MEMOIRS

OF THE

AMERICAN MATHEMATICAL SOCIETY

Number 105

COMPACTLY COVERED REFLECTIONS, EXTENSION OF UNIFORM DUALITIES AND GENERALIZED ALMOST PERIODICITY

by

MICHAEL H. POWELL

Published by the
American Mathematical Society
Providence, Rhode Island
1970

Key Words and Phrases

covered sets, monoids and algebras; category of covered objects; Cartesian category; uniformizing rule; compactly covered object; covered uniform monoids and locally convex algebras; compactly covered reflection; uniform duality; bounded duality; almost periodic functions and linear forms; Bohr compactly covered reflection; extension context; extension property; double sequence property; Arens' multiplication; weakly almost periodic functions and linear forms; convolution; weakly almost periodic compactly covered reflection; linear extension context; linear extension property; weakly almost periodic module.

AMS 1970 Subject Classifications 18B99, 46A05, 46M99; 43A60

Abstract

This monograph begins in Chapter 2 by proving a category-theoretic result which asserts that, in certain categories whose objects are equipped with uniform structures, the compactly covered objects always form a reflective subcategory. As special cases, one can prove the existence of Bohr compactly covered reflections and weakly almost periodic compactly covered reflections for covered uniform monoids and covered locally convex algebras.

In Chapter 3, the notion of a uniform duality is then introduced and an abstract version of Ascoli's Theorem proved. This theorem is then applied in Chapter 4 to give explicit constructions of Bohr compactly covered reflections for covered uniform monoids and covered locally convex algebras by means of a theory of almost periodic functions and linear forms.

In Chapter 5, a theory of extension contexts for a uniform duality is developed and theorems proved which state the equivalence between the existence of extensions of such dualities to dualities involving compactly covered objects and certain conditions involving weak compactness or involving double sequence properties or double limit properties. This theory is strengthened in Chapter 6 by combinatorial methods in those cases where extension to closed convex hulls is desired. These results are applied to give explicit constructions for weakly almost periodic compactly covered reflections of covered uniform monoids and covered locally convex algebras by means of a theory of weakly almost periodic functions and linear forms.

FOREWORD

This monograph is organized into chapters and, within the chapters into sections. Within the sections the definitions and results are numbered consecutively. For reference purposes within a given section the definitions and results of that section are referred to simply by number, e.g. Proposition 1. The definitions and results of another section within the same chapter are referred to by section number and number, e.g. Proposition 2.1. The definitions and results of another chapter are referred to by chapter number, section number and number, e.g. Proposition 2.2.1. The sections of the same chapter are referred to by number, e.g. §1, those of another chapter by chapter number and section number, e.g. §1.1.

I should like to dedicate this monograph to the two people who--at least in an immediate sense--were most responsible for my being able to produce it: My advisor, Professor Ky Fan, and my beloved wife, Jo Anne.

I should also like to acknowledge the fact that, during the time this monograph was being written, I was supported first by an NSF Graduate Fellowship and later as a research assistant under NSF Grant GP8394.

Michael H. Powell
University of California at
Santa Barbara
June 1969

In addition to the above acknowledgements, I should like also to express my gratitude to the referee for a large number of suggestions. These were helpful in enabling me to rewrite large parts of Chapter 2 and in revising the rest of the monograph.

Michael H. Powell
University of Maryland
February 1970

TABLE OF CONTENTS

		Page No.
FOREWORD		
INTRODUCTION		1
Chapter 1:	Preliminaries	5
1	Synopsis	5
2	Terminology from Set Theory and Topology	6
3	Terminology Concerning Categories	10
4	Terminology Concerning Uniform Structures	13
5	Terminology Concerning Algebra	17
6	Terminology from the Theory of Locally Convex Spaces	20
Chapter 2:	Compactly Covered Reflections	24
1	Synopsis	24
2	Cartesian Categories	26
3	Examples of Cartesian Categories	30
4	Uniformizing Rules for Cartesian Categories	32
5	Examples of Uniformizing Rules for Cartesian Categories	38
6	Dual Objects	41
7	Compactly Covered Reflections in Cartesian Categories	44
8	Examples of Compactly Covered Reflections	50
Chapter 3:	Uniform Dualities	55
1	Synopsis	55
2	Basic Definitions and Terminology Concerning Uniform Dualities	55
3	Transpose Maps	61
4	Completeness in a Uniform Duality	65
5	Precompactness in a Uniform Duality	71

Chapter 4:	Almost Periodic Functions and Linear Forms	76
1	Synopsis	76
2	Action of a Monoid on a Duality	77
3	Action of a Covered Monoid on a Duality	80
4	Almost Periodic Elements in a Duality	84
5	Almost Periodic Functions on a Covered Uniform Monoid	91
6	Almost Periodic Linear Forms on a Covered Locally Convex Algebra	99
Chapter 5:	Extension of Uniform Dualities	106
1	Synopsis	106
2	Extension Contexts in a Duality of Sets	107
3	Extension Contexts in a Duality in a Cartesian Category	113
4	Extension Contexts over a Uniformized Object	119
5	The Double Sequence Property	125
6	The Double Sequence Property and Extension Contexts	130
7	An Application: Arens Multiplication in the Bidual of a Bornological Algebra	136
8	A Generalized Eberlein-Grothendieck Theorem	151
9	Extension Theorems	155
10	An Application: Weakly Almost Periodic Linear Forms on a Covered Locally Convex Algebra	159
Chapter 6:	Linear Extension of Uniform Dualities	173
1	Synopsis	173
2	Linear Extension Contexts	174
3	The Convex Double Sequence Property	181
4	Pták's Combinatorial Lemma and the Double Limit Property	184
5	The Convex Double Sequence Property and Linear Extension Contexts	186
6	A Generalized Eberlein-Grothendieck-Krein Theorem	187
7	Linear Extension Theorems	191

8	An Application: Weakly Almost Periodic Functions on a Covered Uniform Monoid	197
9	Compact Reflections of Uniform Monoids: Extensions of Some Results of De Leeuw and Glicksberg	208
Symbol Index		221
Terminology Index		224
Bibliography		233

INTRODUCTION

The first problem with which this monograph is concerned is to state and prove existence theorems for what I have chosen to call compactly covered reflections in certain kinds of categories. This is done in Chapter 2. The method that is used can be briefly described as follows:

First the notion is introduced of a category of covered objects (§2.2). In essence, this is simply a category in which to every object there corresponds an underlying space (a set) and a directed covering of that space. Morphisms in such categories are always functions from one underlying space to another which take coverings to families which refine the covering in the codomain. A certain number of additional restrictions are then imposed, the most critical being that the category contain products and that the underlying space of a product should be the product of the underlying spaces. Because of the crucial role that this particular restriction plays, the resulting general type of category is called a Cartesian category (§2.2).

Secondly, the notion is introduced of a uniformizing rule for a Cartesian category (§2.4). Such a rule assigns to each object of the category a family of uniform structures on the underlying space, subject to certain restrictions. If we apply such a rule to a Cartesian category, we can obtain a new "uniformized" category. An example would be the uniformizing rule which assigns to an object in the Cartesian category of abelian groups (and group homomorphisms) the family of all uniform structures on a given group which make it a topological

---

Received by the editors November 12, 1969 and, in revised form, September 25, 1970.

group. The uniformized category would be the category of abelian topological groups (and continuous homomorphisms). An object of a general uniformized category is called <u>compactly covered</u> if each set in its covering family is contained in some compact set of its covering family (§2.4). The main theorem of the chapter, Theorem 2.7.1, states that the compactly covered objects form a reflective subcategory. In the above special case we could get as a corollary the existence of Bohr compactifications for abelian topological groups. Several examples of this kind are given in Section 2.8.

While much of the material presented in later chapters has intrinsic interest even without the notion of compactly covered reflection, the principal application of the general theories developed in Chapters 3, 5 and 6 is in giving explicit constructions of certain compactly covered reflections. The particular reflections for which explicit constructions are given are for <u>covered uniform monoids</u> and <u>covered locally convex algebras</u> (§2.5). In each of these cases, two different kinds of compactly covered reflections are explicitly constructed. The first kind arises when a type of joint uniform continuity is demanded of the multiplication. In this case, the principal tool turns out to be an Ascoli Theorem (§3.5) which is applied to produce a general theory of <u>almost periodic functions and linear forms</u> (Chapter 4). With the aid of this theory one can explicitly construct what I have called <u>Bohr compactly covered reflections</u>, a construction which is well-known in the special case of the Bohr compactification of a topological group. The second kind of compactly covered reflection arises when no joint continuity restriction whatever is demanded and all that is required is separate uniform continuity of the multiplication. In this case the principal tools which are used are the extension theorems of Chapters 5 and 6. With the aid of these theorems a general theory is developed of <u>weakly almost periodic functions and linear forms</u> (§5.10, §6.8) and this theory is in turn applied to obtain explicit constructions of what I have called <u>weakly almost periodic compactly covered reflections</u>. Once again this generalizes a known construction in the special case of monoids, that of Deleeuw and Glicksberg [2].

Not too much need be said of the Ascoli theorems and other results which are stated in Chapter 3. These results are by and large simply adaptations of standard results from the theory of function spaces to a duality-theoretic situation. The concept is introduced of a *uniform duality* (§3.2) and notation and terminology are developed, along with elementary results, concerning those "uniform convergence" structures which a uniform duality yields. Some results on transpose maps and completeness are also proved, but the main purpose of the chapter is to state and prove, in a duality-theoretic setting, the Ascoli theorems of §3.5. As mentioned above, these are applied extensively in Chapter 4.

After Chapter 4, aside from the applications mentioned above, the rest of the monograph is devoted mainly to the problem of trying to "extend" a uniform duality to a new duality in which all the objects involved are compactly covered. The theorems which are proved (in Section 5.9 and Section 6.7) generalize the extension theorem of Pták [2] and therefore, as Pták noticed, are quite intimately connected with the fundamental results concerning weak compactness in the theory of locally convex spaces. In fact, in the process of leading up to the extension theorems proved in Sections 5.9 and 6.7, auxillary results are proved which directly generalize the Eberlein-Grothendieck theorem (§5.8) and Krein's Theorem (§6.6). It has also been noticed (see Simons [2]) that Pták's extension theorem is a kind of Fubini Theorem. This is implicit in the procedure involving *extension contexts* which is used in Chapters 5 and 6 and explicit in the Fubini theorem which is stated in Section 6.7 as a corollary of the extension theorem 6.7.1.

The principal tool which Pták used to prove his extension theorem was *the double limit property*. The results of Chapters 5 and 6 do not assume that the duality is over a sequentially compact space and so a more suitable analogue for this tool had to be developed and I have called it the *double sequence* property (§5.5). In Chapter 6, a slightly more specialized property was called for, which I have called the convex double sequence property (§6.3). The procedures of Chapters 5 and 6 are quite similar to one another and, in fact, the extension problems of Chapter 6 are reduced to problems which were treated in Chapter 5 by combinatorial methods. In Chapter 5, the use of extension contexts and the double sequence property to prove extension theorems is broken into two steps, the second of which cannot be attempted until the first is taken. The first step is the more difficult, since it requires a generalized Eberlein-Grothendieck theorem to take it. Under certain circumstances however the difficulty in the first step does not occur and extension theorems can be proved without too much difficulty. This is the case, for instance, in Section 5.7, where less difficult extension theorems are applied to give results about regularity of Arens' multiplication in the bidual of a bornological algebra.

The monograph concludes with a section (§6.9) which extends some results of Deleeuw and Glicksberg concerning certain monoids of operators on Banach spaces. The extended results concern themselves instead with certain kinds of actions of uniform monoids on locally convex spaces, producing what I have called weakly almost periodic modules. The ideal theory of the weakly almost periodic compact reflection of the uniform monoid can then be used to give, in certain cases, direct sum decompositions of the module. Also, the existence of an almost periodic submodule is proved and the ideal theory of the Bohr compact reflection of the uniform monoid is used to give, in certain cases, direct sum decompositions of it.

Chapter 1. PRELIMINARIES

§1 Synopsis

The intent of this chapter is to set down the terminology which is of a general nature and will be used in the other chapters, along with certain facts which will be used without further comment.

The titles of the sections are self explanatory, but some preliminary comments may be in order: As far as standard references goes, the terminology and notation with regard to topology and uniform space theory is probably closer to that of Bourbaki ([1] and [2]) than to Kelley ([1]). Consequently, much of Sections 2 and 4 is devoted to listing that terminology with which a person used to the latter reference might feel uncomfortable. This is not meant to imply however that all the terminology in these sections is that of Bourbaki. Also, the treatment of uniform space terminology is more detailed than that on topology, since it seemed to me more likely that some readers might be unfamiliar with the terminology in the theory of uniform spaces, and since uniform structures play a much larger part in this paper than do topologies.

Considerable use is made throughout this monograph of a very elementary kind of category theory, especially in Chapter 2. A section on terminology in this area has therefore to be included if only for the reason that the monograph is primarily about functional analysis and so it is not unlikely that many readers will be even less familiar with category theory than is the author. Moreover, the notion of "reflection" plays such a large part that it seemed imperative to say something about it at least. It should be mentioned that the word "reflection" is used both in its conventional sense as defined in Freyd [1] (not as defined in Mitchell [1], where it would be "coreflection") but also in a slightly more general sense. For instance, a "semi-group algebra" would be considered in this treatise as a reflection for the monoid in the category of algebras (via a forgetful functor). This language will be used rather than the "universal mapping" language which would be used in the treatise of Herrlich [1]. The principal motivation for this is to preserve economy of terminolgy (better yet, to prevent cumbersome terminology from being even worse). So Section 3 of this chapter is recommended reading.

Little need be said about Section 5 unless the reader is unfamiliar with the word "monoid" or is unused to the convention that all rings have identities.

The terminology introduced in Section 6 differs very little from that in the books of Horváth [1] and Schaefer [1]. It is included here only as a convenience.

§2. Terminology from Set Theory and Topology

Let X be a given set. Let $\mathcal{A}$ be a family of subsets of X. We denote

$$\bigcup\mathcal{A} = \{x\in X: \exists A\in\mathcal{A} \text{ s.t. } x\in A\}$$

$$\bigcap\mathcal{A} = \{x\in X: \forall A\in\mathcal{A},\ x\in A\}$$

where $\exists$ means "there exists", s.t. stands for "such that" and $\forall$ means "for every". We note that $\bigcup\mathcal{A}$ remains the same regardless of our initial choice of X, as does $\bigcap\mathcal{A}$, except in the case where $\mathcal{A}$ is the empty set, which we will always denote by $\emptyset$. In this case, we have

$$\bigcap\emptyset = X .$$

A family $\mathcal{A}$ of subsets of X is said to be a covering of X if we have $X = \bigcup\mathcal{A}$.

If $\mathcal{A}$ and $\mathcal{B}$ are families of subsets of X, we say that $\mathcal{A}$ refines $\mathcal{B}$ if for each set $A\in\mathcal{A}$ there is some set $B\in\mathcal{B}$ such that $A\subset B$. If $\mathcal{B}$ also refines $\mathcal{A}$, we say $\mathcal{A}$ and $\mathcal{B}$ are equivalent and we write $\mathcal{A} \sim \mathcal{B}$.

By a relation in X, we mean a subset of the Cartesian product X × X. If S and T are relations in X, we write

$$S^{-1} = \{(x,y): (y,x)\in S\}$$

$$T\circ S = \{(x,z): \exists y\in X \text{ s.t. } (x,y)\in S,\ (y,z)\in T\}$$

$$S^n = S\circ\ldots\circ S \quad (n \text{ times})$$

where n is an integer, $n \geq 1$. If $A \subset X$, $x \in X$ and S is a relation in X, we write

$$S(x) = \{y \in X: \quad (x,y) \in S\}$$

$$S(A) = \{y \in X: \quad \exists x \in A \text{ s.t. } y \in S(x)\}$$

By the identity relation in X, or the diagonal of X × X, we mean the set

$$\Delta_X = \{(x,x): \quad x \in X\}$$

which is simply written in most cases as

$$\Delta_X = \Delta .$$

If $\mathcal{A}$ is a covering of X, the relation $\bigcup\{A \times A: \quad A \in \mathcal{A}\}$ in X is called the graph of $\mathcal{A}$.

The family of all subsets of X is partially ordered by inclusion. Unless we explicitly state otherwise, if we say that a subset of this set has a particular property of partially ordered sets, we will means that it has this property with respect to this partial ordering. In particular, a family $\mathcal{A}$ of subsets of X is called directed if for every pair A, $B \in \mathcal{A}$, there is some $C \in \mathcal{A}$ such that $A \cup B \subset C$.

If X and Y are non-empty sets,

$$\phi: X \to Y$$

is a function, $\mathcal{A}$ is a family of subsets of X we denote

$$\phi(\mathcal{A}) = \{\phi(B): \quad B \in \mathcal{A}\}$$

If $\mathcal{B}$ is a family of subsets of Y then we denote

$$\phi^{-1}(\mathcal{B}) = \{\phi^{-1}(C): \quad C \in \mathcal{B}\}$$

ϕ is called injective (an injection) if $x, y \in X$ and $x \neq y$ implies $\phi(x) \neq \phi(y)$. ϕ is called surjective (a surjection) if $\phi(X) = Y$. ϕ is called bijective (a bijection) if it is both injective and surjective.

The set of all functions from X to Y is denoted Y^X.

For the rest of this section, X will denote a fixed, non-empty set.

Let $\mathcal{F}$ be a family of subsets of X. Let

$$\mathcal{G} = \{\bigcap \mathcal{H}: \mathcal{H} \text{ is a finite subset of } \mathcal{F}\}$$

(The empty set is considered finite, so we have $X = \bigcap \emptyset \in \mathcal{G}$.) $\mathcal{F}$ is called a <u>filter subbase</u> if $\emptyset \notin \mathcal{G}$. $\mathcal{F}$ is called a <u>filter base</u> if, in addition, every set of $\mathcal{G}$ contains a set of $\mathcal{F}$. If $\mathcal{F}$ is a filter subbase, $\mathcal{G}$ is a filter base. $\mathcal{F}$ is called <u>a filter</u> on X if it is a filter base and if whenever $F \in \mathcal{F}$ and $F \subset Y \subset X$, then $Y \in \mathcal{F}$. Notice that if $\mathcal{F} = \emptyset$, then $\mathcal{G} = \{X\}$ and so $\mathcal{F}$ is a filter subbase and $\mathcal{G}$ is a filter on X. If $\mathcal{F}$ is a filter subbase, then $\mathcal{G}$ is called <u>the filter base generated by $\mathcal{F}$</u> and the family $\{Y \subset X: \exists\, G \in \mathcal{G} \text{ s.t. } G \subset Y\}$ is called <u>the filter generated by $\mathcal{F}$</u>.

The set of all filters on X is inductively ordered by set inclusion and so, by Zorn's Lemma, contains maximal elements. Such an element is called an <u>ultrafilter</u> on X.

Now let $\mathcal{T}$ be a topology on X. If $\mathcal{F}$ is a filter base on X, then the $\mathcal{T}$-adherence of $\mathcal{F}$ is defined to be $\bigcap \mathcal{H}$, where $\mathcal{H}$ is the family of all $\mathcal{T}$-closed sets in the filter generated by $\mathcal{F}$. A point $x \in X$ in the $\mathcal{T}$-adherence of $\mathcal{F}$ is called <u>a $\mathcal{T}$-adherent point</u> of $\mathcal{F}$. This is the case if and only if every $\mathcal{T}$-neighborhood of x meets every set of $\mathcal{F}$. In particular, this is the case if every $\mathcal{T}$-neighborhood of x contains a set of $\mathcal{F}$. In this case, we say that <u>$\mathcal{F}$ converges to x with respect to $\mathcal{T}$</u> and we write

$$x = \lim \mathcal{F}$$

(<u>This is not to imply that if $y \in X$ and $y = \lim \mathcal{F}$, then $x=y$.</u>) $\mathcal{F}$ is said to <u>$\mathcal{T}$-converge</u> if it converges to some point of X with respect to $\mathcal{T}$.

By <u>a sequence</u> in X, we mean a function

$$n \to x_n$$

from the positive integers to X. Such a sequence is denoted by $\{x_n\}$. By <u>a subsequence</u> of $\{x_n\}$, we mean the composition of a a strictly increasing function

$$i \to n_i$$

of the positive integers into themselves with the function

$$n \to x_n$$

Such a composition is denoted by $\{x_{n_i}\}$. By the <u>elementary filter base of $\{x_n\}$</u> we mean the filter base

$$F = \{\{x_n: \ n \geq p\}: \ p \geq 1\}$$

A point $x \in X$ is called a <u>T-adherent point of $\{x_n\}$</u> if it is a T-adherent point of F. <u>$\{x_n\}$ is said to converge to x with respect to T</u> if we have $x = \lim F$. In this case, we write $x = \lim_n x_n$. $\{x_n\}$ is said to T-converge if it converges to some point of X with respect to T.

We are interested in the following conditions which the topology T on X might satisfy:

If every pair of distinct points of X has a pair of disjoint neighborhoods, T is called a Hausdorff topology.

If every covering of X by open sets has a finite subcovering, T is said to be quasi-compact. This is equivalent to the condition that every filter on X have a T-adherent point.

If T is a Hausdorff topology which is quasi-compact, T is called <u>compact</u>.

If every sequence in X has a T-adherent point, T is called <u>countably compact</u>.

If every sequence in X has a convergent subsequence, T is called <u>sequentially compact</u>.

By a <u>pseudo-metric</u> on X, we mean a function

$$g: \ X \times X \to [o, +\infty)$$

where for all $x, y, z \in X$, $0 = g(x,x) \leq g(z,x) = g(x,z) \leq g(x,y) + g(y,z)$. If g is a pseudo-metric on X, there is a (unique) topology on X such that for each $x \in X$, $\{\{y \in X: \ g(x,y) < \epsilon\}: \epsilon > o\}$ is a base for the filter of neighborhoods of x. This is called the <u>topology determined by g</u>. If T can be determined by a pseudo-metric, T is said to be <u>pseudo-metrizable</u>. In this case, T is quasi-compact if and only if T is countably compact if and only if T is sequentially compact.

When we are given a topology T on X, we denote the pair (X,T) by $X[T]$ and call $X[T]$ a topological space. If we say $X[T]$ has some property which pertains to T, we shall mean that T has that property.

We shall consider T as being identical with its family of open sets. Therefore, if Y is another non-empty set, S is a topology on Y and

$$\phi: \quad X \to Y$$

is a function, $\phi^{-1}(S)$ is a topology on X. We say that ϕ is continuous (with respect to T and S) if $\phi^{-1}(S) \subset T$. If $x \in X$, we say that ϕ is continuous at x if $\phi^{-1}(G) \subset F$ where F is the filter of T-neighborhoods of x and G is the filter of S-neighborhoods of $\phi(x)$. ϕ is continuous if and only if it is continuous at each point of x.

If $X[T]$ and $E[S]$ are topological spaces, if ϕ: $X \to E$ is a continuous surjection, and if T is quasi-compact, so is S. If $X[T]$ is compact, if ϕ is a continuous bijection, and if $E[S]$ is a Hausdorff space, $E[S]$ is compact and ϕ^{-1} is continuous.

$X[T]$ is said to be locally compact, if T is Hausdorff and each element of X has a compact neighborhood.

§3 Terminology Concerning Categories

By a category, C, we mean

(1) a collection of objects, denoted Obj C

(2) for each pair A, B $\in$ Obj$C$ a set of morphisms, denoted Mor (A,B)

(3) For each triple A, B, C $\in$ Obj$C$ a law of composition

$$\text{Mor}(B,C) \times \text{Mor}(A,B) \to \text{Mor}(A,C)$$

$$(f,g) \to fg$$

all subject to the following demands:

(a) If A $\in$ Obj C, there is a morphism $I_A \in \text{Mor}(A,A)$ with the property that for every B $\in$ Obj C, every $f \in \text{Mor}(A,B)$ and every $g \in \text{Mor}(B,A)$, we have $fI_A = f$ and $I_A g = g$.

(b) If A, B, C, $D \in \mathrm{Obj}\,\mathcal{C}$ and if $f \in \mathrm{Mor}(A,B)$, $g \in \mathrm{Mor}(B,C)$, $h \in \mathrm{Mor}(C,D)$, then $h(gf) = (hg)f$.

If A, $B \in \mathrm{Obj}\,\mathcal{C}$ and $f \in \mathrm{Mor}(A,B)$, then f is called a coretraction (retraction) if there is some $g \in \mathrm{Mor}(B,A)$ such that $gf = I_A$ $(fg = I_B)$. If there exist g, $h \in \mathrm{Mor}(B,A)$ such that $gf = I_A$ and $fh = I_B$, then we have $g = gI_B = g(fh) = (gf)h = I_A h = h$ and we write $g = h = f^{-1}$. In this case, we call f a $\mathcal{C}$-isomorphism and call f^{-1} the inverse of f.

If $\mathcal{C}$ and $\mathcal{D}$ are categories, then a covariant (contravariant) functor, T, from $\mathcal{C}$ to $\mathcal{D}$ consists of the following:

(4) A rule which associates to each $A \in \mathrm{Obj}\,\mathcal{C}$ some $T(A) \in \mathrm{Obj}\,\mathcal{D}$

(5) For each pair A, $B \in \mathrm{Obj}\,\mathcal{C}$ a function
$T\colon\ \mathrm{Mor}_{\mathcal{C}}(A,B) \to \mathrm{Mor}_{\mathcal{D}}(T(A),T(B))$
(a function
$T\colon\ \mathrm{Mor}_{\mathcal{C}}(A,B) \to \mathrm{Mor}_{\mathcal{D}}(T(B),T(A)))$

all subject to the following demands:

(c) If $A \in \mathrm{Obj}\,\mathcal{C}$, then $T(I_A) = I_{T(A)}$

(d) If A, B, $C \in \mathrm{Obj}\,\mathcal{C}$ and if $f \in \mathrm{Mor}(A,B)$, $g \in \mathrm{Mor}(B,C)$, then we have

$$T(gf) = T(g)\,T(f)$$

$$(T(gf) = T(f)\,T(g))$$

A covariant functor T from $\mathcal{C}$ to $\mathcal{D}$ is called <u>faithful</u> if for each pair A, $B \in \mathrm{Obj}\,\mathcal{C}$, the function

$$T\colon\ \mathrm{Mor}_{\mathcal{C}}(A,B) \to \mathrm{Mor}_{\mathcal{C}}(T(A),T(B))$$

is injective.

If we are given a category $\mathcal{D}$, then by a subcategory of $\mathcal{D}$ we mean a pair $(\mathcal{C},T)$, where $\mathcal{C}$ is a category, where T is a covariant functor from $\mathcal{C}$ to $\mathcal{D}$, and where $T(A) = A$ for each object A of $\mathcal{C}$ and $T(f) = f$ for each morphism f of $\mathcal{C}$. Obviously, given $\mathcal{C}$, there is a unique choice of T and so T is suppressed and we simply say that $\mathcal{C}$ is a subcategory of $\mathcal{D}$. We say that a subcategory of $\mathcal{C}$ of $\mathcal{D}$ is a full subcategory if we have $Mor_{\mathcal{C}}(A,B) = Mor_{\mathcal{D}}(A,B)$ for each pair A, B Obj$\mathcal{C}$.

We now consider a fixed category $\mathcal{C}$. An object A of $\mathcal{C}$ is called a final (initial) object of $\mathcal{C}$ if for each $B \in Obj\mathcal{C}$, Mor(B,A)(Mor(A,B)) contains precisely one element. Clearly, if an object B of $\mathcal{C}$ is also a final (initial) object, then the unique element in Mor(A,B) must be a $\mathcal{C}$-isomorphism.

If $\{A_\nu\}_{\nu \in I}$ is an indexed family of objects of $\mathcal{C}$, then we can define a new category, $\mathcal{D}$, as follows: An object of $\mathcal{D}$ is a pair $(A, \{\phi_\nu\}_{\nu \in I})$ where $A \in Obj\mathcal{C}$ and where, for each $\nu \in I$, $\phi_\nu \in Mor_{\mathcal{C}}(A, A_\nu)$. If $X = (A, \{\phi_\nu\}_{\nu \in I})$ and $Y = (B, \{\psi_\nu\}_{\nu \in I})$ are objects of $\mathcal{D}$, then a morphism, θ, from X to Y is a $\mathcal{C}$-morphism $\theta \in Mor(A,B)$ such that $\phi_\nu = \psi_\nu \theta$ for each $\nu \in I$. Any final object in $\mathcal{D}$ is called a product in $\mathcal{C}$ of the family $\{A_\nu\}_{\nu \in I}$. If every family of objects in $\mathcal{C}$ has a product in $\mathcal{C}$, then we say that $\mathcal{C}$ has products (or that products exist in $\mathcal{C}$).

Now let A be an object of $\mathcal{C}$, let $\mathcal{E}$ be another category, and let T be a covariant functor from $\mathcal{E}$ to $\mathcal{C}$. We can construct a new category $\mathcal{F}$ as follows: An object of $\mathcal{F}$ is a pair (B,ϕ) where $B \in Obj\mathcal{E}$ and $\phi \in Mor(A,T(B))$. If $X = (B,\phi)$ and $Y = (C,\psi)$ are objects of $\mathcal{F}$, then a morphism, θ, from X to Y is a morphism $\theta \in Mor(B,C)$ such that $\psi = T(\theta)\phi$. An initial object in $\mathcal{F}$ will be called <u>a reflection for A in $\mathcal{E}$ via T</u>. In case T is understood, we say simply "<u>a reflection for A in $\mathcal{E}$</u>". In many cases of interest in this monograph, T will be understood to be a "forgetful" functor of some kind. It should be pointed out that <u>the above terminology is not standard</u>. The standard use of this terminology comes in the special case where $\mathcal{E}$ is a subcategory of $\mathcal{C}$ and T the embedding functor. In the general case, if every object of $\mathcal{C}$ has reflections in $\mathcal{E}$ (via T), we say that <u>$\mathcal{C}$ has reflections in $\mathcal{E}$ (via T)</u>. If $\mathcal{E}$ is a subcategory of $\mathcal{C}$, we say simply that <u>$\mathcal{E}$ is reflective</u>.

<u>By the category of sets, we mean the category whose objects are (all) non-empty sets and whose morphisms are functions</u>. That is, if A, B are sets, then $B^A = Mor(A,B)$. Morphism

composition is, of course, simply function composition. Isomorphisms in this category are simply bijections. This category has products. In fact, let $\{X_\nu\}_{\nu\in I}$ be an indexed family of sets. Let X be the cartesian product $\Pi_{\nu\in I}X_\nu$, i.e., all functions

$$I \to \cup_{\nu\in I} X_\nu$$

$$\nu \to x_\nu$$

such that $x_\nu \in X_\nu$. (Such a function is denoted by $\{x_\nu\}_{\nu\in I}$.) <u>We will always denote by</u>

$$\pi_\nu: \quad X \to X_\nu$$

<u>the map</u>

$$\{x_\mu\}_{\mu\in I} \to x_\nu,$$

called projection on the νth co-ordinate, $\nu\in I$. The pair $(X, \{\pi_\nu\}_{\nu\in I})$ is a product of the family $\{X_\nu\}_{\nu\in I}$ in this category.

§4. <u>Terminology Concerning Uniform Spaces</u>

Let X be a non-empty set. A filter $\mathcal{U}$ on the Cartesian product X × X will be called <u>a uniform structure on X</u> if the following three conditions are satisfied:

(i) If $U\in\mathcal{U}$, then $U \supset \Delta$

(ii) If $U\in\mathcal{U}$, then $U^{-1}\in\mathcal{U}$

(iii) If $U\in\mathcal{U}$, then there is some $V\in\mathcal{U}$ such that $\overset{2}{V}\subset U$.

Each set $U\in\mathcal{U}$ will be called <u>an entourage</u> of $\mathcal{U}$. A filter base (subbase) $\mathcal{V}$ on X × X which generates $\mathcal{U}$ will be called <u>a basic (sub-basic) system of entourages for $\mathcal{U}$</u>. A basic system of entourages of $\mathcal{U}$ is often called <u>a fundamental system of entourages for $\mathcal{U}$</u>.

<u>If Φ is a set of uniform structures on X, then $\cup\Phi$ is a subbasic system of entourages for a uniform structure on X,</u> denoted $\vee\Phi$. In the particular case where $\Phi = \emptyset$, we have $\vee\Phi = \{X \times X\}$. <u>This particular uniform structure on X will be called the chaotic structure</u>.

If Y is another non-empty set and if $\mathcal{U}$ is a uniform structure on Y, each function f: $X \to Y$ defines a uniform structure on X denoted by $f^{-1}(\mathcal{U})$. If X is a subset of Y and if f is the inclusion map, we denote $f^{-1}(\mathcal{U}) = \mathcal{U}|_X$.

If $\{X_\nu\}_{\nu \in I}$ is a family of non-empty sets, if $\mathcal{U}_\nu$ is a uniform structure on X_ν for each $\nu \in I$, and if $(X, \{\phi_\nu\}_{\nu \in I})$ is any product of the family $\{X_\nu\}_{\nu \in I}$ in the category of sets, we define the product uniform structure of the $\mathcal{U}_\nu$ on X relative to the maps ϕ_ν to be the uniform structure $\bigvee_{\nu \in I} \phi_\nu^{-1}(\mathcal{U}_\nu)$. In the particular case of the Cartesian product, $X = \Pi_{\nu \in I} X_\nu$, $\phi_\nu = \pi_\nu (\nu \in I)$, we generally suppress the family $\{\pi_\nu\}_{\nu \in I}$ and speak simply of the product uniform structure of the $\mathcal{U}_\nu$ on X. In this case we write $\Pi_{\nu \in I} \mathcal{U}_\nu = \bigvee_{\nu \in I} \pi_\nu^{-1}(\mathcal{U}_\nu)$. In the particular case where $I = \{1,2\}$, we write $X = X_1 \times X_2$ and $\Pi_{\nu \in I} \mathcal{U}_\nu = \mathcal{U}_1 \times \mathcal{U}_2$.

If X and Y are non-empty sets, if $\mathcal{U}$ is a uniform structure on X and if $\mathcal{V}$ is a uniform structure on Y, a function

$$f: \quad X \to Y$$

is called $\mathcal{U}$-$\mathcal{V}$ uniformly continuous on a subset $\emptyset \neq A \subset X$ if we have $f^{-1}(\mathcal{V})|_A \subset \mathcal{U}|_A$.

We now consider a non-empty set X and a uniform structure $\mathcal{U}$ on X. We denote the pair $(X,\mathcal{U})$ by $X[\mathcal{U}]$ and call such a pair a uniform space. When we attribute a property which pertains to $\mathcal{U}$ to $X[\mathcal{U}]$, we shall mean that $\mathcal{U}$ has that property.

$\mathcal{U}$ is said to be <u>separated</u> if we have $\bigcap \mathcal{U} = \Delta$.

There is a (unique) topology, denoted $t(\mathcal{U})$, on X such that if $x \in X$, the filter of neighborhoods of x is $\{U(x): U \in \mathcal{U}\}$. $\mathcal{U}$ is separated if and only if $t(\mathcal{U})$ is a Hausdorff topology. $t(\mathcal{U})$ is called <u>the topology determined by $\mathcal{U}$</u>.

<u>$\mathcal{U}$ is said to be quasi-compact if $t(\mathcal{U})$ is quasi-compact</u>. <u>$\mathcal{U}$ is said to be compact if it is quasi-compact and separated</u>, i.e., if $t(\mathcal{U})$ is compact.

If $Y[\mathcal{V}]$ is another uniform space, a $\mathcal{U}$-$\mathcal{V}$ uniformly continuous function f: $X \to Y$ is always $t(\mathcal{U})$ - $t(\mathcal{V})$ continuous. A function which has this latter property is said to be $\mathcal{U}$-$\mathcal{V}$

continuous. In general, if we assert properties of uniform structures which pertain to the topologies they determine, we will mean that those topologies have these properties. In case $\mathcal{U}$ is quasi-compact, the converse to the above assertion holds, i.e., a $\mathcal{U}$-$\mathcal{V}$ continuous function f: $X \to Y$ is $\mathcal{U}$-$\mathcal{V}$ uniformly continuous. If $\mathcal{W}$ is another uniform structure on X, if $\mathcal{U}$ is quasi-compact, and if $t(\mathcal{U}) = t(\mathcal{W})$, then $\mathcal{U}=\mathcal{W}$.

We call $\mathcal{U}$ <u>precompact</u> if for every $U \in \mathcal{U}$ there is a finite covering $\mathcal{A}$ of X whose graph is contained in U. If Φ is a family of precompact uniform structures of X, then $\vee\Phi$ is also precompact. There is a strongest precompact uniform structure on X. A fundamental system of entourages for this uniform structure can be got by taking all graphs of finite coverings of X. <u>This uniform structure is therefore called the uniform structure of finite coverings of X</u>. There is a strongest uniform structure on X which is weaker than $\mathcal{U}$ and is precompact. <u>This uniform structure is called the Samuel structure of $\mathcal{U}$</u>. $\mathcal{U}$ and its Samuel structure determine the same topology on X.

A filter base $\mathcal{F}$ on X is said to be <u>a $\mathcal{U}$-Cauchy filter base</u> if for each $U \in \mathcal{U}$ there is some $F \in \mathcal{F}$ such that $F \times F \subset U$. $\mathcal{F}$ is a $\mathcal{U}$-Cauchy Filter base if and only if it generates a $\mathcal{U}$-Cauchy filter. Any $\mathcal{U}$-convergent filter is a $\mathcal{U}$-Cauchy filter. <u>$\mathcal{U}$ is said to be complete</u> if the converse holds, i.e., if every $\mathcal{U}$-Cauchy filter is convergent.

$\mathcal{U}$ is quasi-compact if and only if $\mathcal{U}$ is pre-compact and complete.

There is a strongest uniform structure on X. It is called the discrete uniform structure and is characterized by the fact that Δ is an entourage for it.

Let $Y[\mathcal{V}]$ be another uniform space and let f: $X \to Y$ be a function. If $\mathcal{V}$ is precompact, so is $f^{-1}(\mathcal{V})$. If f is a $\mathcal{U}$-$\mathcal{V}$ uniformly continuous surjection and if $\mathcal{U}$ is precompact, then $\mathcal{V}$ is precompact.

The category of uniform spaces is the category whose objects are uniform spaces and whose morphisms are uniformly continuous functions. The separated uniform spaces, resp. the

separated complete uniform spaces, resp. the compact uniform
spaces form a full subcategory. Moreover, it is reflective.
A reflection of $X[U]$ in this subcategory is called a <u>separation</u>,
resp. a <u>completion</u>, resp. a <u>Samuel compact reflection</u> of $X[U]$.
$(Y[V],p)$ is a separation, resp. completion, resp. Samuel compact reflection of $X[U]$ if and only if $p(X) = Y$ and $p^{-1}(V) = U$,
resp. $p(X)$ is dense in Y and $p^{-1}(V) = U$, resp. $p(X)$ is dense in
Y and $p^{-1}(V)$ is the Samuel structure of U.

Now let T be a topology on X. There is a strongest uniform
structure V on X such that $t(V) \subset T$. The Samuel structure of V
is the strongest precompact uniform structure W on X such that
$t(W) \subset T$. W is also called the Čech structure of T. <u>Any Samuel</u>
<u>compact reflection</u> of $X[V]$ is called a Stone-Čech compact reflec-
<u>tion of $X[T]$. In case $T = t(V)$, we call any such compact reflec-</u>
<u>tion a Stone-Čech compactification of $X[T]$.</u> A Stone-Cech com-
pact reflection $(Y[S], \phi)$ of $X[T]$ is characterized by the
following properties.

(1) $Y[S]$ is a compact uniform space

(2) ϕ: X → Y is $T-S$ continuous

(3) If $Z[R]$ is any compact uniform space and ψ: X → Z is
     any $T-R$ continuous map, then there is a unique con-
     tinuous map θ: Y → Z such that $\psi = \theta \phi$.

Now let g be a pseudo-metric on X. g determines a uniform
structure V on X (<u>called the uniform structure determined by g</u>)
by taking all sets of the form $\{(x,y): g(x,y) < \epsilon\}$, $\epsilon > 0$, as a
fundamental system of entourages for V. $t(V)$ is just the
topology determined by g. If U can be determined by some
pseudo-metric, then U is called <u>pseudo-metrizable</u>. In this
case, $t(U)$ is pseudo-metrizable. The converse is not true in
general.

Now let $\{g_V\}_{V \in I}$ be a family of pseudo-metrics on X. Let
g_V determine the uniform structure U_V. Let $V = \vee_{V \in I} U_V$. Then
V is called <u>the uniform structure determined by the family</u>
$\underline{\{g_V\}_{V \in I}}$. Each g_V is $\underline{V - \text{uniformly continuous}}$. That is, the

map

$$X \times X \to [o, +\infty)$$
$$(x,y) \to g_\nu(x,y)$$

is $\mathcal{V} \times \mathcal{V}$ - uniformly continuous. It is a very important fact that if $\{g_\nu\}_{\nu\in I}$ is the family of all $\mathcal{U}$-uniformly continuous pseudo-metrics on X, then $\{g_\nu\}_{\nu\in I}$ determines $\mathcal{U}$. $\mathcal{U}$ is pseudo-metrizable if and only if $\mathcal{U}$ has a countable fundamental system of entourages if and only if there is a countable family of $\mathcal{U}$-uniformly continuous pseudo-metrics which determines $\mathcal{U}$.

Now let $\{X_\nu[\mathcal{V}]\}_{\nu\in I}$ be any family of uniform spaces. We denote by $\Pi_{\nu\in I}X_\nu[\mathcal{U}_\nu]$ the uniform space $(\Pi_{\nu\in I}X_\nu, \Pi_{\nu\in I}\mathcal{U}_\nu)$. In the category of uniform spaces, $(\Pi_{\nu\in I}X_\nu[\mathcal{U}_\nu], \{\pi_\nu\}_{\nu\in I})$ is a product of the family $\{X_\nu[\mathcal{U}_\nu]\}_{\nu\in I}$. If $(Y[\mathcal{U}], \{\phi_\nu\}_{\nu\in I})$ is assumed to be any such product, then the following assertions are true:

(1) $Y[\mathcal{V}]$ is separated if and only if each $X_\nu[\mathcal{U}_\nu]$ is separated.

(2) $Y[\mathcal{V}]$ is precompact if and only if each $X_\nu[\mathcal{U}_\nu]$ is precompact.

(3) $Y[\mathcal{V}]$ is complete if and only if each $X_\nu[\mathcal{U}_\nu]$ is complete.

(4) $Y[\mathcal{U}]$ is compact if and only if each $X_\nu[\mathcal{U}_\nu]$ is compact.

(5) A separation of $Y[\mathcal{V}]$ is a product of separations of the $X_\nu[\mathcal{U}_\nu]$.

(6) A completion of $Y[\mathcal{V}]$ is a product of completion of the $X_\nu[\mathcal{U}_\nu]$.

Finally, if, for each $\nu\in I$, $X[\mathcal{U}] = X_\nu[\mathcal{U}_\nu]$, then we write $\Pi_{\nu\in I}X_\nu[\mathcal{U}_\nu]$ as $X[\mathcal{U}]^I$.

§5. Terminology from Algebra

By a monoid, we mean a non-empty set X, together with an associative internal law of composition which admits an identity. Unless we state otherwise, we shall always assume that the law of composition in a monoid X is written by juxtaposition

$$X \times X \to X$$

$$(x,y) \to xy$$

and that the identity is denoted by 1.

If o is an internal law of composition in a set X, then by the opposite law of o we mean the law

$$X \times X \to X$$

$$(x,y) \to y \circ x$$

If $M = (X,\cdot)$ is a monoid, then we call the set X, together with the opposite law of $\cdot$, the opposite monoid of M and denote it by M^o.

Let M be a monoid and let X be a non-empty set. By an action of M on the left of X, we mean a map

$$M \times X \to X$$

$$(a,x) \to a \cdot x$$

such that $a \cdot (b \cdot x) = (ab) \cdot x$, $1 \cdot x = x$ for all $a, b \in M$, $x \in X$. By an action of M on the right (resp. both sides) of X, we mean an action of M^o (resp. $M \times M^o$) on the left of X.

If M,N are monoids, then by a monoid homomorphism $M \xrightarrow{\phi} N$, we mean a function ϕ: $M \to N$ such that $\phi(ab) = \phi(a)\phi(b)$, $\phi(1)=1$ for all $a, b \in M$.

If M is a monoid, X and Y are non-empty sets and M acts on the left of both X and Y, then by an action homomorphism ${}_MX \xrightarrow{\phi} {}_MY$ we mean a function ϕ: $X \to Y$ such that $\phi(a \cdot x) = a \cdot \phi(x)$ for all $a \in M$, $x \in X$.

If M is a monoid, a family $\mathcal{M}$ of subsets of M is called stable if whenever we are given $S, T \in \mathcal{M}$ there is some $R \in \mathcal{M}$ such that $ST = \{st: s \in S, t \in T\} \subset R$.

If a monoid M acts on the left of a set X, a family $\mathcal{A}$ of subsets of X is called stable (with respect to the action of M) if for each $a \in M$ and each $Y \in \mathcal{A}$ there is some $Z \in \mathcal{A}$ such that $a \cdot Y = \{a \cdot y: y \in Y\} \subset Z$.

We denote the real number field by R. We denote the complex number field by C. We use the symbol K to stand for either R or C. (That is, if we develop a theory for K, we mean that if either R or C is substituted in every place that one finds K, then the resulting theory is true.)

If E is a K - vector space, then by a linear form on E, we mean a linear map $E \overset{\phi}{\to} K$. By a linear transformation of E we mean a linear map $E \overset{\phi}{\to} E$. A linear transformation of E is also called a linear operator on E. We denote by E* the set of all linear forms on E, together with the usual K-vector space structure. By the canonical form

$$\langle\, ,\, \rangle : \quad E \times E^* \to K$$

we mean the map

$$E \times E^* \to K$$

$$(x,f) \to \langle x,f \rangle = f(x) \quad .$$

By a K - algebra or an algebra over K, we mean a set A, together with an addition and a scalar multiplication which make A a K-vector space, together with a bilinear internal law of composition (called multiplication)

$$A \times A \to A$$

$$(x,y) \to xy$$

which makes A a (multiplicative) monoid. Notice that our definition of a K-algebra will always assume the existence of a multiplicative identity. This identity will usually, like that of K, be denoted by 1.

If A and B are K-algebras, then by a K-algebra homomorphism $A \overset{\phi}{\to} B$, we mean a linear map ϕ which is also a multiplicative monoid homomorphism (Notice that a K-algebra homomorphism takes 1 to 1.).

If E is a K-vector space, then we denote by $L(E)$ the set of all linear operators on E, together with the usual K-algebra structure. $L(E)$ is called the algebra of all linear operators on E.

§6. Terminology from the Theory of Locally Convex Spaces

Let E be a K-vector space. A subset F of E is called convex if $F \neq \emptyset$ and if for all x, $y \in F$ and all $\lambda \in R$ such that $0 \leq \lambda \leq 1$, we have $\lambda x + (1-\lambda)y \in F$. F is called balanced if $F \neq \emptyset$ and for all $x \in F$ and all $\lambda \in K$ such that $|\lambda| \leq 1$, we have $\lambda x \in F$.

A topology, $\mathcal{T}$, on E is called a vector topology if $\mathcal{T}$ makes the addition and scalar multiplication of E both jointly continuous. If $\mathcal{U}$ is the filter of neighborhoods of o in E, then $\mathcal{U}$ has a base which is comprised of balanced, closed sets. If, for each $U \in \mathcal{U}$, we define

$$N_U = \{(x,y) \in E: \quad x-y \in U\}$$

then $\{N_U: \ U \in \mathcal{U}\}$ is a fundamental system of entourages for a uniform structure, $N_{\mathcal{U}}$, on E. We have $t(N_{\mathcal{U}}) = \mathcal{T}$. Moreover, if F is any other K-vector space, if $\mathcal{S}$ is a vector topology on F and if $\mathcal{V}$ is the filter of $\mathcal{S}$-neighborhoods of o in F, then a linear map ϕ: $E \to F$ is $\mathcal{T}$-$\mathcal{S}$ continuous if and only if it is $N_{\mathcal{U}}$-$N_{\mathcal{V}}$ uniformly continuous. For this reason, one tends to obscure the distinction between $\mathcal{T}$ and $N_{\mathcal{U}}$. In the future, we shall refer to both $\mathcal{T}$ and $N_{\mathcal{U}}$ by the same symbol, $\mathcal{T}$. We shall call $\mathcal{T}$ also a vector uniform structure on E. We shall refer to the pair $E[\mathcal{T}] = (E,\mathcal{T})$ as a topological vector space.

By the category of topological vector spaces we mean the category whose objects are topological vector spaces and whose morphisms are continuous linear maps. The separated, complete spaces form a full subcategory which is reflective. If $E[\mathcal{T}]$ is a topological vector space, a reflection of $E[\mathcal{T}]$ in this subcategory is called a completion of $E[\mathcal{T}]$. It is also a completion of $E[\mathcal{T}]$ as a uniform space.

A set $B \subset E[\mathcal{T}]$ is called a $\mathcal{T}$-bounded if for each neighborhood U of 0 in E, there is some $0 \neq \lambda \in K$ such that $\lambda B \subset U$.

$E[\mathcal{T}]$ is called locally convex if there is a base for the filter of $\mathcal{T}$-neighborhoods at 0 comprised of convex sets. In this case, we denote by E' the dual space of E, i.e., the subspace of E* comprised of $\mathcal{T}$-continuous linear forms. A set

$B \subset E'$ is <u>uniformly equicontinuous</u> (i.e., for every entourage U of K, there is an entourage V of E such that $(x,y) \in V$ implies $(\phi(x), \phi(y)) \in U$ for all $\phi \in B$) if and only if B is equicontinuous at o.

If E and F are K-vector spaces, then we say that E and F are <u>in duality over K</u> if we are given a bilinear map

$$\langle\, , \,\rangle : \quad E \times F \to K$$

$$(x,y) \to \langle x,y \rangle$$

Given such a duality over K, we define <u>$\sigma(E,F)$</u> to be the uniform structure on E of simple convergence on F. This is a locally convex structure. A set $B \subset E$ is called bounded, if B is $\sigma(E,F)$ - precompact, i.e., $\sigma(E,F)$-bounded. $\sigma(E,F)$ is the weakest locally convex structure on E such that for each $y \in F$ the form $x \to \langle x,y \rangle$ is continuous. If $\mathcal{B}$ is a directed covering of E by $\sigma(E,F)$-bounded sets then we denote by $T_{\mathcal{B}}$ the locally convex structure on F determined by the pseudo-metrics.

$$F \times F \to [o,\infty)$$

$$(x,y) \to \sup_{z \in B} |\langle z,x \rangle - \langle z,y \rangle|$$

where $B \in \mathcal{B}$. If $B \subset E$, we denote

$$B^{o} = \{x \in F: \ |\langle y,x \rangle| \leq 1 \ \forall \ y \in B\}$$

If $B \in \mathcal{B}$, then B^{oo} is the smallest balanced, convex, $\sigma(E,F)$-closed set containing B. If $\mathcal{B}$ is stable under multiplication by scalars, then

$$\{B^{o}: \ B \in \mathcal{B}\}$$

is a $T_{\mathcal{B}}$-neighborhood base at o in F comprised of $\sigma(F,E)$-closed, balanced, convex sets. If $\mathcal{B}$ is comprised of all of the bounded sets, we denote

$$T_{\mathcal{B}} = \beta(F,E)$$

If $\mathcal{B}$ is comprised of all $\beta(E,F)$-bounded sets, we denote

$$T_{\mathcal{B}} = \beta^{*}(F,E)$$

If E is $\sigma(E,F)$-separated and if $\mathcal{B}$ is comprised of all sets $B \subset E$ such that B^{oo} is $\sigma(E,F)$-compact, then we denote

$$\mathcal{T}_{\mathcal{B}} = \tau(F,E).$$

$\tau(F,E)$ is the strongest locally convex topology on F much that the dual of F is comprised exactly of the forms

$$x \to \langle y, x\rangle \quad (y \in E).$$

Now let $E[\mathcal{T}]$ be a separated locally convex space and let E' be its dual. By the canonical duality of E and E' over K we mean the duality

$$\langle , \rangle \; E \times E' \to K$$

$$(x,f) \to f(x) = \langle x, f\rangle$$

We have

$$\sigma(E,E') \subset \mathcal{T} \subset \tau(E,E') \subset \beta^*(E,E') \subset \beta(E,E').$$

If $B \subset E$ is convex, B is $\mathcal{T}$-closed if and only if B is $\sigma(E,E')$-closed. If B, $C \subset E$ are convex, U is a $\mathcal{T}$-neighborhood of o and $C \cap (B+U) = \emptyset$, then there is a form $f \in E'$ such that

$$\sup\{\mathrm{Re} f(x): \; x \in B\} < \inf\{\mathrm{Re} f(x): \; x \in C\}$$

A set $B \subset E$ is said to be absorbing if for each $x \in E$, we have $\lambda x \in B$ for some $0 \neq \lambda \in K$. A set $B \subset E$ is said to be bornivorous (a bornivore) if for every $\sigma(E,E')$-bounded set $G \subset E$ there is some $0 \neq \lambda \in K$ such that $\lambda G \subset B$. A set $B \subset E$ is $\mathcal{T}$-bounded if and only if it is $\sigma(E,E')$-bounded. A set $B \subset E$ is called a barrel if $B = B^{oo}$ and B is absorbing. The barrels form a neighborhood base at 0 for $\beta(E,E')$. If $\beta(E,E') = \mathcal{T}$, $\mathcal{T}$ is called barrelled. The bornivorous barrels form a neighborhood base at 0 for $\beta^*(E,E')$. If $\beta^*(E,E') = \mathcal{T}$, $\mathcal{T}$ is called quasi-barrelled. If every convex, balanced bornivore is a neighborhood of 0, $\mathcal{T}$ is called bornological. A bornological space is quasi-barrelled. $\tau(E,E')$ is called the Mackey topology. If $\mathcal{T} = \tau(E,E')$, $E[\mathcal{T}]$ is called a Mackey space. $\sigma(E,E')$ is called a weak topology on E. If $\mathcal{T} = \sigma(E,E')$, $\mathcal{T}$ is called a weak topology.

If E is a K-vector space, a semi-norm on E is a positive function p from E to R such that $p(x+y) \leq p(x) + p(y)$ and $p(\lambda x) = |\lambda| p(x)$ for all $x,y \in E$, $\lambda \in K$. If whenever $p(x) = 0$ then $x=0$, p is called a norm. If $\{p_\nu\}_{\nu \in I}$ is any family of semi-norms on E, then the family of all pseudo-metrics of the form

$$(x,y) \to p_\nu(x-y) \quad (\nu \in I)$$

determines a locally convex uniform structure on E called the (locally convex) topology determined by $\{p_\nu\}_{\nu \in I}$. If $\mathcal{T}$ is any locally convex topology on E, then $\mathcal{T}$ is determined by the family of all $\mathcal{T}$-continuous semi-norms on E.

Chapter 2. COMPACTLY COVERED REFLECTIONS

§1. *Synopsis*

Probably the best way to introduce this chapter is to begin with some examples. Consider the following categories: Topological groups and continuous group homomorphisms; Monoids with uniform structures making multiplication *separately* uniformly continuous and uniformly continuous monoid homomorphisms; Monoids with uniform structures making multiplication *jointly* uniformly continuous and uniformly continuous monoid homomorphisms; Topological spaces and continuous functions; Uniform spaces and uniformly continuous functions. In each of these cases, the compact objects clearly form a full subcategory. What is not immediately clear, but nonetheless is true, is that *in each case the subcategory is reflective*. The reflections are (respectively) Bohr "compactifications"; the "weakly almost periodic compactification" of Glicksberg and DeLeeuw [2]; the "almost periodic compactification" of Glicksberg and DeLeeuw [2]; Stone-Cech "compactifications"; Samuel "compactifications".

A slightly less familiar case would be the following: By a covered locally convex algebra, we will mean a pair $(A,\mathcal{A})$ where A is a locally convex algebra and $\mathcal{A}$ is a directed covering of A by balanced, convex, bounded sets which is stable under multiplication and scalar multiplication. A morphism $(A,\mathcal{A}) \xrightarrow{\phi} (B,\mathcal{B})$ is a continuous algebra homomorphism $\phi\colon A \to B$ such that $\phi(\mathcal{A})$ refines $\mathcal{B}$. $(A,\mathcal{A})$ will be called compactly covered if each set of $\mathcal{A}$ is contained in a compact set of $\mathcal{A}$. The compactly covered objects form a full subcategory. Once again, the subcategory is reflective. Also, there is a forgetful functor from this subcategory to the category of covered uniform monoids and, via this functor, uniform monoids have reflections in this subcategory

The purpose of this chapter is to develop a theory which will yield one theorem which directly generalizes all of the above statements. (Corollary 7.6 is such a result.) In order to achieve this end a theory is developed for what I have elected to call "Cartesian categories" and of "uniformizing rules" for such categories. In Section 2, the notion of a category of covered objects is introduced. Briefly put, to each object of such a category there corresponds an underlying space and a directed covering of that space. Morphisms are required to take coverings to families refining the covering in the codomain. If we require additionally 1) the existence of images for morphisms; 2) that those elementary results about factoring morphisms which are true in most algebraic contexts hold in our category; and 3) that products exist and look like Cartesian products, then we call the category "Cartesian". The choice of the name reflects the author's feeling that, while criteria 1) and 2) are important, it is criterion 3) that is the really crucial one. Section 3 is devoted to those examples of Cartesian categories on which interest will center here and in later chapters.

In Section 4, the notion is introduced of a uniformizing rule for a Cartesian category. Such a rule assigns to each object of the category a set of uniform structures on the underlying space. A certain amount of stability is insisted on, e.g., the inverse image of one of these distinguished structures under a morphism is again a distinguished structure and the set of distinguished structures is closed under taking least upper bounds. These requirements force products of "uniformized objects" to exist and to have as their underlying uniform space the product of their respective underlying uniform spaces. In other words, products of uniformized objects look like Cartesian products. This allows us to use Tychonoff's theorem. Indeed, the key role of Tychonoff's theorem in proving the general theorem mentioned above is the reason for requiring products and product structures in the theory to be (essentially) Cartesian products and product structures. A final requirement on the uniformizing rules is imposed to allow us to use the very fundamental uniform space-theoretic fact that a uniformly continuous map from a dense subspace to a separated, complete space has a unique uniformly continuous extension to the whole space. This fact can be applied in the theory of topological groups or of topological vector spaces--as in many other familiar theories--where the extended map is again a morphism if the original map was. We wish to apply it in our general theory and so restrict it accordingly. Section 5 is devoted to those examples of uniformizing rules for Cartesian categories on which interest will center in later chapters.

Section 7 is devoted to proving general theorems of the kind mentioned at the beginning of this section. The easiest result to state is Theorem 7.1. A direct corollary of this theorem would be the existence of all the compact reflections mentioned in the first paragraph of this section and the fact that the compactly covered objects form a reflective subcategory of the covered locally convex algebras. Slightly more general results are easy corollaries of this theorem. Also there are some corollaries dealing with those situations in which the underlying space of a compactly covered reflection can be recovered by uniform space theoretic methods (compactifications).

Section 6 is devoted to the concept of dual objects and the model given by spaces of bounded linear maps. The notion is introduced of a uniformizing rule giving a Cartesian category cover-closed dual objects. This notion will play an important role in later chapters.

§2. Cartesian Categories

1. Definition: By a space functor sp on a category $\mathcal{C}$, we will mean a faithful co-variant functor from $\mathcal{C}$ to the category of sets (see §1.3).

If sp is such a functor, the pair $(\mathcal{C}, \text{sp})$ will be called a concrete category.

2. Definition: By a covered set we mean an ordered pair $(X, \mathcal{A})$ where X is a non-empty set and $\mathcal{A}$ is an increasingly directed covering of X.

By the category of covered sets we mean the category whose objects are covered sets and whose morphisms

$$(X,\mathcal{A}) \xrightarrow{\phi} (Y,\mathcal{B})$$

are functions ϕ: $X \to Y$ such that $\phi(\mathcal{A})$ refines $\mathcal{B}$.

There is a natural space functor on this category, denoted, as will always be the case, by sp.

<u>If $A = (X,\mathcal{A})$ is a covered set, we agree to write $\mathcal{A} = c(A)$</u>.

3. <u>Definition</u>: By a <u>category of covered objects</u> we shall mean a pair ($\mathcal{C}$, csp) where $\mathcal{C}$ is a category and csp is a <u>faithful covariant</u> functor--called <u>the covered space functor</u>--from $\mathcal{C}$ to the category of covered sets.

We will always denote by sp both the natural space functor on the category of covered sets and the space functor spo csp on $\mathcal{C}$, where ($\mathcal{C}$, csp) is a category of covered objects. Also, if A is an object of $\mathcal{C}$, we will write c(A) instead of c(csp A). <u>c(A) is called the covering family of A</u>. Finally, if A, B are objects of $\mathcal{C}$ and if $\phi \in$Mor(A, B), we will write ϕ instead of either csp(ϕ) or sp(ϕ).

We shall also permit ourselves certain obvious abuses of terminology and notation, i.e., if we say that a category $\mathcal{C}$ is a category of covered objects, we shall mean that we are given a covariant functor from $\mathcal{C}$ to the category of covered sets, this functor always being denoted by csp, and that ($\mathcal{C}$, csp) is a category of covered objects. It will often happen that there is some "natural" choice of csp in the case of some particular category $\mathcal{C}$ and, when we say that $\mathcal{C}$ is a category of covered objects, we will always assume that we have made that choice.

We note at this time that, in the category of covered sets, products always exist. In fact, if $\{(X_\nu, \mathcal{A}_\nu)\}_{\nu \in I}$ is a family of covered sets, we put

$$X = \Pi_{\nu \in I} X_\nu$$

$$\mathcal{A} = \{\Pi_{\nu \in I} A_\nu : \{A_\nu\}_{\nu \in I} \in \Pi_{\nu \in I} \mathcal{A}_\nu\}$$

Then $((X,A), \{\pi_\nu\}_{\nu\in I})$ is a product of the family $\{(X_\nu, A_\nu)\}_{\nu\in I}$ in this category. <u>We shall always refer to this product as the Cartesian product of this family, and denote it by $\Pi_{\nu\in I}(X_\nu, A_\nu)$</u>.

4. <u>Definition</u>: Let $\mathcal{C}$ be a category of covered objects and let A be an object of $\mathcal{C}$. An object B of $\mathcal{C}$ is called <u>a sub-object of A</u> provided that the following conditions are satisfied:

(1) $\text{sp } B \subset \text{sp } A$

(2) c(B) refines c(A)

(3) there is a morphism $\phi\in\text{Mor}(B,A)$ such that the function

$$\phi: \quad \text{spB} \to \text{spA}$$

is the inclusion map

(4) if C is any object of $\mathcal{C}$ and $\psi\in\text{Mor}(C,A)$ satisfies the conditions that $\psi(\text{spC})\subset\text{spB}$ and $\psi(c(C))$ refines c(B), then there is a morphism $\theta\in\text{Mor}(C,B)$ such that $\psi = \phi\circ\theta$ (ϕ the inclusion map).

5. <u>Definition</u>: Let $\mathcal{C}$ be a category of covered objects. We say that <u>$\mathcal{C}$ contains images</u> provided that whenever we are given two objects A, C of $\mathcal{C}$ and a morphism $\psi\in\text{Mor}(C,A)$, then there is a sub-object B of A such that

$$\text{spB} = \psi(\text{spC})$$

$$c(B) \sim \psi(c(C))$$

<u>We denote such an object B by $\psi(C)$</u>.

We note in the above definition that there is nothing to prevent the existence of two distinct objects B, B' which satisfy the stated conditions. However, if this is so, it is also clear that spB = spB', c(B) $\sim$ c(B') and (from (4) of Def. 4) that the identity map on spB is a morphism of both Mor(B,B') and Mor(B',B) and is therefore a $\mathcal{C}$-isomorphism. In other words, for all practical purposes B and B' are the same object and we shall feel free to write B = ψ(C) just as though we were sure that B were unique.

6. Definition: Let $\mathcal{C}$ be a category of covered objects. We say that morphisms can be factored in $\mathcal{C}$ provided that the following condition holds:

Let A, B, C be objects of $\mathcal{C}$, let $\phi \in \mathrm{Mor}(A,B)$ and let $\psi \in \mathrm{Mor}(A,C)$. We suppose the function ϕ to be surjective and that there is a morphism

$$\theta: \ \mathrm{csp}(B) \to \mathrm{csp}(C)$$

in the category of covered sets such that $\psi = \theta\phi$. Then we require that θ be also in Mor(B,C).

7. Definition: A Category of covered objects $\mathcal{C}$ is called Cartesian if the following conditions hold:

(1) $\mathcal{C}$ has products and the covered space functor preserves products.

(2) $\mathcal{C}$ contains final objects, and if A is such an object then spA reduces to a point. Such objects are called the points of $\mathcal{C}$.

(3) $\mathcal{C}$ contains images.

(4) Morphisms can be factored in $\mathcal{C}$.

(Since a product of an empty family of objects is a pair (A,ϕ) where A is a final object (and ϕ an empty family of morphisms), (2) is technically redundant.)

We will conclude this section by introducing one last concept.

8. Definition: Let $\mathcal{C}$ and $\mathcal{D}$ be categories of covered objects. A covariant functor T from $\mathcal{C}$ to $\mathcal{D}$ will be called admissible if we have

$$\mathrm{csp} = \mathrm{csp} \circ T$$

That is, if $A \in \mathrm{Obj}\,\mathcal{C}$ and ϕ is a morphism of $\mathcal{C}$, then we have $\mathrm{csp}(A) = \mathrm{csp}(T(A))$ and $\mathrm{csp}(\phi) = \mathrm{csp}(T(\phi))$.

Clearly, an admissable functor is always faithful. In most cases we will consider, our admissible functors will be forgetful functors of some kind (most of which are clearly admissible). We will be interested in cases where $\mathcal{D}$ has reflections in $\mathcal{C}$ via an admissible functor.

§3. Examples of Cartesian Categories

1. Example: The category of covered sets is Cartesian.

2. Example: We will hereafter always consider the category of sets to be a category covered objects via the covered space functor csp(X) = (X, {X}). As such, it is a Cartesian category.

3. Example: We define the category of monoids to be the category whose objects are monoids and whose morphisms are monoid homomorphisms. We will hereafter always consider this category to be a category of covered objects via the covered space functor csp(M) = (spM, {spM}). As such, it is a Cartesian category.

The above example brings up a rather common abuse of notation which we will use from time to time. If $\mathcal{C}$ is a concrete category and A is an object of $\mathcal{C}$, we will often write A in place of spA. Whenever we do this, we will be careful to preclude any possibility for confusion.

4. Example: We define the category of covered monoids as follows: An object in this category is a pair $(M,\mathcal{M})$, where M is a monoid and $\mathcal{M}$ is a directed covering of M which is stable under multiplication (see §1.5). A morphism

$$(M,\mathcal{M}) \xrightarrow{\phi} (N,\mathcal{N})$$

is a monoid homomorphism ϕ from M to N such that $\phi(\mathcal{M})$ refines $\mathcal{N}$. This is a Cartesian category.

5. Example: We define the category of vector spaces over K to be the category whose objects are vector spaces over K and whose morphisms are linear maps. We will always consider it as a category of covered objects via the functor csp(E) = (E, {E}). As such, it is a Cartesian category.

6. Example: We define the category of covered vector spaces over K to be the category whose objects are pairs $(E,\mathcal{S})$ where E is a vector space over K and $\mathcal{S}$ is a directed covering of E by balanced, convex sets which is stable under multiplication by scalars (see §1.5). A morphism

$$(E,\mathcal{S}) \xrightarrow{\phi} (F,\mathcal{T})$$

is a linear map ϕ from E to F such that $\phi(\mathcal{S})$ refines $\mathcal{T}$. This is a Cartesian category.

7. Example: We define the category of K-algebras in the obvious way. The covered space functor is csp(A) = (A, {A}). This is a Cartesian category.

8. Example: We define the category of covered K-algebras to be the category whose objects are pairs $(A,\mathcal{A})$ where A is an algebra over K and where $\mathcal{A}$ is a directed covering of A by convex, balanced sets which is stable under multiplication and stable under multiplication by scalars. (See §1.5). A morphism

$$(A,\mathcal{A}) \xrightarrow{\phi} (B,\mathcal{B})$$

is a K-algebra homomorphism from A to B such that $\phi(\mathcal{A})$ refines $\mathcal{B}$. This is a Cartesian category.

Examples 1 thru 8 give us a plentiful supply of forgetful functors, as is indicated in the following (commutative) diagram.

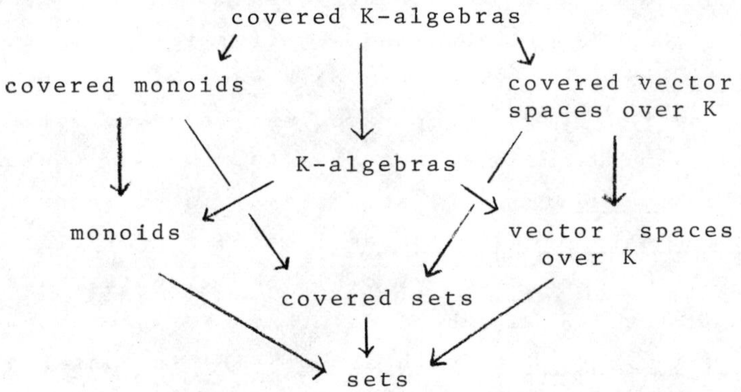

All these functors are admissible. Moreover, they give us several examples of reflections of one category in another. The more familiar ones are the following: Sets have reflections in monoids (free monoids); sets have reflections in vector spaces (the vector space with formal basis X, X a set); monoids have reflections in algebras ("semi-group algebras"); sets have reflections in algebras (free algebras). These reflections are more familiar since they all involve a special kind of category of covered objects, which we will call a category of sets, i.e., a category in which

$$c(A) \sim \{spA\}$$

for each object A. The examples of reflections in the other cases are less familiar, but easily obtained from the others. For instance, covered sets have reflections in covered vector spaces. In fact, if $(X,\mathcal{A})$ is a covered set and (E,ϕ) is a vector space reflection of X, let $\mathcal{S}$ denote the smallest directed family of balanced, convex subsets of E which is stable under scalar multiplication and is refined by $\phi(\mathcal{A})$. Then $((E,\mathcal{S}),\phi)$ is a covered vector space reflection of $(X,\mathcal{A})$. In a similar manner, we can see that covered sets have reflections in covered monoids and in covered algebras. Also, covered monoids have reflections in covered algebras.

§4. Uniformizing Rules for Cartesian Categories

Let $\mathcal{C}$ be a category of covered objects and let A be an object of $\mathcal{C}$. Let $\mathcal{U}$ be a uniform structure on spA. We denote by $A[\mathcal{U}]$ the pair $(A,\mathcal{U})$. $A[\mathcal{U}]$ is called a uniformized object. We say that $A[\mathcal{U}]$ is separated if $\mathcal{U}$ is separated. We say that $A[\mathcal{U}]$ is completely covered if $\mathcal{U}$ is separated and if every set of c(A) is contained in some $\mathcal{U}$-complete set of c(A). We say that $A[\mathcal{U}]$ is precompactly covered, if every set of c(A) is $\mathcal{U}$-precompact. We say that $A[\mathcal{U}]$ is compactly covered if each set of c(A) is contained in some $\mathcal{U}$-compact set of c(A) (this implies that $\mathcal{U}$ is separated). Now let B be a subobject of A. We say that B is cover-closed in A w.r.t. $\mathcal{U}$ if each set of c(B) is contained in some $\mathcal{U}$-closed set of c(B). We say that A is cover-closed w.r.t. $\mathcal{U}$ if A is cover-closed in A w.r.t. $\mathcal{U}$. We denote by $\mathcal{U}|_B$ the uniform structure $\mathcal{U}|_{spB}$. If we say that B is completely covered, precompactly covered, or compactly covered w.r.t. $\mathcal{U}$ we shall mean that $B[\mathcal{U}|_B]$ has this property.

Now suppose that we are given a covered set $(X,\mathcal{A})$ and a set Y. Let ϕ: $X \to Y$ be a function, let $\mathcal{U}$ be a uniform structure (resp. topology) on X and let $\mathcal{V}$ be a uniform structure (resp. topology) on Y. We call ϕ locally $\mathcal{U}$-$\mathcal{V}$ uniformly continuous (resp. locally $\mathcal{U}$-$\mathcal{V}$ continuous) if for each $A \in \mathcal{A}$, the map $\phi|_A$ is $\mathcal{U}|_A$ -$\mathcal{V}$ uniformly continuous (resp. continuous).

1. Definition: By a uniformizing rule for a Cartesian category $\mathcal{C}$, we mean a rule, u, which assigns to each object A of $\mathcal{C}$ a family u(A) of uniform structures on spA such that the following conditions hold:

(1) If A, B are objects of $\mathcal{C}$, if $\phi \in \mathrm{Mor}(A,B)$, and if $\mathcal{U} \in u(B)$,

$$\phi^{-1}(\mathcal{U}) \in u(A)$$

(2) If A is any object of $\mathcal{C}$ and if $\Phi \subset u(A)$, then $\vee\Phi \in u(A)$.

(3) Let A be an object of $\mathcal{C}$ and let B be a sub-object of A. Let $\mathcal{U} \in u(A)$ and suppose that A is cover-closed w.r.t. $\mathcal{U}$. Then there is a sub-object C of A such that the following conditions are satisfied:

(3-a) B is a sub-object of C

(3-b) C is cover-closed w.r.t. $\mathcal{U}$.

(3-c) Each set of c(C) is contained in the $\mathcal{U}$-closure of some set of c(B).

(3-d) If D is any object of $\mathcal{C}$, if $\mathcal{V} \in u(D)$, if $D[\mathcal{V}]$ is separated, and if ϕ is a locally $\mathcal{U}$-$\mathcal{V}$ uniformly continuous morphism from csp(C) to csp(D) such that $\phi|_{spB} \in \mathrm{Mor}(B,D)$ then $\phi \in \mathrm{Mor}(C,D)$.

Now let $\mathcal{C}$ be a Cartesian and let u be a uniformizing rule for $\mathcal{C}$. Let A be an object of $\mathcal{C}$, let B be a sub-object of A, let $\mathcal{U} \in u(A)$ and suppose that A is cover-closed w.r.t. $\mathcal{U}$. If C is a sub-object of A such that the conditions of part (3) of the above definition are satisfied with respect to A, B, C, we call C a cover-closed envelope of B in A w.r.t. $\mathcal{U}$. The following result about these objects is quite important.

2. Proposition: Let $\mathcal{C}$ be a Cartesian category and let u be a uniformizing rule for $\mathcal{C}$. Let A be an object of $\mathcal{C}$ and let B be a subobject of A. Let $\mathcal{U}\in u(A)$, suppose that A is cover-closed w.r.t. $\mathcal{U}$ and let C be a cover-closed envelope of B in A w.r.t. $\mathcal{U}$.

(1) Let C' be a sub-object of A which satisfies conditions (3-a), (3-b), and (3-c) of Definition 1. Then spC = spC' = $\bigcup\{\overline{F}: F\in c(B)\}$. The identity map on spC is a $\mathcal{C}$-isomorphism in Mor(C,C') and C' satisfies (3-d).

(2) Let D be an object of $\mathcal{C}$, let $\mathcal{V}\in u(D)$ and suppose that D[$\mathcal{V}$] is completely covered. Then if ψ is a $\mathcal{U}$-$\mathcal{V}$ uniformly continuous morphism from B to D, there is a $\mathcal{U}$-$\mathcal{V}$ uniformly continuous morphism $\phi\in$ Mor(C,D) such that $\phi|_{spB} = \psi$.

Proof: (1) The first statement is clear as is the fact that c(C) $\sim$ c(C'). But if we apply Definition 2.4 (part (4)) to the inclusion maps C $\to$ A and C' $\to$ A, the fact that c(C) $\sim$ c(C') forces the last statement.

(2) Under the stated hypotheses, there is a morphism ϕ from csp(C) to csp(D) which is $\mathcal{U}$-$\mathcal{V}$ uniformly continuous and satisfies the condition $\phi|_{spB} = \psi$. So we must have $\phi\in$ Mor(C,D) by (3-d).

3. Notation: Let $\mathcal{C}$ be a Cartesian category and let u be a uniformizing rule for $\mathcal{C}$. We denote by $\mathcal{C}_u^{\ell}$ the category whose objects are pairs A[$\mathcal{U}$] = (A,$\mathcal{U}$) where A is an object of $\mathcal{C}$ and $\mathcal{U}\in u(A)$. The morphisms of $\mathcal{C}_u^{\ell}$ are those $\mathcal{C}$-morphisms which are locally uniformly continuous. We denote by $\mathcal{C}_u$ the subcategory of $\mathcal{C}_u^{\ell}$ whose objects are the same and whose morphisms are uniformly continuous. Both $\mathcal{C}_u$ and $\mathcal{C}_u^{\ell}$ are categories of covered objects.

4. Proposition: Let $\mathcal{C}$ be a Cartesian category and let u be a uniformizing rule for $\mathcal{C}$. Let $\{A_\nu\}_{\nu\in I}$ be a family of objects of $\mathcal{C}$ and, for each $\nu\in I$, choose $\mathcal{U}_\nu\in u(A_\nu)$. If (A, $\{\phi_\nu\}_{\nu\in I}$) is a product of the family $\{A_\nu\}_{\nu\in I}$ in $\mathcal{C}$, then $(A[\bigvee_{\nu\in I}\phi_\nu^{-1}(\mathcal{U}_\nu)], \{\phi_\nu\}_{\nu\in I})$ is a product of the family $\{A_\nu[\mathcal{U}_\nu]\}_{\nu\in I}$ in either $\mathcal{C}_u^{\ell}$ or $\mathcal{C}_u$.

Proof: Apply part (1) of Definition 2.7 and parts (1) and (2) of Definition 1.

Let $\mathcal{C}$ be a Cartesian category and let u be a uniformizing rule for $\mathcal{C}$. Let A be an object of $\mathcal{C}$ and let $\mathcal{U}$ be a uniform structure on spA. By the uniform structure in u(A) determined by $\mathcal{U}$, we mean the strongest uniform structure in u(A) which is weaker than $\mathcal{U}$. We sometimes denote this structure by $\mathcal{U}_u$. By the inductive uniform structure in u(A) determined by $\mathcal{U}$, we mean the strongest uniform structure $\mathcal{V}$ in u(A) which makes the identity map on spA locally $\mathcal{U}$-$\mathcal{V}$ uniformly continuous. We sometimes denote this structure by $\mathcal{U}^i_u$. In case $\mathcal{U} \in u(A)$, we often abbreviate $\mathcal{U}^i_u$ to $\mathcal{U}^i$. Now let $\mathcal{T}$ denote any topology on spA. By the uniform structure in u(A) determined by $\mathcal{T}$, we mean the strongest uniform structure $\mathcal{V} \in u(A)$ such that $t(\mathcal{V}) \subset \mathcal{T}$. We sometimes denote this structure by $\mathcal{T}_u$. By the inductive uniform structure in u(A) determined by $\mathcal{T}$, we mean the strongest uniform structure $\mathcal{V} \in u(A)$ which makes the identity map on spA locally $\mathcal{T}$-$\mathcal{V}$ continuous. We sometimes denote this structure by $\mathcal{T}^i_u$.

5. Notation: Let $\mathcal{C}$ be a category of covered objects. We denote by $\mathcal{C}_o$, resp. $\mathcal{C}^\ell_o$, the category whose objects are pairs $A[\mathcal{U}] = (A,\mathcal{U})$ where A is an object of $\mathcal{C}$, $\mathcal{U}$ is any uniform structure on spA, and whose morphisms are the uniformly continuous, resp. locally uniformly continuous, morphisms of $\mathcal{C}$.

We denote by $\mathcal{C}_t$, resp. $\mathcal{C}^\ell_t$, the category whose objects are pairs $A[\mathcal{T}] = (A,\mathcal{T})$ where A is an object of $\mathcal{C}$, $\mathcal{T}$ is any topology on spA, and whose morphisms are the continuous, resp. locally continuous, morphisms of $\mathcal{C}$.

All these categories are categories of covered objects.

6. Proposition: Let $\mathcal{C}$ be a Cartesian category and let u be a uniformizing rule for $\mathcal{C}$. Let $\mathcal{D}$ be a category of covered objects and let T be an admissible functor from $\mathcal{C}$ to $\mathcal{D}$ (see 2.8).

(1) T defines admissible functors, all denoted by T_u, from $\mathcal{C}_u$ to $\mathcal{D}_o$, from $\mathcal{C}_u$ to $\mathcal{D}^\ell_o$, from $\mathcal{C}_u$ to $\mathcal{D}_t$, from $\mathcal{C}_u$ to $\mathcal{D}^\ell_t$, from $\mathcal{C}^\ell_u$ to $\mathcal{D}^\ell_o$ and from $\mathcal{C}^\ell_u$ to $\mathcal{D}^\ell_t$.

(2) Let A be an object of $\mathcal{D}$ and let $\mathcal{U}$ be a uniform structure (topology) on spA. Suppose that A has a reflection in $\mathcal{C}$ via T (see §1.3). Then, considered as an object of $\mathcal{D}_o$ ($\mathcal{D}_t$), $A[\mathcal{U}]$ has a reflection in $\mathcal{C}_u$ via T_u. Considered as an object of $\mathcal{D}_o^\ell$ ($\mathcal{D}_t^\ell$), $A[\mathcal{U}]$ has a reflection in $\mathcal{C}_u$ via T_u. Considered as an object of $\mathcal{D}_o^\ell$ ($\mathcal{D}_t^\ell$), $A[\mathcal{U}]$ has a reflection in $\mathcal{C}_u^\ell$ via T_u.

(3) If $\mathcal{D}$ has reflections in $\mathcal{C}$ via T, then $\mathcal{D}_o$ and $\mathcal{D}_t$ have reflections in $\mathcal{C}_u$ via T_u, $\mathcal{D}_o^\ell$ and $\mathcal{D}_t^\ell$ have reflections in $\mathcal{C}_u$ via T_u, and $\mathcal{D}_o^\ell$ and $\mathcal{D}_t^\ell$ have reflections in $\mathcal{C}_u$ via T_u.

Proof: (1) The definition of T_u is, of course,

$$T_u\colon\ A[\mathcal{U}] \to T(A)[\mathcal{U}]$$

$$\phi \to \phi$$

as a functor from $\mathcal{C}_u$ to $\mathcal{D}_o$ or $\mathcal{D}_o^\ell$ and from $\mathcal{C}_u^\ell$ to $\mathcal{D}_o^\ell$ and

$$T_u\colon\ A[\mathcal{U}] \to T(A)[t(\mathcal{U})]$$

$$\phi \to \phi$$

as a functor from $\mathcal{C}_u$ to $\mathcal{D}_t$ or $\mathcal{D}_t^\ell$ and from $\mathcal{C}_u^\ell$ to $\mathcal{D}_t^\ell$.

Now (3) follows immediately from (2). Also, if $A[\mathcal{U}]$ is an object of $\mathcal{D}_o^\ell$ or $\mathcal{D}_t^\ell$ then a reflection for $A[\mathcal{U}]$ in $\mathcal{C}_u$ via T_u is also a reflection in $\mathcal{C}_u^\ell$. Finally, since the topological case is analogous to the uniform structure case, our problem reduces to showing that if $A[\mathcal{U}]$ is an object of either $\mathcal{D}_o$ or $\mathcal{D}_o^\ell$ then $A[\mathcal{U}]$ has a reflection in $\mathcal{C}_u$ if A has a reflection in $\mathcal{C}$.

Suppose A is an object of $\mathcal{D}$, $\mathcal{U}$ is a uniform structure on spA, and (B,ϕ) is a reflection for A in $\mathcal{C}$ via T. Let $\mathcal{V}$, resp. $\mathcal{W}$, be the strongest uniform structure in u(B) making ϕ uniformly continuous, resp. locally uniformly continuous, with respect to $\mathcal{U}$. Now let C be any object of $\mathcal{C}$ and suppose that $\psi \in \mathrm{Mor}(A,T(C))$. Let $\mathcal{Z} \in u(C)$. There is a unique morphism $\theta \in \mathrm{Mor}(B,C)$ such that $\psi = \theta\phi$.

If ψ is $\mathcal{U}$-$\mathcal{Z}$ uniformly continuous, then $\psi^{-1}(\mathcal{Z})\subset\mathcal{U}$. So $\phi^{-1}\theta^{-1}(\mathcal{Z})\subset\mathcal{U}$. So ϕ is $\mathcal{U}$-$\theta^{-1}(\mathcal{Z})$ uniformly continuous. But $\theta^{-1}(\mathcal{Z})\in u(B)$. So, by definition, $\theta^{-1}(\mathcal{Z})\subset\mathcal{V}$. So θ is $\mathcal{V}$-$\mathcal{Z}$ uniformly continuous. So $(B[\mathcal{V}],\phi)$ is a reflection for $A[\mathcal{U}]$, considered as an object of $\mathcal{D}_o$.

If ψ is locally $\mathcal{U}$-$\mathcal{Z}$ uniformly continuous and if $F\in c(A)$, then $\psi^{-1}(\mathcal{Z})|_F\subset\mathcal{U}|_F$. So $\phi^{-1}\theta^{-1}(\mathcal{Z})|_F\subset\mathcal{U}|_F$. So ϕ is locally $\mathcal{U}$-$\theta^{-1}(\mathcal{Z})$ uniformly continuous. But $\theta^{-1}(\mathcal{Z})\in u(B)$. So, by definition, $\theta^{-1}(\mathcal{Z})\subset\mathcal{W}$. So θ is $\mathcal{W}$-$\mathcal{Z}$ uniformly continuous. So $(B[\mathcal{W}],\phi)$ is a reflection for $A[\mathcal{U}]$, considered as an object of $\mathcal{D}_o^\ell$.

7. <u>Definition</u>: Let $\mathcal{C}$ be a Cartesian category, u a uniformizing rule for $\mathcal{C}$. Let $\mathcal{D}$ be a category of covered objects and let T be an admissible functor from $\mathcal{C}$ to $\mathcal{D}$ (2.8). Let A be an object of $\mathcal{D}$, $\mathcal{U}$ a uniform structure (topology) on spA, and suppose A has a reflection in $\mathcal{C}$ via T (see §1.3).

If we consider $A[\mathcal{U}]$ as an object of $\mathcal{D}_o(\mathcal{D}_t)$ then a reflection for $A[\mathcal{U}]$ in $\mathcal{C}_u$ via T_u will be called <u>a reflection for $A[\mathcal{U}]$ in $\mathcal{C}$ with respect to u via T</u>.

If we consider $A[\mathcal{U}]$ as an object of $\mathcal{D}_o^\ell$ $(\mathcal{D}_t^\ell)$ then a reflection for $A[\mathcal{U}]$ in $\mathcal{C}_u$ via T_u will be called <u>an inductive reflection for $A[\mathcal{U}]$ in $\mathcal{C}$ with respect to u via T</u>.

If we consider $A[\mathcal{U}]$ as an object of $\mathcal{D}_o^\ell$ $(\mathcal{D}_t^\ell)$ then a reflection for $A[\mathcal{U}]$ in $\mathcal{C}_u^\ell$ via T_u will be called <u>a local reflection for $A[\mathcal{U}]$ in $\mathcal{C}$ with respect to u via T</u>.

8. <u>Corollary</u>: Let $\mathcal{C}$ be a Cartesian category, let $\mathcal{D}$ be another category of covered objects and let T be an admissible functor from $\mathcal{C}$ to $\mathcal{D}$. Suppose that $\mathcal{D}$ has reflections in $\mathcal{C}$ via T.

Let A be an object of $\mathcal{D}$ and let $\mathcal{U}$ be a uniform structure (topology) on spA. Let (B,ϕ) be a reflection for A in $\mathcal{C}$ via T and let $\mathcal{V}$, resp. $\mathcal{W}$ be the strongest uniform structure in u(B) making ϕ uniformly continuous (continuous), resp. locally uniformly continuous (locally continuous).

(1) $(B[\mathcal{V}],\phi)$ is a reflection for $A[\mathcal{U}]$ in $\mathcal{C}$ with respect to u via T.

(2) $(B[\mathcal{W}],\phi)$ is an inductive reflection for $A[\mathcal{U}]$ in $\mathcal{C}$ with respect to u via T.

Proof: See the proof of Proposition 6.

9. Definition: Let $\mathcal{C}$ and $\mathcal{D}$ be Cartesian categories and let u, resp. v, be a uniformizing rule for $\mathcal{C}$, resp. $\mathcal{D}$. Let T be an admissible functor from $\mathcal{C}$ to $\mathcal{D}$. T will be called compatible with u and v if $u(A) \subset v(T(A))$ for every object A of $\mathcal{C}$.

10. Corollary: Let $\mathcal{C}$ and $\mathcal{D}$ be Cartesian categories, let u, resp. v, be a uniformizing rule for $\mathcal{C}$, resp. $\mathcal{D}$. Let T be an admissible functor from $\mathcal{C}$ to $\mathcal{D}$, compatible with u and v.

(1) T defines admissible functors, all denoted T_{uv}, from $\mathcal{C}_u$ to $\mathcal{D}_v$, from $\mathcal{C}_u$ to $\mathcal{D}^{\ell}_v$, and from $\mathcal{C}^{\ell}_u$ to $\mathcal{D}^{\ell}_v$.

(2) Let A be an object of $\mathcal{D}$, $\mathcal{U} \in v(A)$ and suppose A has a reflec-in $\mathcal{C}$ via T. Considering $A[\mathcal{U}]$ as an object of $\mathcal{D}_v$, any reflection of $A[\mathcal{U}]$ in $\mathcal{C}$ w.r.t. u via T is a reflection for $A[\mathcal{U}]$ in $\mathcal{C}_u$ via T_{uv}. Considering $A[\mathcal{U}]$ as an object of $\mathcal{D}^{\ell}_v$, any inductive reflection of $A[\mathcal{U}]$ in $\mathcal{C}$ w.r.t. u via T is a reflection for $A[\mathcal{U}]$ in $\mathcal{C}_u$ via T_{uv}. Considering $A[\mathcal{U}]$ as an object of $\mathcal{D}^{\ell}_v$, any local reflection of $A[\mathcal{U}]$ in $\mathcal{C}$ w.r.t. u via T is a reflection for $A[\mathcal{U}]$ in $\mathcal{C}^{\ell}_u$ via T_{uv}.

(3) If $\mathcal{D}$ has reflections in $\mathcal{C}$ via T, then $\mathcal{D}_v$ has reflections in $\mathcal{C}_u$ via T_{uv}, $\mathcal{D}^{\ell}_v$ has reflections in $\mathcal{C}_u$ via T_{uv} and $\mathcal{D}^{\ell}_v$ has reflections in $\mathcal{C}^{\ell}_u$ via T_{uv}.

If, in Definition 7, T is understood, the phrase "via T" will be omitted.

§5. Examples of Uniformizing Rules for Cartesian Categories

1. Example: Let $\mathcal{C}$ denote the category of covered sets. The rule u which assigns to each object A of $\mathcal{C}$ the set u(A) of all uniform structures on spA is a uniformizing rule for $\mathcal{C}$. $\mathcal{C}_u$ will be called the category of covered uniform spaces.

If $\mathcal{D}$ is any other projective category and v is a uniformizing rule for $\mathcal{D}$, then there are forgetful functors from $\mathcal{D}_v^\ell$ to $\mathcal{C}_u^\ell$ and from $\mathcal{D}_v$ to $\mathcal{C}_u$. We note the following two important facts about them:

(1) Each of them preserves products (by Proposition 4.3).

(2) If A is an object of $\mathcal{D}$, $\mathcal{U} \in v(A)$, A is cover-closed w.r.t. $\mathcal{U}$, B is a subobject of A, and C is a cover-closed envelope of B in A w.r.t. $\mathcal{U}$, then we have $spC = \bigcup\{\overline{F}: F \in c(B)\}$. c(C) is equivalent to $\{\overline{F}: F \in c(B)\}$. Therefore, the identity map on spC is a $\mathcal{C}$-isomorphism from csp(C) to $(spC, \{\overline{F}: F \in c(B)\})$.

2. <u>Example</u>: Let $\mathcal{C}$ denote the category of sets.

The rule u which assigns to each set X the set u(X) of all uniform structures on X is a uniformizing rule for $\mathcal{C}$. $\mathcal{C}_u$ is called <u>the category of uniform spaces</u>.

3. <u>Example</u>: Let $\mathcal{C}$ denote the category of monoids.

The rule u which assigns to each monoid M the set u(M) of all uniform structures on M which make the multiplication of M <u>separately</u> uniformly continuous is a uniformizing rule for $\mathcal{C}$. $\mathcal{C}_u$ is called <u>the category of uniform monoids</u>.

The rule e which assigns to each monoid M the set e(M) of all uniform structures on M which make the multiplication of M <u>jointly</u> uniformly continuous is a uniformizing rule for $\mathcal{C}$.

In the above example, as in all examples of uniformizing rules for Cartesian categories of sets, the following holds: Let $\mathcal{C}$ be a Cartesian category of sets and let u be a uniformizing rule for $\mathcal{C}$. We can state a result analogous to that we stated after Example 1: There is a forgetful functor from $\mathcal{C}_u$ to the category of uniform spaces. We note the following two important facts about it:

(1) It preserves products.

(2) If A is an object of $\mathcal{C}$, $\mathcal{U} \in u(A)$, B is a subobject of A and C is a (cover-) closed envelope of B in A w.r.t. $\mathcal{U}$, then we have

$$spC = \overline{spB}$$

4. Example: Let C denote the category of covered monoids.

The rule u which assigns to each covered monoid $(M,\mathcal{M})$ the set of all uniform structures on M which make the multiplication of M separately uniformly continuous is a uniformizing rule for C. C_u will be called the category of covered uniform monoids.

The rule e which assigns to each covered monoid $(M,\mathcal{M})$ the set of all uniform structures on M which make the multiplication of M separately uniformly continuous on M and jointly uniformly continuous on each set of $\mathcal{M}$ is a uniformizing rule for C.

5. Example: Let C denote the category of vector spaces over K. The rule u which assigns to each vector space E the set u(E) of all locally convex topologies on E is a uniformizing rule for C. C_u will be called the category of locally convex spaces.

The rule w which assigns to E the set w(E) of all weak topologies in u(E) is a uniformizing rule for C. (See Köthe [1], §22.5.)

6. Example: Let C denote the category of covered vector spaces over K.

The rule u which assigns to each covered vector space $(E,\mathcal{S})$ the set of all locally convex uniform structures on E which make each set of $\mathcal{S}$ a bounded set is a uniformizing rule for C. C_u will be called the category of covered locally convex spaces.

The rule w which assigns to each covered vector space $(E,\mathcal{S})$ the set of all weak topologies in $u(E,\mathcal{S})$ is a uniformizing rule for C. C_w is called the category of covered weak locally convex spaces.

7. Example: Let C denote the category of K-algebras. The uniformizing rule u which assigns to each algebra A the set u(A) of all locally convex topologies on A which make the multiplication of A separately continuous is a uniformizing rule for C. C_u will be called the category of locally convex algebras (over K).

The rule w which assigns to each algebra A the set w(A) of all weak topologies in u(A) is a uniformizing rule for C.

8. Example: Let $\mathcal{C}$ denote the category of covered K-algebras. the uniformizing rule u which assigns to each covered algebra $(A,\mathcal{A})$ the set $u(A,\mathcal{A})$ of all locally convex topologies on A which make A a locally convex algebra and make each set of $\mathcal{A}$ bounded is a uniformizing rule for $\mathcal{C}$. $\mathcal{C}_u$ will be called the category of covered locally convex algebras (over K).

The uniformizing rule $\mathcal{W}$ which assigns to each covered algebra $(A,\mathcal{A})$ the set $\mathcal{W}(A,\mathcal{A})$ of all weak topologies in $u(A,\mathcal{A})$ is a uniformizing rule for $\mathcal{C}$. $\mathcal{C}_{\mathcal{W}}$ will be called the category of covered weak locally convex algebras.

The uniformizing rule e which assigns to each covered algebra $(A,\mathcal{A})$ the set $e(A,\mathcal{A})$ of all topologies in $u(A,\mathcal{A})$ which make multiplication jointly uniformly continuous on each set of $\mathcal{A}$ is a uniformizing rule for $\mathcal{C}$.

The uniformizing rule $\mathcal{W}e$ which assigns to each covered algebra $(A,\mathcal{A})$ the set $\mathcal{W}e(A,\mathcal{A}) = \mathcal{W}(A,\mathcal{A}) \cap e(A,\mathcal{A})$ is a uniformizing rule for $\mathcal{C}$.

In Section 3, we mentioned that in Examples 1 thru 8 we have many forgetful functors, all of which are admissible and many of which yield reflections. In each such case Proposition 4.6 guarantees us reflections in the uniformized categories mentioned in this section. I will state explicitly at this time only the cases which will be of most interest in later chapters:

Let $S[\mathcal{U}]$ be a covered uniform monoid. Then $S[\mathcal{U}]$ has reflections, local reflections and inductive reflections in the category of covered locally convex algebras over K and in the category of covered weak locally convex algebras over K. Analogous results hold with respect to the rules e and $\mathcal{W}e$ for the category of covered algebras. (These rules are defined as in Example 8.)

§6 Dual Objects

1. Definition: Let $\mathcal{C}$ be a category of covered objects and let E be an object of $\mathcal{C}$. If A is any object of $\mathcal{C}$ and if $\mathrm{Mor}(A,E) \neq \emptyset$, we define the dual object of A over E to be the covered set

$$\mathcal{D}(A, E)$$

whose space is Mor(A,E) and whose covering family consists of all subsets $S \subset \mathrm{Mor}(A,E)$ such that for each $F \in c(A)$, the set $\{\phi(x): \phi \in S, x \in F\}$ is contained in some set of c(E). Such a set S will be called <u>bounded</u>.

If $\mathcal{C}$ is a category of pairs, if E is an object of $\mathcal{C}$, and if $\mathrm{Mor}(A,E) \neq \emptyset$ for each object A of $\mathcal{C}$, then we can define a natural functor from $\mathcal{C}$ to the category of covered sets as follows: If A is an object of $\mathcal{C}$, the functor takes A to $\mathcal{D}(A,E)$. If A, B are objects of $\mathcal{C}$ and if $\phi \in \mathrm{Mor}(A,B)$, then the functor takes ϕ to <u>the transpose of ϕ over E</u>, usually denoted simply by ${}^t\phi$, which is defined as follows:

$$
\begin{aligned}
{}^t\phi: \quad & \mathcal{D}(B,E) \to \mathcal{D}(A,E) \\
& \psi \to \psi\phi
\end{aligned}
$$

This functor is (clearly) contravariant and will be called <u>the transpose functor over E</u>.

3. <u>Definition</u>: Let $\mathcal{C}$ be a Cartesian category and let u be a uniformizing rule for $\mathcal{C}$. If A, B are objects of $\mathcal{C}$, if $\mathrm{Mor}(A,B) \neq \emptyset$, and $\mathcal{U} \in u(A)$, $\mathcal{V} \in u(B)$, we define the <u>local dual of $A[\mathcal{U}]$ over $B[\mathcal{V}]$</u> to be the covered set

$$L\mathcal{D}(A[\mathcal{U}],B[\mathcal{V}])$$

whose space is the set of all locally $\mathcal{U}$-$\mathcal{V}$ uniformly continuous morphisms in Mor(A,B) and whose covering family is all locally uniformly equicontinuous and bounded subsets of that space. We define <u>the dual of $A[\mathcal{U}]$ over $B[\mathcal{V}]$</u> to be the covered set

$$\mathcal{D}(A[\mathcal{U}], B[\mathcal{V}])$$

whose space is the set of all $\mathcal{U}$-$\mathcal{V}$ uniformly continuous morphisms in Mor(A,B) and whose covering family is all bounded and uniformly equicontinuous subsets of that space.

4. <u>Proposition</u>: Let $\mathcal{C}$ be a Cartesian category and let u be a uniformizing rule for $\mathcal{C}$.

Let A, B, E be objects of $\mathcal{C}$, let $\mathcal{V} \in u(A)$, $\mathcal{W} \in u(B)$ and $\mathcal{U} \in u(E)$. Suppose $\mathrm{Mor}(A,E) \neq \emptyset \neq \mathrm{Mor}(B,E)$.

Let $\phi \in \mathrm{Mor}(A,B)$

(I) The map

$$^{t}\phi: \quad \mathcal{D}(B,E) \to \mathcal{D}(A,E)$$

is uniformly continuous with respect to the subspace uniform structures got from the product uniform spaces $spE[\mathcal{U}]^{spB}$ and $spE[\mathcal{U}]^{spA}$.

(II) If ϕ is locally $\mathcal{U}$-$\mathcal{W}$ uniformly continuous, then

$$^{t}\phi: \quad L\mathcal{D}(B[\mathcal{W}],\ E[\mathcal{U}]) \to L\mathcal{D}(A[\mathcal{V}],\ E[\mathcal{U}])$$

is a covered set morphism.

(III) If ϕ is $\mathcal{V}$-$\mathcal{W}$ uniformly continuous, then

$$^{t}\phi: \quad \mathcal{D}(B[\mathcal{W}],\ E[\mathcal{U}]) \to \mathcal{D}(A[\mathcal{V}],\ E[\mathcal{U}])$$

is a covered set morphism.

It is a trivial matter to check that if A and E are objects in a category of covered objects and if $\mathrm{Mor}(A,E) \neq \emptyset$, then $\mathcal{D}(A,E)$ is a subobject of the product covered set $csp(E)^{spA}$. Also, if $\mathcal{U}$ is a uniform structure on spE making the covered uniform space $csp(E)[\mathcal{U}]$ cover-closed, then the product covered uniform space $csp(E)[\mathcal{U}]^{spA}$ is also cover-closed. (Recall that a subobject of a covered uniform space is cover-closed if each set in its covering is contained in a closed set of its covering.)

5. <u>Definition</u>: Let $\mathcal{C}$ be a Cartesian category and let u be a uniformizing rule for $\mathcal{C}$. If for each pair A, E of objects of $\mathcal{C}$ such that $\mathrm{Mor}(A,E) \neq \emptyset$, and each uniform structure $\mathcal{U} \in u(E)$ making $E[\mathcal{U}]$ separated and cover-closed, $\mathcal{D}(A,E)$ is a cover-closed subobject of the product covered uniformed space $csp(E)[\mathcal{U}]^{spA}$, then we say <u>u gives $\mathcal{C}$ cover-closed dual objects</u>.

In each of the Cartesian categories introduced in §3 we have $\emptyset \neq \mathrm{Mor}(A,E)$ for all objects A, E of the category. Each of the examples of uniformizing rules given §5 gives the category involved cover-closed dual objects.

The most usual way in which covered vector spaces over K arise is the case where we are given a locally convex space $B[\mathcal{T}]$ and we take our covered vector space to be $(B,\mathcal{B}) = E$ where $\mathcal{B}$ is the family of bounded, convex, balanced subsets of B. If $A[\mathcal{S}]$ is another locally convex space, $\mathcal{A}$ is the family of bounded, convex, balanced subsets of A, and $F = (A,\mathcal{A})$, then Mor(E,F) is usually called <u>the space of bounded linear maps from B to A</u>.

If we take simply the closure of Mor(E,F) in A^B, and if $\mathcal{S}$ is separated, then we obtain a linear subspace of A^B comprised of linear maps, but they need not be bounded linear maps. For instance, in the case where A=K, the closure is all of B*, the algebraic dual of B. However, $\mathcal{D}(E,F)$ is a cover closed subobject of $A[\mathcal{S}]^B$ if $\mathcal{S}$ is separated.

In the case where $B[\mathcal{T}]$ is bornological, we have $\phi \in$ Mor(E,F) if and only if ϕ is a continuous linear map from B to A.

In the case where A=K, we will often denote Mor(E,F) by B^b, the space of bounded linear forms on $B[\mathcal{T}]$. In this case the covering family of $\mathcal{D}(E,F)$ is the family of all $\beta(B^b,B)$-bounded subsets of B^b. (K, of course, is considered as a covered vector space with its balanced, convex, bounded sets as its covering family.)

§7. <u>Compactly Covered Reflections in a Cartesian Category</u>

Throughout this section, $\mathcal{C}$ will denote a fixed Cartesian category and u will denote a fixed uniformizing rule for $\mathcal{C}$.

As a preliminary, it should be mentioned that if we replace "compact" by "complete" thruout this section (both as words and as parts of other words) the entire section would still be true, word for word. (All that one would have to check would be Theorem 1, Corollary 5 and Corollary 10, since all other proofs are categorical.) However, the interest in later chapters is in the case stated, so we will not explicitly carry the other case.

1. <u>Theorem</u>: <u>The compactly covered objects form a full, reflective subcategory of $\mathcal{C}_u$</u>.

<u>Proof</u>: It is clearly full. Let $A[\mathcal{U}]$ be an object of $\mathcal{C}_u$.

There is an index set I and an indexed family $\{B[\mathcal{V}_\nu], \phi_\nu\}_{\nu \in I}$ which has the following properties:

(a) For each $\nu \in I$, $B_\nu[\mathcal{V}_\nu]$ is a compactly covered object of $\mathcal{C}_u$ and ϕ_ν is a $\mathcal{U}$-$\mathcal{V}_\nu$ uniformly continuous morphism in Mor(A,B_ν).

(b) For each $\nu \in I$, B_ν is the cover-closed envelope of $\phi_\nu(A)$ in B_ν w.r.t. $\mathcal{V}_\nu$.

(c) If $B[\mathcal{V}]$ is any compactly covered object of $\mathcal{C}_u$ and if $\phi \in$ Mor(A,B) is $\mathcal{U}$-$\mathcal{V}$ uniformly continuous, then $\phi^{-1}(\mathcal{V}) = \phi_\nu^{-1}(\mathcal{V}_\nu)$ for some $\nu \in I$.

Since $\mathcal{C}_u$ contains points (by part (2) of Definition 2.7 and part (2) of Definition 4.1), $I \neq \emptyset$. We now choose any product $(C[\mathcal{W}], \{\psi_\nu\}_{\nu \in I})$ of the family $\{B_\nu[\mathcal{V}_\nu]\}_{\nu \in I}$ in $\mathcal{C}_u$. This is possible by Proposition 4.3 and by that result, $C[\mathcal{W}]$ is compactly covered. By the definition of a product, there is a unique morphism $\phi \in$ Mor$(A[\mathcal{U}], C[\mathcal{W}])$ of $\mathcal{C}_u$ such that $\psi_\nu \phi = \phi_\nu$ for each $\nu \in I$. We now let B denote a cover-closed envelope of $\phi(A)$ in C w.r.t. $\mathcal{W}$ and let $\mathcal{V} = \mathcal{W}|_B$. We let $\iota \in$ Mor(B,C) denote the inclusion map. We choose the unique morphism $\theta \in$ Mor(A,B) such that $\phi = \iota\theta$.

Now let $D[\mathcal{Z}]$ be a compactly covered object of $\mathcal{C}_u$ and let $\rho \in$ Mor$(A[\mathcal{U}], D[\mathcal{Z}])$. Choose $\nu \in I$ such that $\rho^{-1}(\mathcal{Z}) = \phi_\nu^{-1}(\mathcal{V}_\nu)$. Then, since each set of $c(B_\nu)$ is contained in the $\mathcal{V}_\nu$-closure of some set of $c(\phi_\nu(A))$, there is a unique $\mathcal{V}_\nu$-$\mathcal{Z}$ uniformly continuous covered set morphism

$$\lambda\colon \quad \text{csp}(B_\nu) \to \text{csp}(D)$$

Such that $\rho = \lambda\phi_\nu$. Moreover, since morphisms can be factored in $\mathcal{C}$, $\lambda|_{\phi_\nu(A)}$ must be in Mor$(\phi_\nu(A),D)$. But then, since B_ν is the cover-closed envelope of $\phi_\nu(A)$ in B_ν w.r.t. $\mathcal{V}_\nu$, it follows that $\lambda \in$ Mor(B_ν,D). But then we have

$$\begin{aligned}(\lambda\psi_\nu\iota)\theta &= \lambda\psi_\nu(\iota\theta)\\ &= \lambda\psi_\nu\phi\\ &= \lambda\phi_\nu\\ &= \rho\end{aligned}$$

and so, since B is the cover-closed envelope of $\theta(A)$ in B w.r.t. $\mathcal{V}$, $\lambda\psi_{\mathcal{V}}\iota$ is the unique $\mathcal{V}$-$\mathcal{Z}$ uniformly continuous morphism in Mor(B,D) such that $(\lambda\psi_{\mathcal{V}}\iota)\theta = \rho$.

We have just proved that $(\theta, B[\mathcal{V}])$ is a reflection for $A[\mathcal{U}]$ in the compactly covered objects of C_u.

2. <u>Lemma</u>: Let $\mathcal{D}$, $\mathcal{E}$, $\mathcal{F}$ be categories, T a covariant functor from $\mathcal{D}$ to $\mathcal{E}$ and S a covariant functor from $\mathcal{E}$ to $\mathcal{F}$. If A is an object of $\mathcal{F}$, if (B,ϕ) is a reflection for A in $\mathcal{E}$ via S, and if (C,ψ) is a reflection for B in $\mathcal{D}$ via T, then $(C, S(\psi)\phi)$ is a reflection for A in $\mathcal{D}$ via ST.

So if $\mathcal{F}$ has reflections in $\mathcal{E}$ via S and $\mathcal{E}$ has reflections in $\mathcal{D}$ via T, then $\mathcal{F}$ has reflections in $\mathcal{D}$ via ST.

<u>Proof</u>: Let D be an object of $\mathcal{D}$ and let $\theta \in \mathrm{Mor}(A, ST(D))$. There is a unique $\rho \in \mathrm{Mor}(B,T(D))$ such that $\theta = S(\rho)\phi$. There is a unique $\sigma \in \mathrm{Mor}(C,D)$ such that $\rho = T(\sigma)\psi$. We have $\theta = S(\rho)\phi = S(T(\sigma)\psi)\phi = ST(\sigma)(S(\psi)\phi)$. Now suppose $\pi \in \mathrm{Mor}(C,D)$ and $\theta = ST(\pi)(S(\psi)\phi)$. Then we have $T(\pi)\psi \in \mathrm{Mor}(B,D)$ and $\theta = S(T(\pi)\psi)\phi$. So, by the uniqueness of ρ, we have $\rho = T(\pi)\psi$. But then, by the uniqueness of σ, $\pi = \sigma$. So there is a unique $\sigma \in \mathrm{Mor}(C,D)$ such that $ST(\sigma)(S(\psi)\phi) = \theta$. So $(C, S(\psi)\phi)$ is a reflection for A in $\mathcal{D}$ via ST.

3. <u>Corollary</u>: The compactly covered objects of C_u form a reflective subcategory of both C_o and C_t.

<u>Proof</u>: The identity functor on C is, of course, admissible. So we may apply Proposition 4.6 and Lemma 2, along with Theorem 1.

4. <u>Definition</u>: Let A be an object of C and let $\mathcal{U}$ be a uniform structure (topology) on spA.

Any reflection for $A[\mathcal{U}]$ in the compactly covered objects of C_u will be called <u>a compactly covered reflection of $A[\mathcal{U}]$ with respect to u</u>.

If $(\phi, B[\mathcal{V}])$ is a compactly covered reflection of $A[\mathcal{U}]$ with respect to u and if $\phi^{-1}(\mathcal{V}) = \mathcal{U}(t(\phi^{-1}(\mathcal{V})) = \mathcal{U})$ then we will call $(\phi, B[\mathcal{V}])$ <u>a compactification of $A[\mathcal{U}]$</u> and say that $\mathcal{U}$--or $A[\mathcal{U}]$--is <u>compactifiable with respect to u</u>.

5. <u>Corollary</u>: Let A be an object of $\mathcal{C}$ and let $\mathcal{U}$ be a uniform structure (topology) on spA. Let $B[\mathcal{V}]$ be a compactly covered object of $\mathcal{C}_u$ and let $\phi \in Mor(A,B)$ be $\mathcal{U}$-$\mathcal{V}$ uniformly continuous (continuous).

(1) $(\phi, B[\mathcal{V}])$ is a compactly covered reflection of $A[\mathcal{U}]$ with respect to u if and only if B is the cover-closed envelope of $\phi(A)$ in B w.r.t. $\mathcal{V}$ and $\phi^{-1}(\mathcal{V})$ is the strongest uniform structure in u(A) which is compactifiable with respect to u and which is weaker than $\mathcal{U}$ (determines a topology which is weaker than $\mathcal{U}$).

(2) <u>$(\phi, B[\mathcal{V}])$ is a compactification of $A[\mathcal{U}]$ if and only if B is the cover-closed envelope of $\phi(A)$ in B w.r.t. $\mathcal{V}$ and $\mathcal{U} = \phi^{-1}(\mathcal{V})$</u>.

(3) <u>Now suppose that $(B[\mathcal{V}], \phi)$ is a compactification of $A[\mathcal{U}]$ and that $(X[\mathcal{W}], j)$ is a completion of the uniform space $spA[\mathcal{U}]$. Then there is a unique $\mathcal{V}$-$\mathcal{W}$ uniform embedding</u>

$$\theta: \quad spB \to X$$

<u>such that $j = \theta\phi$. Moreover, if $\mathcal{A} = \{\overline{j(F)}: \ F \in c(A)\}$ and $Y = \bigcup \mathcal{A}$, then θ is an isomorphism of the covered set csp(B) to the covered set $(Y, \mathcal{A})$</u>.

6. <u>Corollary</u>: Let $\mathcal{D}$ be another category of covered objects and let T be an admissible functor from $\mathcal{C}$ to $\mathcal{D}$. Suppose that $\mathcal{D}$ has reflections in $\mathcal{C}$ via T.

Let $\mathcal{C}_{uc}$, resp. $\mathcal{C}^{\ell}_{uc}$, denote the full subcategory of $\mathcal{C}_u$, resp. $\mathcal{C}^{\ell}_u$, whose objects are the compactly covered objects of $\mathcal{C}_u$, resp. $\mathcal{C}^{\ell}_u$.

(1) $\mathcal{D}_o$ has reflections in $\mathcal{C}_{uc}$ via T_u.
(2) $\mathcal{D}_t$ has reflections in $\mathcal{C}_{uc}$ via T_u.
(3) $\mathcal{D}^{\ell}_{o}$ has reflections in $\mathcal{C}_{uc}$ via T_u.
(4) $\mathcal{D}^{\ell}_t$ has reflections in $\mathcal{C}_{uc}$ via T_u.
(5) $\mathcal{D}^{\ell}_o$ has reflections in $\mathcal{C}^{\ell}_{uc}$ via T_u.
(6) $\mathcal{D}^{\ell}_t$ has reflections in $\mathcal{C}^{\ell}_{uc}$ vía T_u.

<u>Proof</u>: Apply Proposition 4.6, Lemma 2 and Theorem 1.

7. Definition: Let $\mathcal{D}$ be another category of covered objects and let T be an admissible functor from $\mathcal{C}$ to $\mathcal{D}$ such that $\mathcal{D}$ has reflections in $\mathcal{C}$ via T.

Let A be an object of $\mathcal{D}$ and let $\mathcal{U}$ be a uniform structure (topology) on spA.

(1) If we consider $A[\mathcal{U}]$ as an object of $\mathcal{D}_o$ ($\mathcal{D}_t$) then a reflection for $A[\mathcal{U}]$ in $\mathcal{C}_{uc}$ via T_u will be called a compactly covered reflection of $A[\mathcal{U}]$ in $\mathcal{C}$ with respect to u via T.

(2) If we consider $A[\mathcal{U}]$ as an object of $\mathcal{D}_o^{\ell}$ ($\mathcal{D}_t^{\ell}$) then a reflection for $A[\mathcal{U}]$ in $\mathcal{C}_{uc}$ via T_u will be called an inductive compactly covered reflection of $A[\mathcal{U}]$ in $\mathcal{C}$ with respect to u via T.

(3) If we consider $A[\mathcal{U}]$ as an object of $\mathcal{D}_o^{\ell}$ ($\mathcal{D}_t^{\ell}$), then a reflection of $A[\mathcal{U}]$ in $\mathcal{C}_{uc}^{\ell}$ via T_u will be called a compactly covered local reflection of $A[\mathcal{U}]$ in $\mathcal{C}$ with respect to u via T.

In case the functor T is understood (as is usually the case) then the phrase "via T" is omitted thruout. In the even more special case where $\mathcal{D}=\mathcal{C}$ and T is the identity functor, then the phrase "in $\mathcal{C}$" is also omitted thruout.

In the general case, if $\mathcal{C}$ is also a category of sets we replace the phrase "compactly covered" with "compact" thruout.

8. Corollary: Let $\mathcal{D}$ be another category of covered objects and let T be an admissible functor from $\mathcal{C}$ to $\mathcal{D}$ such that $\mathcal{D}$ has reflections in $\mathcal{C}$ via T.

Let A be an object of $\mathcal{D}$ and let $\mathcal{U}$ be a uniform structure (topology) on spA.

Let $(B[\mathcal{V}], \phi)$, resp. $(C[\mathcal{W}], \psi)$, be a reflection, resp. an inductive reflection, for $A[\mathcal{U}]$ in $\mathcal{C}$ with respect to u via T. Let $(D[\mathcal{Y}],\theta)$, resp. $(E[\mathcal{Z}],\rho)$, be a compactly covered reflection, resp. an inductive compactly covered reflection, of $B[\mathcal{V}]$, resp. $C[\mathcal{W}]$.

Then $(D[\mathcal{Y}], T(\theta)\phi)$, resp. $(E[\mathcal{Z}], T(\rho)\psi)$, is a compactly covered reflection, resp. an inductive compactly covered reflection, in $\mathcal{C}$ w.r.t. u via T.

Proof: Apply Lemma 2.

9. *Definition*: Let A be an object of $\mathcal{C}$ and let $\mathcal{U}$ be a uniform structure (topology) on spA.

A compactly covered local reflection (ϕ, B[$\mathcal{V}$]) of A[$\mathcal{U}$] with respect to u will be called *a local compactification* of A[$\mathcal{U}$] if $\phi^{-1}(\mathcal{V})|_F = \mathcal{U}|_F$ ($t(\phi^{-1}(\mathcal{V}))|_F = \mathcal{U}|_F$) for each $F \in c(A)$. In this case, we will say that *$\mathcal{U}$* (or A[$\mathcal{U}$]) *is locally compactifiable with respect to u*.

10. *Corollary*: *Let A be an object of $\mathcal{C}$ and let $\mathcal{U}$ be a uniform structure (topology) on spA*.

(1) *If (ϕ, B[$\mathcal{V}$]) is a compactly covered local reflection of A[$\mathcal{U}$] with respect to u, then (ϕ, B[$\mathcal{V}^i$]) is an inductive compactly covered reflection of A[$\mathcal{U}$] with respect to u*.

(2) *If (ϕ, B[$\mathcal{V}$]) is a local compactification of A[$\mathcal{U}$] with respect to u, and if (j,X[$\mathcal{W}$]) is a completion of the uniform space spA[$\mathcal{U}$], then there is a unique local $\mathcal{V}$-$\mathcal{W}$ embedding*

$$\theta: \ spB \to X$$

such that $j = \theta\phi$. Moreover, if $\mathcal{A} = \{\overline{j(F)}: F \in c(A)\}$ and $Y = \bigcup\mathcal{A}$, then θ is a covered set isomorphism of csp(B) to (Y,$\mathcal{A}$).

(3) *If A[$\mathcal{U}$] is compactifiable with respect to u and if (ϕ, B[$\mathcal{V}$]) is a compactly covered reflection of A[$\mathcal{U}$] with respect to u, then it is also a compactly covered local reflection of A[$\mathcal{U}$] with respect to u*.

Proof: (1) and (2) are quite clear.

Assume A[$\mathcal{U}$] is compactifiable and (ϕ, B[$\mathcal{V}$]) is a compactly covered reflection of A[$\mathcal{U}$]. Let (ψ, C[$\mathcal{W}$]) be a compactly covered local reflection of A[$\mathcal{U}$] and let $\theta \in Mor(C,B)$ be the unique locally $\mathcal{W}$-$\mathcal{V}$ uniformly continuous morphism such that $\phi = \theta\psi$. Since $\mathcal{V}$ is compactifiable, we have

$$\phi^{-1}(\mathcal{V})|_F = \mathcal{U}|_F = \psi^{-1}(\mathcal{W})|_F$$

for each $F \in c(A)$. It follows from this that θ is a bijection and that θ^{-1} is a covered set isomorphism of csp(B) to csp(C). Since we can factor morphisms in $\mathcal{C}$, $\theta^{-1}|_{\phi(A)}$ is in Mor(ϕ(A), C). Moreover, θ^{-1} is clearly locally $\mathcal{V}$-$\mathcal{W}$ uniformly continuous. Therefore, since B is the cover-closed envelope of ϕ(A) w.r.t. $\mathcal{V}$, $\theta^{-1} \in$ Mor(B,C). This forces (ϕ, B[$\mathcal{V}$]) to be a compactly covered local reflection for A[U].

11. Note: Part (3) of Corollary 5 and part (2) of Corollary 10 give us a way of describing the underlying covered set of a compactly covered reflection or compactly covered local reflection in the case where A[$\mathcal{U}$] is compactifiable or locally compactifiable. So if one wishes to use a compactly covered reflection or local reflection of A[$\mathcal{U}$] as an aid in analyzing A[$\mathcal{U}$] one will have a considerable advantage in the case where A[$\mathcal{U}$] is compactifiable or locally compactifiable. Accordingly, we will devote considerable time in later chapters to theorems about compactifiability and local compactifiability in certain special cases.

§8. Examples of Compactly Covered Reflections

1. Example: Let $\mathcal{C}$ denote the category of covered sets and let u be the rule which assigns to each object A of $\mathcal{C}$ the set u(A) of all uniform structures on spA. A uniform structure $\mathcal{U} \in$ u(A) is compactifiable if and only if each set of c(A) is $\mathcal{U}$-precompact. In this case, we can obtain a compactification of A[$\mathcal{U}$] by choosing a completion (X[$\mathcal{V}$], j) of spA[$\mathcal{U}$] and taking ((Y,$\mathcal{A}$)[$\mathcal{V}|_Y$], j) as our compactification, where $\mathcal{A} = \{\overline{j(F)}: F \in c(A)\}$, Y = $\bigcup \mathcal{A}$.

2. Example: Let $\mathcal{C}$ denote the category of sets and let u be the rule which assigns to each set X the set u(X) of all uniform structures on X.

If X is a set and $\mathcal{U}$ is a uniform structure on X, then a compact reflection of X[$\mathcal{U}$] with respect to u is just a Samuel compact reflection of X[$\mathcal{U}$].

If X is a set and $\mathcal{T}$ is a topology on X, then a compact reflection of X[$\mathcal{T}$] w.r.t. u is just a Stone-Čech compact reflection of X[$\mathcal{T}$].

3. Example: Let $\mathcal{C}$ denote the category of monoids and let u be the rule which assigns to each monoid M the set u(M) of all uniform structures on M which make the multiplication separately uniformly continuous. Let e be the rule which assigns to each monoid M the set e(M) of all uniform structures on M which make the multiplication jointly uniformly continuous. If M is a monoid and if $\mathcal{U} \in u(M)$, then a compact reflection of $M[\mathcal{U}]$ with respect to e (e - not u) is called a Bohr compact reflection of $M[\mathcal{U}]$. A compact reflection of $M[\mathcal{U}]$ in w.r.t. u is simply called a compact reflection of $M[\mathcal{U}]$.

4. Proposition: We adopt the notation of Example 3. Let M be a monoid, let $\mathcal{U} \in u(M)$ be precompact, and let $(E[\mathcal{V}], j)$ be a compactification of the uniform space $spM[\mathcal{U}]$.

(1) $\mathcal{U}$ is compactifiable with respect to u if and only if there is a separately uniformly continuous map

$$\theta: \; E[\mathcal{V}] \times E[\mathcal{V}] \to E[\mathcal{V}]$$

such that

$$\theta(j(m), j(n)) = j(mn)$$

for each pair m, $n \in M$. In this case θ is a law of composition making E a monoid and $(E[\mathcal{V}], j)$ becomes a compact reflection of $M[\mathcal{U}]$ with respect to u.

(2) Therefore, if $\mathcal{U} \in e(M)$, $M[\mathcal{U}]$ is compactifiable with respect to e.

5. Example: Let $\mathcal{C}$ denote the category of covered monoids. Let u be the rule which assigns to each covered monoid $(M,\mathcal{M})$ the set $u(M,\mathcal{M})$ of all uniform structures on M which make the multiplication separately uniformly continuous. Let e be the rule which assigns to each covered monoid $(M,\mathcal{M})$ the set $e(M,\mathcal{M})$ of all uniform structures in $u(M,\mathcal{M})$ which make the multiplication jointly uniformly continuous on each set of $\mathcal{M}$.

The following proposition holds:

6. <u>Proposition</u>: We adopt the notation of Example 5. Let $(M,\mathcal{M})$ be a covered monoid, let $\mathcal{U}\in u(M,\mathcal{M})$, let $(M,\mathcal{M})[\mathcal{U}]$ be precompactly covered, and let $(E[\mathcal{V}], j)$ be a completion of the uniform space $spM[\mathcal{U}]$. Let $\mathcal{A} = \{\overline{j(L)}: L\in\mathcal{M}\}$ and let $Y = \cup\mathcal{A}$.

(1) $(M,\mathcal{M})[\mathcal{U}]$ is locally compactifiable w.r.t. u if and only if there is a map

$$\theta: \; Y[\mathcal{V}] \times Y[\mathcal{V}] \to Y[\mathcal{V}]$$

which is separately uniformly continuous on each set of $\mathcal{A}$ and which satisfies the condition that

$$\theta(j(m), j(n)) = j(mn)$$

for each pair $m, n\in M$. In this case, θ is a law of composition making $(Y,\mathcal{A})$ a covered monoid. If $\mathcal{W}$ is the strongest uniform structure on Y which agrees with $\mathcal{V}$ on each set of $\mathcal{A}$, then $(j, (Y,\mathcal{A})[\mathcal{W}])$ becomes an inductive compactly covered reflection of $(M,\mathcal{M})[\mathcal{U}]$ with respect to u.

(2) Therefore, if $\mathcal{U}\in e(M,\mathcal{M})$, $(M,\mathcal{M})[\mathcal{U}]$ is locally compactifiable with respect to e.

It is not at all an easy matter to decide whether or not a uniform monoid, resp. a covered uniform monoid, is compactifiable, resp. locally compactifiable. Giving criteria for this to be the case and explicit constructions for compact reflections, resp. inductive compactly covered reflections, in the general case forms the major application of the extension theory in Chapter 6.

7. <u>Example</u>: Let $\mathcal{C}$ denote the category of covered vector spaces over K and let w denote the rule which assigns to each covered vector space $(E,\mathcal{S})$ the set of all locally convex uniform structures $\mathcal{U}$ on E such that (1) each set of $\mathcal{S}$ is $\mathcal{U}$-bounded and (2) $\mathcal{U} = \sigma(E,E[\mathcal{U}]')$. Let $(E,\mathcal{S})$ be a covered vector space and let $\mathcal{U}\in w(E,\mathcal{S})$. Let e be the natural (evaluation) map of E into E″ where E″ is the dual of $E[\mathcal{U}]'$ when the latter space is given the uniform structure of uniform convergence on sets of $\mathcal{S}$. Let $\mathcal{T}$ denote the family of all equicontinuous subsets of E″. Then

$$((E'',\mathcal{T})[\sigma(E'', E')], e)$$

is a compactification of $(E,\mathcal{S})[\sigma(E,E')]$ w.r.t. $\mathcal{W}$.

If we refer to Example 8 of Section 5, then we have several uniformizing rules for the category of covered K-algebras. With respect to these rules we have various kinds of compactly covered reflections for a given covered locally convex algebra. Explicit constructions for the compactly covered reflections with respect to the rules e and $\mathcal{W}$e will be given in Chapter 4 in a utilization of Ascoli's theorem, as will explicit constructions for compactly covered reflections with respect to the rule e on covered monoids (and monoids).

Explicit constructions for compactly covered reflections of a covered locally convex algebra with respect to the rules **u** and $\mathcal{W}$ are more difficult to give (in the author's opinion) and giving them forms the major application of the extension theory developed in Chapter 5.

For now, the important thing to remember is that we know these various kinds of compactly covered reflections of covered uniform monoids and covered locally convex algebras exist, even though we may have no explicit constructions of them. We also know that a covered uniform monoid has compactly covered reflections in the category of covered algebras with respect to each of the four rules we defined for this latter category.

There is one simplification in the problem of compactly covered reflections in the category of covered K-algebras which we can make at this time. We do so in the following proposition.

8. Proposition: Let $\mathcal{C}$ denote the category of covered K-algebras and let the rules u, $\mathcal{W}$, e, $\mathcal{W}$e be defined as in Example 8 of Section 5. Let $\mathcal{D}$ be another category of covered objects and let T be an admissible functor from $\mathcal{C}$ to $\mathcal{D}$. Suppose that $\mathcal{D}$ has reflections in $\mathcal{C}$ via T.

Let X be an object of $\mathcal{D}$ and let $\mathcal{U}$ be a uniform structure on spX. Let $E[\mathcal{T}]$ be a covered locally convex K-algebra where $E = (A,\mathcal{A})$ and let ϕ be a morphism from X to T(E).

(1) <u>If $(E[\mathcal{T}], \phi)$ is an (inductive) compactly covered reflection of $X[\mathcal{U}]$ w.r.t. u, resp. w.r.t. e, via T, then $(E[\sigma(A, A')], \phi)$ is an (inductive) compactly covered reflection of $X[\mathcal{U}]$ w.r.t. $\mathcal{W}$, resp. w.r.t. $\mathcal{W}e$, via T</u>.

(2) <u>If $(E[\mathcal{T}], \phi)$ is an (inductive) compactly covered reflection of $X[\mathcal{U}]$ w.r.t. $\mathcal{W}$, resp. w.r.t. $\mathcal{W}e$, via T then there is a family $\mathcal{M}$ of $\sigma(A',A)$ compact subsets of A' such that $(E[\mathcal{T}_m], \phi)$ is a compactly covered reflection of $X[\mathcal{U}]$ w.r.t</u>. <u>u, resp. w.r.t. e, via T</u>.

<u>Proof</u>: (2) is a corollary of (1). The proof of (1) rests almost entirely on the fact that a continuous linear map is always weakly continuous (see 3.3.7).

Suppose that $(E[\mathcal{T}], \phi)$ is an (inductive) compactly covered reflection of $X[\mathcal{U}]$ w.r.t. u, resp. w.r.t. e. Let $F[\mathcal{S}]$ be a compactly covered object of $\mathcal{C}_{\mathcal{W}}$, resp. $\mathcal{C}_{\mathcal{W}e}$, and let $\psi \in Mor(X, T(F))$ be (locally) uniformly continuous with respect to $\mathcal{U}$ and $\mathcal{S}$. Then, by definition, there is a unique continuous morphism $\theta: E \to F$ such that $\psi = T(\theta)\,\phi$. Since θ is continuous and since $\mathcal{S}$ is a weak topology, θ is $\sigma(A,A')$-$\mathcal{S}$ continuous. The proof will be complete if we show that $\sigma(A,A') \in u(E)$, resp. $\sigma(A,A') \in e(E)$, and that $E[\sigma(A,A')]$ is compactly covered.

If $a \in A$ then the maps $x \to ax$ and $x \to xa$ are continuous w.r.t. $\mathcal{T}$. So, being linear, they are continuous w.r.t. $\sigma(A,A')$. So $\sigma(A,A') \in u(E)$. If, in addition, $\mathcal{T} \in e(E)$ and $B \in \mathcal{A}$ then there is a compact set $C \in \mathcal{A}$ such that $B \cup BB \subset C$. But, by compactness, since $\sigma(A,A')$ is separated and weaker than $\mathcal{T}$, $\mathcal{T}|_C = \sigma(A,A')|_C$ (as uniform structures). So the uniform continuity of the map

$$B \times B \to C$$
$$(a,b) \to ab$$

with respect to $\mathcal{T}$ implies it with respect to $\sigma(A,A')$. So $\sigma(A,A') \in e(E)$. That $E[\sigma(A,A')]$ is compactly covered also follows from the fact that $\sigma(A,A')$ is separated and weaker than $\mathcal{T}$.

Chapter 3. UNIFORM DUALITIES

§1. Synopsis

The object of this section is to state the definitions and fundamental results which concern uniform dualities. Many of these definitions and results are simply lifted from the elementary theory of function spaces. The reason for preferring a duality theory instead is the obvious one: It is symmetric. This has been noticed and fruitfully applied by many in the theory of locally convex spaces, which heavily influences my treatment here.

The most important results are the Ascoli Theorem presented in §5, together with its corollaries, and the results on completeness presented in §4 which will be used extensively in my treatment of almost periodic functions and linear forms in Chapter 4.

Before one reads this chapter, a very strong warning concerning Chapter 2 is in order: While the approach initiated there has its difficulties, having initiated it I intend to be quite thoroughly consistent in following it. If the reader has not familiarized himself with the definitions in Sections 2.2 and 2.4, he will have some difficulty following this chapter or, if he can follow it, tend to misinterpret it. The same warning would apply to Section 2 of this chapter. As a special instance, we remind the reader that if $A = (X, \mathcal{A})$ is a covered set and if $\mathcal{U}$ is a uniform structure on X, then the pair $A[\mathcal{U}] = (A, \mathcal{U})$ is called a covered uniform space. It is called precompactly covered if each set of $\mathcal{A}$ is precompact.

§2. Basic Definitions and Terminology Concerning Uniform Dualities

1. Definition: Let $\mathcal{C}$ be a category of covered objects. By a duality in $\mathcal{C}$ we mean the following:

(1) Three objects A, B, E of $\mathcal{C}$

(2) A function

$$\langle\, , \rangle\ \mathrm{sp}A \times \mathrm{sp}B \to \mathrm{sp}E$$
$$(x,y) \to \langle x,y\rangle$$

such that

(a) For each $x \in spA$, the map

$$spB \to spE$$

$$y \to \langle x,y\rangle$$

is in $Mor(B,E)$.

(b) For each $y \in spB$, the map

$$spA \to spE$$

$$x \to \langle x,y\rangle$$

is in $Mor(A,E)$.

We abbreviate this by saying that we have a duality $\langle A,B\rangle$ over E in $\mathcal{C}$. The duality is said to be <u>bounded</u> if for each $F \in c(A)$ and each $G \in c(B)$, the set

$$\{\langle x,y\rangle : \ x \in F, \ y \in G\}$$

is contained in some set of $c(E)$. If $\mathcal{C}$ is the category of covered sets, a duality in $\mathcal{C}$ is called <u>a duality of covered sets</u>.

Let $\mathcal{C}$ be a category of covered objects and let $\langle A,B\rangle$ be a duality over E in $\mathcal{C}$. <u>We will usually denote by</u>

$$r_A\colon \ spA \to Mor(B,E)$$

$$r_B\colon \ spB \to Mor(A,E)$$

the functions defined as follows:

$$(r_A x)(y) = \langle x,y\rangle = (r_B y)(x)$$

where $x \in spA$, $y \in spB$. If the duality is bounded, then r_A is a covered set morphism from $csp(A)$ to $\mathcal{D}(B,E)$ and r_B is a covered set morphism from $csp(B)$ to $\mathcal{D}(A,E)$. If either of these statements is true, then the duality is bounded and both of the statements are true.

2. <u>Definition</u>: Let $\mathcal{C}$ be a category of covered objects. By <u>a (locally) uniform duality $\langle A[\mathcal{V}], B[\mathcal{W}]\rangle$ over $E[\mathcal{U}]$ in $\mathcal{C}$, we mean</u>

(1) A duality $\langle A,B\rangle$ over E in $\mathcal{C}$.

(2) Uniform structures $\mathcal{U}$ on spE, $\mathcal{V}$ on spA, $\mathcal{W}$ on spB such that

each $x \in spA$ the map

$$spB \to spE$$
$$y \to \langle x,y \rangle$$

is (locally) $\mathcal{W}$-$\mathcal{V}$ uniformly continuous and for each $y \in spB$ the map

$$spA \to spE$$
$$x \to \langle x,y \rangle$$

is (locally) $\mathcal{V}$-$\mathcal{U}$ uniformly continuous.

3. Convention: In this section and in many other parts of this paper we shall state definitions and results about a duality which admit an obvious symmetric analogue. We shall never bother to state the analogue.

4. Notation: Let $\mathcal{C}$ be a category of covered objects and let $\langle A,B \rangle$ be a duality over E in $\mathcal{C}$. Let $\mathcal{U}$ be a uniform structure on spE.

If $F \subset spB$ and $U \in \mathcal{U}$, we denote by

$$N(F,U)$$

the set $\{(x_1,x_2): (\langle x_1,y \rangle)(x_2,y \rangle) \in U \ \forall\ y \in F\}$ in $spA \times spA$. If C is a subobject of B we denote by

$$N(C,\mathcal{U})$$

the uniform structure on spA which has $\{N(F,U): F \in c(C),\ U \in \mathcal{U}\}$ as a fundamental system of entourages. We denote by

$$\sigma(C,\mathcal{U})$$

the uniform structure on spA which has $\{N(y,U): y \in spC,\ U \in \mathcal{U}\}$ as a subbasic system of entourages. (Of course, $N(y,U)$ denotes $N(\{y\}, U)$).

There are some simple computational rules in connection with the above notation: Let F_1, F_2, $F_3 \subset spB$ and let U_1, U_2, $U_3 \in \mathcal{U}$. We have

(1) If $F_1 \cup F_2 \subset F_3$ and $U_3 \subset U_1 \cap U_2$ then $N(F_3, U_3) \subset N(F_1, U) \cap N(F_2, U_2)$.

(2) If $U_1^2 \subset U_2$, then $N^2(F_1, U_1) \subset N(F_1, U_2)$

(3) If $U_1 \subset U_2^{-1}$, then

$$N(F_1, U_1) \quad N^{-1}(F_1, U_2)$$

Also, it is clear that if C and D are subobjects of B and D is a subobject of C, then $N(D,\mathcal{U})$ is weaker than $N(C,\mathcal{U})$. If we only assume that $spD \subset spC$, then $\sigma(D,\mathcal{U})$ is weaker than $\sigma(C,\mathcal{U})$. If $\mathcal{Z}$ is a uniform structure on spE which is stronger (weaker) than $\mathcal{U}$, then $N(C,\mathcal{Z})$ is stronger (weaker) than $N(C,\mathcal{U})$ and $\sigma(C,\mathcal{Z})$ is stronger (weaker) than $\sigma(C,\mathcal{U})$.

If $\mathcal{C}$ is a Cartesian category, u a uniformizing rule for $\mathcal{C}$, and if $\mathcal{U} \in u(E)$, then $\sigma(C,\mathcal{U})$ is in u(A).

5. *Convention*: For the rest of this section, we assume that we are given a fixed duality <A,B> over E in a category of covered objects $\mathcal{C}$.

6. *Definition*: Let $\mathcal{U}$ be a uniform structure on spE, $\mathcal{V}$ a uniform structure on spA.

An element $y \in spB$ is said to be $\mathcal{V}$-$\mathcal{U}$ uniformly continuous on set $F \subset spA$ if this is true of the map $r_B y$. A set $G \subset spB$ is said to be $\mathcal{V}$-$\mathcal{U}$ uniformly continuous on a set $F \subset spA$ if this is true of each of the maps $r_B y$ $(y \in G)$. A subobject C of B is said to be $\mathcal{V}$-$\mathcal{U}$ uniformly continuous on a set $F \subset spA$ if this is true of spC.

A set $G \subset spB$ is said to be (locally) $\mathcal{V}$-$\mathcal{U}$ uniformly continuous on a subobject D of A if this is true of each of the morphisms $r_B y$ $(y \in G)$.

A subobject C of B is said to be (locally) $\mathcal{V}$-$\mathcal{U}$ uniformly continuous on a subobject D of A if this is true of spC.

A set $G \subset spB$ is said to be $\mathcal{V}$-$\mathcal{U}$ uniformly equicontinuous on a set $F \subset spA$ if this is true of the family of maps $r_B y$ $(y \in G)$. A subobject C of B is said to be $\mathcal{V}$-$\mathcal{U}$ uniformly equicontinuous on a set $F \subset spA$ if this is true of each set in c(C).

<u>A subobject C of B is said to be $\mathcal{V}$-$\mathcal{U}$ uniformly equicontinuous on a subobject D of A if C is $\mathcal{V}$-$\mathcal{U}$ uniformly equicontinuous on spD</u>.

<u>A subobject C of B is said to be locally $\mathcal{V}$-$\mathcal{U}$ uniformly equicontinuous on a subobject D of A if C is $\mathcal{V}$-$\mathcal{U}$ uniformly equicontinuous on each set of c(D)</u>.

7. <u>Lemma</u>: Let $\mathcal{U}$ be a uniform structure on spE, $\mathcal{V}$ a uniform structure on spA, $\mathcal{W}$ a uniform structure on spB.

Let $F \subset$ spA, $G \subset$ spB.

(1) G is $\mathcal{V}$-$\mathcal{U}$ uniformly equicontinuous on F if and only if $N(G,U)|_F$ is an entourage of $\mathcal{V}|_F$ for each $U \in \mathcal{U}$.

(2) If G is $\mathcal{V}$-$\mathcal{U}$ uniformly equicontinuous on F, then so is the closure of G in spB with respect to the uniform structure of $\mathcal{U}$-simple convergence on **F**.

(3) G is $\mathcal{V}$-$\mathcal{U}$ uniformly equicontinuous on F and F is $\mathcal{W}$-$\mathcal{V}$ uniformly equicontinuous on G if and only if the map

$$F \times G \to \text{spE}$$
$$(x,y) \to \langle x,y\rangle$$

is $\mathcal{V} \times \mathcal{W}$-$\mathcal{U}$ uniformly continuous.

<u>Proof</u>: (1) is a triviality

(2) Suppose G is $\mathcal{V}$-$\mathcal{U}$ uniformly equicontinuous on F. Let $U \in \mathcal{U}$, choose $V \in \mathcal{V}$ s.t. $(x,z) \in V|_F \to (\langle x,y\rangle, \langle z,y\rangle) \in U \; \forall y \in G$.

Now let w be in the closure of G with respect to the uniform structure of $\mathcal{U}$-simple convergence on F. We claim that if $(x,z) \in V|_F$ then $(\langle x,w\rangle, \langle z,w\rangle) \in \overset{3}{U}$. It clearly suffices to establish this claim.

Choose $x,z \in F$ s.t. $(x,z) \in V$. $\exists\, y \in G$ s.t. $(\langle x,w\rangle, \langle x,y\rangle) \in U$ and $(\langle z,w\rangle, \langle z,y\rangle) \in U^{-1}$. But then, since $(\langle x,y\rangle, \langle z,y\rangle) \in U$, it follows that $(\langle x,w\rangle, \langle z,w\rangle) \in \overset{3}{U}$.

We now prove (3). Suppose G is $\mathcal{V}$-$\mathcal{U}$ uniformly equicontinuous on F and F is $\mathcal{W}$-$\mathcal{U}$ uniformly equicontinuous on G. Let $U \in \mathcal{U}$ and choose $V \in \mathcal{V}$, $W \in \mathcal{W}$ s.t. $(x,z) \in V|_F \to (\langle x,y\rangle, \langle z,y\rangle) \in U \; \forall y \in G$ and $(y,w) \in W|_G \to (\langle x,y\rangle, \langle x,w\rangle) \in U \; \forall x \in F$. Then $(x,z) \in V|_F$ and

$(y,w) \in W|_G \to (\langle x,y\rangle, \langle z,y\rangle) \in U$ and $(\langle z,y\rangle, \langle z,w\rangle) \in U \to (\langle x,y\rangle, \langle z,w\rangle) \in U^2$.

Conversely, suppose the map is $\mathcal{V} \times \mathcal{W}$-$\mathcal{U}$ uniformly continuous. Let $U \in \mathcal{U}$. Choose $V \in \mathcal{V}$, $W \in \mathcal{W}$ s.t. $(x,z) \in V|_F$, $(y,w) \in W|_G \to (\langle x, y\rangle, \langle z,w\rangle) \in U$. Then $(x,z) \in V|_F \to (\langle x,y\rangle, \langle z,y\rangle) \in U \ \forall\ y \in G$ and $(y,w) \in W|_G \to (\langle x,y\rangle, \langle x,w\rangle) \in U \ \forall\ x \in F$.

8. <u>Proposition</u>: <u>Let $\mathcal{U}$ be a uniform structure on spE. Let $\mathcal{V}$ be a uniform structure on spA. Let $\mathcal{W}$ be a uniform structure on spB. Let D be a subobject of A and let C be a subobject of B.</u>

(1) <u>C is (locally) $\mathcal{V}$-$\mathcal{U}$ uniformly continuous on D if and only if the identity morphism on D is (locally) $\mathcal{V}$-σ $(C,\mathcal{U})$ uniformly continuous</u>.

(2) <u>C is (locally) $\mathcal{V}$-$\mathcal{U}$ uniformly equicontinuous on D if and only if the identity morphism on D is (locally) $\mathcal{V}$-$\mathcal{N}$ $(C,\mathcal{U})$ continuous</u>.

(3) <u>If $E[\mathcal{U}]$ is cover-closed and if C is (locally) $\mathcal{V}$-$\mathcal{U}$ uniformly equicontinuous on D, so is the cover-closed envelope of csp(C) in sp(B) w.r.t. $\sigma(D,\mathcal{U})$</u>.

(4) <u>C is locally $\mathcal{V}$-$\mathcal{U}$ uniformly equicontinuous on D and D is locally $\mathcal{W}$-$\mathcal{V}$ uniformly equicontinuous on C if and only if for each $F \in c(D)$ and each $G \in c(C)$ map</u>

$$F \times G \to spE$$

$$(x,y) \to \langle x,y\rangle$$

<u>is $\mathcal{V} \times \mathcal{W}$-$\mathcal{U}$ uniformly continuous</u>.

<u>Proof</u>: (1) is a triviality. (2), (3) and (4) follow directly from Lemma 7.

9. <u>Convention</u>: In the special case where $\mathcal{U}$ is determined by a single pseudo-metric g, we shall often write E[g] in place of $E[\mathcal{U}]$, and $\mathcal{N}(C,g)$ in place of $\mathcal{N}(C,\mathcal{U})$. If $F \subset spB$, $\epsilon > 0$ and $U = \{(x,y): g(x,y) < \epsilon\}$, we shall write $N(F,\epsilon)$ in place of $N(F,U)$. We shall also write $\sigma(C,g)$ in place of $\sigma(C,\mathcal{U})$. In

case E is the scalar field K and $g(x,y) = |x-y|$, we shall often suppress $\mathcal{U}$ entirely, writing, for instance, $\mathcal{N}(C)$ in place of $\mathcal{N}(C,\mathcal{U})$ and $\sigma(C)$ in place of $\sigma(C,\mathcal{U})$.

§3. Transpose Maps

1. Convention: Throughout this section, $\mathcal{C}$ will denote a fixed category of covered objects in which products exist and for which the covered space functor preserves products.

2. Lemma: Let E be an object of $\mathcal{C}$. Let S and T be non-empty sets. Let $(F, \{\phi\}_{s\in S})$ be a product in $\mathcal{C}$ of a family of objects, indexed by S, each term of which is E. Let $(G, \{\psi_t\}_{t\in T})$ be a product in $\mathcal{C}$ of a family of objects, indexed by T, each term of which is E.

Let θ: $S \to T$ be a function.

(1) There is a unique morphism

$$\rho \in \mathrm{Mor}(G,F)$$

such that for each $s\in S$, we have

$$\phi_s\rho = \psi_{\theta(s)}$$

(2) There is a unique bijection

$$\alpha: \quad (\mathrm{sp}E)^S \to \mathrm{sp}F$$

with the property that for each $s\in S$ we have

$$\phi_s\alpha: \quad f \to f(s)$$

(3) There is a unique bijection

$$\beta: \quad (\mathrm{sp}E)^T \to \mathrm{sp}G$$

with the property that for each $t\in T$ we have

$$\psi_t\beta: \quad f \to f(t)$$

(4) The following diagram is commutative:

$$\begin{array}{ccc} (\mathrm{spE})^T & \xrightarrow{t_\theta} & (\mathrm{spE})^S \\ \beta\downarrow & & \downarrow\alpha \\ \mathrm{spG} & \xrightarrow{\rho} & \mathrm{spF} \end{array}$$

where

$$^t\theta: \quad \sigma \to \sigma\theta$$

Proof: Use the fact that the space functor preserves products.

3. *Convention*: Let E be an object of $\mathcal{C}$ and let S be a non-empty set. *We shall generally denote any product of a family of objects in $\mathcal{C}$, indexed by S, each term of which is E, by $(E^S, \{e(s)\}_{s\in S})$* (the "e" stands for "evaluation"). *In case $f\in sp(E^S)$ and $s\in S$, we shall often write f(s) for the value of e(s) at f. If T is another non-empty set and ϕ: $S \to T$ is a function, we shall denote by $^t\phi$ the unique morphism in $Mor(E^T, E^S)$ such that $e(s)\,^t\phi = e(\phi(s))$ for each $s\in S$.* Since the family of maps $\{e(s)\}s\in S$ is always denoted by the same symbols, *we shall often write E^S instead of $(E^S, \{e(s)\}s\in S)$.*

Now suppose that A is another object of $\mathcal{C}$. *We shall often write E^A in place of E^{spA}.* In this case, there is a unique embedding of Mor(A,E) into $sp(E^A)$ such that all the proper diagrams commute. *We shall often simply consider Mor(A,E) as a subspace of $sp(E^A)$ via this embedding.*

4. *Convention*: Let E be an object of $\mathcal{C}$, let $\mathcal{U}$ be a uniform structure on spE, and let S be a non-empty set. *We shall denote by $E[\mathcal{U}]^S$ any product $(E^S, \{e(s)\}_{s\in S})$ in $\mathcal{C}$, together with the uniform structure $\bigvee_{s\in S} e(s)^{-1}(\mathcal{U})$ on $sp(E^S)$.* Note that, under the space functor, $E[\mathcal{U}]^S$ goes to a product uniform space, $spE[\mathcal{U}]^S$.

The point of the above development is the following: Under the given hypotheses on $\mathcal{C}$, and with the notation we just introduced, we may as well assume that $\mathcal{C}$ is the category of sets for a good number of applications. This is a fact we shall make use of in Chapter 5. For the present, the results of the previous section can be applied to the special case where C is indeed the category of sets.

If A and E are non-empty sets, then by the <u>canonical duality $\langle E^A, A\rangle$ over E</u>, we mean the duality given by $\langle f,x\rangle = f(x)$ ($f \in E^A$, $x \in A$). The following proposition is entirely simple, but quite useful:

5. <u>Proposition</u>: <u>Let A, B, E be non-empty sets. Let $\mathcal{U}$ be a uniform structure on E. Let C be a subobject of the covered set E^A and let D be a subobject of the covered set E^B.</u>

<u>Let $\phi \in B^A$.</u>

(1) ${}^t\phi$: <u>$E[\mathcal{U}]^B \to E[\mathcal{U}]^A$ is uniformly continuous.</u>

(2) <u>ϕ is $\mathcal{N}(C,\mathcal{U})$ - $\mathcal{N}(D,\mathcal{U})$ uniformly continuous if and only if for each set $F \in c(D)$, ${}^t\phi(F)$ is an $\mathcal{N}(C,\mathcal{U})$ -$\mathcal{U}$ uniformly equicontinuous subset of E^A.</u>

<u>Therefore, if we assume that ${}^t\phi$ restricts to a covered set morphism from D to C, then we have</u>

(3) <u>ϕ is $\mathcal{N}(C,\mathcal{U})$ - $\mathcal{N}(D,\mathcal{U})$ uniformly continuous</u>

(4) <u>ϕ is $\sigma(C,\mathcal{U})$ - $\sigma(D,\mathcal{U})$ uniformly continuous</u>

<u>Proof</u>: Only (2) needs any comment. But it is clear that if ϕ is $\mathcal{N}(C,\mathcal{U})$ - $\mathcal{N}(D,\mathcal{U})$ uniformly continuous and if $F \in c(D)$, then since F is $\mathcal{N}(D,\mathcal{U})$ - $\mathcal{U}$ uniformly equicontinuous, ${}^t\phi(F) = \{\psi\phi : \psi \in F\}$ is $\mathcal{N}(C,\mathcal{U})$ - $\mathcal{U}$ uniformly equicontinuous. Conversely, suppose this condition holds. Let $U \in \mathcal{U}$ and let $F \in c(D)$. Then $N({}^t\phi(F),U)$ is an entourage of $\mathcal{N}(C,\mathcal{U})$ by Lemma 2.7. The result now follows from the following lemma.

6. <u>Lemma</u>: Let A, B, E be non-empty sets, let $\mathcal{U}$ be a uniform structure on E and let $\phi \in B^A$.

Let ${}^t\phi$: $E^B \to E^A$, let $F \subset E^B$ and let $U \in \mathcal{U}$.

Then, if x, $y \in A$, we have

$$(x,y) \in N({}^t\phi(F),U) \leftrightarrow (\phi(x),\phi(y)) \in N(F,U)$$

7. Example: We consider the category $\mathcal{C}$ of vector spaces over K (2.3.5).

The rule u which assigns to each object E the set u(E) of all locally convex topologies on E is a uniformizing rule for this Cartesian category. $\mathcal{C}_u$ is called the category of locally convex spaces. If E is any vector space over K, then $\mathcal{D}(E, K)$ is just the algebraic dual E^* (as a covered set, it is isomorphic to $(E^*, \{E^*\})$). If $\mathcal{T}$ is a locally convex topology on E, then $\mathcal{D}(E[\mathcal{T}], K)$ is just the dual space E'. In this setting, Proposition 2.4 and Proposition 5 allow us the following line of reasoning.

Let $E[\mathcal{T}]$ and $F[\mathcal{S}]$ be separated locally convex spaces over K and let ϕ: $E \to F$ be a linear map.

(1) ${}^t\phi$: $F^* \to E^*$ is $\sigma(F^*,F)$ - $\sigma(E^*,E)$ continuous.

(2) ϕ is $\sigma(E,E')$ - $\phi(F,F')$ continuous if and only if ${}^t\phi(F') \subset E'$.

Therefore, if ϕ is $\mathcal{T}$-$\mathcal{S}$ continuous, it follows that

(3) ϕ is $\sigma(E,E')$ - $\sigma(F,F')$ continuous.

Also from the fact that $\phi' = {}^t\phi|_{E'}$ is a $\sigma(F',F)$ - $\sigma(E',E)$ continuous linear (easily checked) map from F' to E', we get

(4) ϕ' maps balanced, convex, $\sigma(F',F)$-compact sets to balanced, convex, $\sigma(E',E)$-compact sets.

(5) ϕ' maps $\sigma(F',F)$-bounded sets to $\sigma(E',E)$-bounded sets.

Proposition 1 translates these statements to

(4') ϕ is $\tau(E,E')$ - $\tau(F,F')$ continuous.

(5') ϕ is $\beta(E,E')$ - $\beta(F,F')$ continuous.

But now if we make the usual identification of E, resp. F, with $E'[\sigma(E',E)]'$, resp. $F'[\sigma(F',F)]'$. we can then identify ϕ with ϕ'' and we obtain, by applying the above arguments to $F'[\sigma(F',F)]$, $E'[\sigma(E',E)]$ and ϕ' in place of $E[\mathcal{T}]$, $F[\mathcal{S}]$ and ϕ, the following statements.

(6) ϕ' is $\tau(F',F)$ - $\tau(E',E)$ continuous

(7) ϕ' is $\beta(F',F)$ - $\beta(E',E)$ continuous.

But then the two statements

(8) ϕ maps $\beta(E,E')$-bounded sets to $\beta(F,F')$ bounded sets

(9) ϕ' maps $\beta(F',F)$-bounded sets to $\beta(E',E)$-bounded sets

which we get from statements (5') and (7) translate through Proposition 1 to

(8') ϕ' is $\beta^*(F',F)-\beta^*(E',E)$ continuous

(9') ϕ is $\beta^*(E,E')-\beta^*(F,F')$ continuous.

§4. Completeness in a Uniform Duality

Having introduced those uniform structures which we defined in Section 1, one of the first questions which must come to mind is that of completeness. Happily, one can quite often reduce questions concerning completeness in these settings to questions about product uniform structures. The following two propositions are fundamental.

1. Proposition: Let $\langle A,B\rangle$ be a duality over E in a category of covered objects $\mathcal{C}$. Let $\mathcal{U}$ be a uniform structure on spE. Let C be a subobject of B.

Let $\mathcal{F}$ be an $\mathcal{N}(C,\mathcal{U})$-Cauchy filter on spA.

If $\mathcal{F}$ converges to a point $x \in$ spA with respect to $\sigma(C,\mathcal{U})$, then $\mathcal{F}$ converges to x with respect to $\mathcal{N}(C,\mathcal{U})$.

Proof: Let $U \in \mathcal{U}$, $G \in c(C)$ be given. Choose $F \in \mathcal{F}$ such that $F \times F \subset N(G,U)$.

Let $z \in F$ be given. We have

$$(\langle z,y\rangle, \langle w,y\rangle) \in U \ \forall\ y \in G,\ w \in F$$

But x is in the $\sigma(C,\mathcal{U})$-closure of F, so, for each $y \in G$, $\exists w \in F$ s.t.

$$(\langle w,y\rangle, \langle x,y\rangle) \in U$$

Therefore,

$$(\langle z,y\rangle, \langle x,y\rangle) \in \overset{2}{U} \ \forall\ y \in G.$$

Since this is true for an arbitrary $z \in F$, we have

$$(z,x) \in N(G,\overset{2}{U}) \ \forall \ z \in F.$$

That is, we have shown that $\mathcal{F}$ converges to x with respect to $N(C,\mathcal{U})$.

2. <u>Proposition</u>: <u>Let <A,B> be a duality over E in a category of covered objects $\mathcal{C}$. Let $\mathcal{U}$ be a uniform structure on spE, let $\mathcal{W}$ be a uniform structure on spB.</u>

<u>Let C be a subobject of B and let X denote the set of all points $x \in spA$ such that the map</u>

$$spC \to spE$$

$$y \to \langle x,y \rangle$$

<u>is locally $\mathcal{W}$-$\mathcal{U}$ uniformly continuous.</u>

<u>X is $N(C,\mathcal{U})$-closed in spA.</u>

<u>Proof</u>: Let x be a point in the $N(C,\mathcal{U})$-closure of X in spA. Let $G \in c(C)$ and let $U = \overset{-1}{U} \in \mathcal{U}$. Choose $z \in X$ such that

$$(x,z) \in N(G,U).$$

Now let $W \in \mathcal{W}$ be chosen so that $(y_1,y_2) \in W \cap (G x G) \to (\langle z,y_1 \rangle, \langle z,y_2 \rangle) \in U$. Then, if $(y_1,y_2) \in W \cap (G x G)$, we have

$$(\langle x,y_1 \rangle, \langle z,y_1 \rangle) \in U$$

$$(\langle z,y_1 \rangle, \langle z,y_2 \rangle) \in U$$

$$(\langle z,y_2 \rangle, \langle x,y_2 \rangle) \in U$$

and therefore

$$(\langle x,y_1 \rangle, \langle x,y_2 \rangle) \in \overset{3}{U}$$

This completes the proof.

3. <u>Corollary</u>: <u>Let $A[\mathcal{V}]$ be a covered uniform space. Let $E[\mathcal{U}]$ denote a separated, complete uniform space.</u>

<u>Let B denote a closed subspace of the product space $E[\mathcal{U}]^{spA}$.</u>

<u>Let C denote the set of all locally $\mathcal{V}$-$\mathcal{W}$ uniformly continuous functions in B.</u>

<u>$C[\mathcal{N}(A,\mathcal{U})]$ is separated and complete</u>.

<u>Proof</u>: It is clearly separated. Let $\mathcal{F}$ be an $\mathcal{N}(A,\mathcal{U})$-Cauchy filter on C. Then $\mathcal{F}$ is a $\sigma(A,\mathcal{U})$ Cauchy filter base on B. Since $E[\mathcal{U}]$ is complete and B is closed in $E[\mathcal{U}]^{spA}$, B is $\sigma(A,\mathcal{U})$-complete. So $\mathcal{F}$ converges to a point $x \in B$ with respect to $\sigma(A,\mathcal{U})$. By Proposition 1, $\mathcal{F}$ converges to x with respect to $\mathcal{N}(A,\mathcal{U})$. By Proposition 2, x is therefore locally $\mathcal{V}$-$\mathcal{W}$ continuous. That is, $x \in C$. This completes the proof.

Now suppose we are given a duality <A,B> over E in a category of covered objects $\mathcal{C}$. We recall from Section 2 that we have natural maps

$$r_A\colon\ spA \to Mor(B,E) \subset spE^{spB}$$

$$r_B\colon\ spB \to Mor(A,E) \subset spE^{spA}$$

associated with this duality. We have then a natural commutative diagram

$$\begin{array}{ccccccc} spA & \longrightarrow & spA & \qquad & spB & \longleftarrow & spB \\ {\scriptstyle r_A}\downarrow & & \downarrow{\scriptstyle j_A} & & {\scriptstyle j_B}\downarrow & & \downarrow{\scriptstyle r_B} \\ Mor(B,E) & \longrightarrow & spE^{spB} & & spE^{spA} & \longleftarrow & Mor(A,E) \end{array}$$

Now let N be a subset of Mor(A,E) such that $r_B(spB)$ is contained in N. We have a natural "evaluation" map

$$e\colon\ spA \to spE^N$$

From this, we obtain a natural commutative diagram

$$\begin{array}{ccccccc} & & spA & \qquad & spB & \longleftarrow & spB \\ & {\scriptstyle e}\swarrow & \downarrow{\scriptstyle j_A} & & {\scriptstyle j_B}\downarrow & & \downarrow{\scriptstyle j_{BN}} \\ spE^N & \xrightarrow[{}^t j_{BN}]{} & spE^{spB} & & spE^{spA} & \longleftarrow & N \end{array}$$

<u>We will utilize the notation introduced here in the statement and proof of the next theorem</u>.

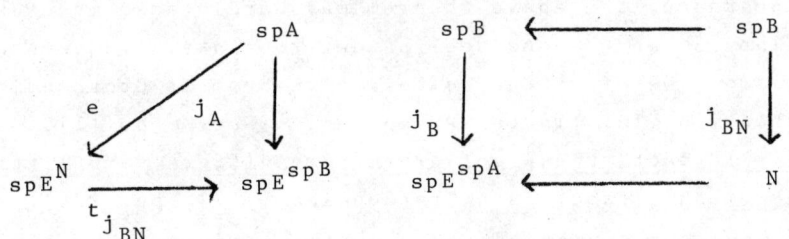

4. Theorem: Let $\mathcal{C}$ denote a category of covered objects. Let <A,B> be a duality over E in $\mathcal{C}$. Let $\mathcal{U}$ be a complete, separated uniform structure on spE and assume that $E[\mathcal{U}]$ is compactly covered. (I.e., each set of c(E) is contained in a compact set of c(E).)

We suppose moreover that Mor(A,E) is closed in the product space $spE[\mathcal{U}]^{spA}$.

Let N denote the subset of Mor(A,E) consisting of all those morphisms which are locally $\sigma(B,\mathcal{U})$ $-\mathcal{U}$ uniformly continuous on A.

(I) $N[\mathcal{N}(A,\mathcal{U})]$ is complete and separated

(II) j_{BN}^{-1} $(\mathcal{N}(A,\mathcal{U})) = \mathcal{N}(A,\mathcal{U})$ (on spB)

(III) ${}^t j_{BN}$ maps the cover-closed envelope of e(A) in $spE[\mathcal{U}]^N$ bijectively onto the cover-closed envelope of $j_A(A)$ in $spE[\mathcal{U}]^{spB}$.

Proof: (I) follows directly from Corollary 3.

(II) this is obvious.

(III) Each of these cover-closed envelopes is a local compactification of the covered uniform space $A[\sigma(B,\mathcal{U})]$. For in the case of the envelope in $spE[\mathcal{U}]^{spB}$, this is a trivial consequence of the fact that each set $\{<x,y>: x \in F\}$ where $y \in B$ and $F \in c(A)$ is relatively compact in $E[\mathcal{U}]$. In the case of the envelope in $spE[\mathcal{U}]^N$, one must also use the local uniform continuity assumption imposed on the points of N. Since ${}^t j_{BN}$, as a transpose map, is uniformly continuous, it maps the closed envelope in $spE[\mathcal{U}]^N$ to that in $spE[\mathcal{U}]^{spB}$. But then, by the properties of local compactifications, it must do so bijectively.

In appearance, the above theorem may hardly seem much deeper than Corollary 3, and a good deal harder to state. To counter this impression, we offer the following theorem of Grothendieck from the theory of locally convex spaces. (See Köthe [1], pp. 271-2.) In fact, the proof given here differs very little from Grothendieck's proof (see Grothendieck, [2], pg. 128).

5. <u>Corollary</u>: Let E and F be vector spaces over K and suppose we are given a bilinear map

$$<,>: \quad F \times E \to K$$

$$(x,y) \to <x,y>$$

Let $\mathcal{B}$ be a directed covering of F by balanced, convex, $\sigma(F,E)$-bounded sets which is stable under multiplication by scalars. Let B denote the covered set $(spF, \mathcal{B})$

Let N denote the set of all linear forms on F which are $\sigma(F,E)$-continuous on each set of $\mathcal{B}$.

The pair $(j_{EN}, N[\mathcal{N}(B)])$ is a completion of the locally convex space $E[\mathcal{N}(B)]$.

<u>Proof</u>: Before trying to apply Theorem 4, we must note that we face a difficulty: Elements of N are not assumed to be $\sigma(F,E)$-<u>uniformly</u> continuous on each set of $\mathcal{B}$. However, a very simple lemma of Grothendieck's (See Köthe [1], pg. 267.) proves that a linear form is uniformly continuous on a balanced, convex subset of a locally convex space if and only if it is continuous on that set, in fact, if and only if it is continuous at 0. So our difficulty was only apparent.

That $\mathcal{N}(B)$ is a locally convex topology on both N and E is a triviality, as is the fact that j_{EN} is linear. So if we apply Theorem 4, all we need to show is that $j_{EN}(E)$ is dense in N. To this end, it suffices (by the Hahn-Banach theorem) to show that ${}^t j_{EN}$ maps N' injectively into E'. However, it is an elementary fact in the theory of locally convex spaces that the dual of E, resp. N, is just the cover-closed envelope of $j_{\mathcal{B}}(B)$ in K^E, resp. the cover-closed envelope of e(B) in K^N. But Theorem 4 then states that ${}^t j_{EN}$ maps N' bijectively onto E'.

6. <u>Corollary</u>: Let $E[\mathcal{T}]$ be a separated locally convex space. The following statements are equivalent:

(1) $E[\mathcal{T}]$ is complete.

(2) If ϕ is a linear form on the dual space, E', of $E[\mathcal{T}]$, and if the restriction of ϕ to each equicontinuous set of E' is

$\sigma(E',E)$-continuous, then ϕ has the form

$$\phi: \quad f \to f(x)$$

for some x E.

The proof of Corollary 5 should give an intuition for how close Theorem 4 comes to giving a general characterization of the completion of a function space. What is lacking in general is a Hahn-Banach Theorem--something to allow us to pass from the statement that ${}^{t}j_{BN}$ is injective on the closed envelope of e(A) to the statement that $j_{EN}(spB)$ is dense in N.

While the above results on completeness are very useful, there is another, still more general result. The above results we proved here because this can be done within the more abstract setting which I am treating. Unfortunately, the more general result is very definitely properly within the theory of locally convex spaces. Since I will have use for the more general result in my treatment of almost periodic and weakly almost periodic linear forms, I wish to have it available. Unfortunately, the standard references (Horvath [1], Chapter 3, §11, Theorem 1 or Schaefer [1], Chapter IV, §6, Theorem 2) on this result impose too many restrictions in the hypotheses. So I will state the result, reduce the proof to the case where the hypotheses are so restricted, and refer the reader to either of the above references.

7. Theorem: Let $F[S]$ be a locally convex space, F' its dual. Let $\mathcal{B}$ be a covering of F by balanced, convex, bounded sets and assume $\mathcal{B}$ is directed (by set inclusion). Let $\mathcal{T}_{\mathcal{B}}$ be the topology on F' of uniform convergence on sets of $\mathcal{B}$.

Let $\tilde{F}'$ consist of all linear forms on F which are continuous on each set of $\mathcal{B}$ with respect to S. (We do not assume such

<u>a form to be $\sigma(F,F')$-continuous on each set of B!!). Then $\tilde{F}'[T_{\mathcal{B}}]$ is a completion of $F'[T_{\mathcal{B}}]$.</u>

<u>Proof</u>: First, it is a triviality that we may as well assume S is separated. So in order to reduce the proof to the special case proved in the references, we need only show that we may assume that each set of $\mathcal{B}$ is closed, i.e., we must show that if $\phi\in\tilde{F}'$, then ϕ is S-continuous on each $\overline{B}$, $B\in\mathcal{B}$. But, by Grothendieck's Lemma (See Köthe [1], pg. 267.) ϕ is S-uniformly continuous on each set of $\mathcal{B}$. So, for each $B\in\mathcal{B}$, we can (uniquely) define a uniformly continuous function

$$\phi_B; \quad \overline{B} \to K$$

such that $\phi_B(x) = \phi(x)$ $(x\in B)$. Since $\mathcal{B}$ is a directed covering of F it follows by continuity that $\phi_B(x) = \phi(x)$ $(x\in\overline{B})$ for each $B\in\mathcal{B}$. Indeed, if $C\in\mathcal{B}$ and $B\cup\{x\}\subset C$ then $\phi_C|_{\overline{B}} = \phi_B$. So $\phi_B(x) = \phi_C(x) = \phi(x)$.

8. <u>Corollary</u>: <u>Let $E[T]$ be a covered locally convex space (see 2.5.6), let $F[S]$ be any locally convex space and let</u>

$$\phi: \quad E \to F$$

<u>be a locally T-S continuous linear map. Then, if $E = (A,\mathcal{A})$, ϕ is locally $\sigma(A,A') - \sigma(F,F')$ continuous.</u>

<u>Proof</u>: If $\alpha\in F'$, then $\alpha\phi$ is locally T-continuous. By Theorem 7 and Corollary 5, $\alpha\phi$ is locally $\sigma(A,A')$-continuous. If $\tilde{A}'$ denotes the space of all linear forms on A with this latter property the statement becomes ${}^t\phi(F')\subset\tilde{A}'$. So ϕ is $\sigma(A,\tilde{A}') - \sigma(F,F')$ continuous, i.e., locally $\sigma(A,A') - \sigma(F,F')$ continuous.

§5. <u>Precompactness in a Uniform Duality</u>

If we are given a duality $\langle A,B\rangle$ over E in a category of covered objects C, if $\mathcal{U}$ is a uniform structure on spE, and if C is a subobject of B, then the question of $\sigma(C,\mathcal{U})$-precompactness is a simple one: A set $F\subset$ spA is $\sigma(C,\mathcal{U})$-precompact if and only if for each $y\in$spC, the set $\{\langle x,y\rangle: x\in F\}$ is precompact in spE[$\mathcal{U}$].

The following results go somewhat deeper:

1. Ascoli's Theorem: Let <A,B> be a duality over E in a category of covered objects.

Let $\mathcal{U}$ be a uniform structure on spE.

If $B[\mathcal{N}(A,\mathcal{U})]$ is precompactly covered, then the uniform structures $\mathcal{N}(B,\mathcal{U})$ and $\sigma(B,\mathcal{U})$ are locally equivalent on A. (That is, the identity morphism on A is locally $\sigma(B,\mathcal{U})$ - $\mathcal{N}(B,\mathcal{U})$ uniformly continuous.)

Proof: Suppose $B[\mathcal{N}(A,\mathcal{U})]$ is precompactly covered. Let $F \in c(A)$, $G \in c(B)$, $U = U^{-1} \in \mathcal{U}$.

$\exists$ a finite set $H \subset G$ s.t. for each $y \in G$ $\exists$ $w \in H$ s.t. $(y,w) \in N(F,U)$. We claim that we have

$$N(H,U)|_F \subset N(G,\overset{3}{U})|_F$$

Clearly, if we show this, the proof will be complete. But suppose $(x,z) \in (F\times F) \cap N(H,U)$. Let $y \in G$. $\exists$ $w \in H$ s.t. $(y,w) \in N(F,U)$. Hence, we have

$$(\langle x,y\rangle, \langle x,w\rangle) \in U$$

$$(\langle x,w\rangle, \langle z,w\rangle) \in U$$

$$(\langle z,w\rangle, \langle z,y\rangle) \in U$$

Therefore, we have

$$(\langle x,y\rangle, \langle z,y\rangle) \in \overset{3}{U}$$

Since $y \in G$ was arbitrarily chosen, this completes the proof.

2. Corollary: Let <A,B> be a duality over E in a category of covered objects.

Let $\mathcal{U}$ be a uniform structure on spE and let $\mathcal{V}$ be a uniform structure on spA.

We suppose that B is locally $\mathcal{V}$-$\mathcal{U}$ uniformly continuous on A.

Then, if $B[\mathcal{N}(A,\mathcal{U})]$ is precompactly covered, B is locally $\mathcal{V}$-$\mathcal{U}$ uniformly equicontinuous on A.

Proof: By Proposition 2.8, we must show that the identity morphism on A is locally $\mathcal{V}$-$\mathcal{N}(B,\mathcal{U})$ uniformly continuous. But by

Theorem 1, it suffices to show it is locally $\mathcal{V}$-$\sigma(B,\mathcal{U})$ uniformly continuous. But by 2.8 the hypotheses force this.

3. Corollary: *Let $\langle A,B\rangle$ be a duality over E in a category of covered objects.*

We assume $A(\mathcal{V})$ is precompactly covered.

If B is locally $\mathcal{V}$-$\mathcal{U}$ uniformly equicontinuous on A, then $\mathcal{N}(A,\mathcal{U})$ and $\sigma(A,\mathcal{U})$ are locally equivalent on B.

Proof: Since $A(\mathcal{V})$ is precompact, and since, by Proposition 2.8, the identity morphism on A is locally $\mathcal{V}$-$\mathcal{N}(B,\mathcal{U})$ uniformly continuous, it follows that $A[\mathcal{N}(B,\mathcal{U})]$ is precompactly covered. The result now follows from Theorem 1.

4. Corollary: *Let $\langle A,B\rangle$ be a duality over E in a category of covered objects.*

Let $\mathcal{U}$ be a uniform structure on spE and let $\mathcal{V}$ be a uniform structure on spA.

We suppose that B is locally $\mathcal{V}$-$\mathcal{U}$ uniformly continuous on A.

We suppose $A[\mathcal{V}]$ and $B[\sigma(A,\mathcal{U})]$ are precompactly covered.

The following statements are equivalent:

(I) *$B[\mathcal{N}(A,\mathcal{U})]$ is precompactly covered.*

(II) *B is locally $\mathcal{V}$-$\mathcal{U}$ uniformly equicontinuous on A.*

(III) *$\mathcal{N}(A,\mathcal{U})$ is locally equivalent to $\sigma(A,\mathcal{U})$ on B.*

Proof: (I) $\rightarrow$ (II) by Corollary 2. (II) $\rightarrow$ (III) by Corollary 3. (III) $\rightarrow$ (I) since $B[\sigma(A,\mathcal{U})]$ is precompactly covered.

The following corollary is a direct generalization of a theorem of Grothendieck in the theory of locally convex spaces. (See Köthe, [1], pg. 268.)

5. Corollary: *(A Symmetric Ascoli Theorem)*

Let $\langle A[\mathcal{V}], B[\mathcal{W}]\rangle$ be a locally uniform duality over $E[\mathcal{U}]$ in a category of covered objects. We suppose that both $A[\mathcal{V}]$ and $B[\mathcal{W}]$ are precompactly covered.

The following statements are all equivalent:

(1) *$A[\mathcal{N}(B,\mathcal{U})]$ is precompactly covered.*

(2) *$B[\mathcal{N}(A,\mathcal{U})]$ is precompactly covered.*

(3) A is locally $\mathcal{W}$-$\mathcal{U}$ uniformly equicontinuous on B.

(4) B is locally $\mathcal{V}$-$\mathcal{U}$ uniformly equicontinuous on A.

(5) The identity morphism on B is locally $\mathcal{W}$-$\mathcal{N}$ (A,$\mathcal{U}$) uniformly continuous.

(6) The identity morphism on A is locally $\mathcal{V}$-$\mathcal{N}$ (B,$\mathcal{U}$) uniformly continuous.

(7) $\mathcal{N}(B,\mathcal{U})$ is locally equivalent to $\sigma(B,\mathcal{U})$ on A.

(8) $\mathcal{N}(A,\mathcal{U})$ is locally equivalent to $\sigma(A,\mathcal{U})$ on B.

(9) For each $F \in c(A)$, $G \in c(B)$ the map

$$F \times G \to spE$$

$$(x,y) \to \langle x,y \rangle$$

is $\sigma(B,\mathcal{U}) \times \sigma(A,\mathcal{U})$-$\mathcal{U}$ uniformly continuous

(10) For each $F \in c(A)$, $G \in c(B)$ the map

$$F \times G \to spE$$

$$(x,y) \to \langle x,y \rangle$$

is $\mathcal{V} \times \mathcal{W}$ - $\mathcal{U}$ uniformly continuous.

Proof: By Corollary 4, we have (1)$\leftrightarrow$(3)$\leftrightarrow$(7), (2)$\leftrightarrow$(4)$\leftrightarrow$(8). By Proposition 2.8, we have (5)$\leftrightarrow$(7) and (6)$\leftrightarrow$(8). But, by Theorem 1, we have (1) $\to$ (8) and (2) $\to$ (7). Since (8) $\to$ (2) and (7) $\to$ (1), this proves that (1) through (8) are equivalent.

But, by Proposition 2.8, we have [(7) and (8)]$\leftrightarrow$(9) and we have [(5) and (6)] $\leftrightarrow$(10).

We will state one more corollary of Theorem 1, this one being a mere special case of the last. My reason for stating it is that it is explicitly suggestive of the theory of almost periodic functions, where I intend to use it in the next chapter.

6. Corollary: (A Symmetric Ascoli Theorem)

Let $\langle A,B \rangle$ be a duality over E in a category of covered objects.

Let $\mathcal{U}$ be a uniform structure on spE and suppose that

$A[\sigma(B,\mathcal{U})]$ and $B[\sigma(A,\mathcal{U})]$ are precompactly covered. (This is always true if $E[\mathcal{U}]$ is precompactly covered.)

The following statements are all equivalent:

(1) *$A[\mathcal{N}(B,\mathcal{U})]$ is precompactly covered.*

(2) *$B[\mathcal{N}(A,\mathcal{U})]$ is precompactly covered.*

(3) *Let $F \in c(A)$, $G \in c(B)$, $U \in \mathcal{U}$. Then there is a finite covering $G = \bigcup_{i=1}^{n} G_i$ of G such that if $(y,w) \in \bigcup_{i=1}^{n} G_i \times G_i$, then, $(\langle x,y\rangle, \langle x,w\rangle) \in U$ for all $x \in F$.*

(4) *Let $F \in c(A)$, $G \in c(B)$, $U \in \mathcal{U}$. Then there is a finite covering $F = \bigcup_{i=1}^{n} F_i$ of F such that if $(x,z) \in \bigcup_{i=1}^{n} F_i \times F_i$, then $(\langle x,y\rangle, \langle z,y\rangle) \in U$ for all $y \in G$.*

(5) *$\mathcal{N}(B,\mathcal{U})$ is locally equivalent to $\sigma(B,\mathcal{U})$ on A.*

(6) *$\mathcal{N}(A,\mathcal{U})$ is locally equivalent to $\sigma(A,\mathcal{U})$ on B.*

(7) *For each $F \in c(A)$, $G \in c(B)$, the map*

$$F \times G \to spE$$
$$(x,y) \to \langle x,y\rangle$$

is $\sigma(B,\mathcal{U}) \times \sigma(A,\mathcal{U}) - \mathcal{U}$ uniformly continuous.

Proof: Let $\mathcal{V}$ be the uniform structure of all finite coverings on spA and let $\mathcal{W}$ be the uniform structure of all finite coverings on spB. Notice the hypothesis that $A[\sigma(B,\mathcal{U})]$ and $B[\sigma(A,\mathcal{U})]$ be precompactly covered forces both $\{\langle z,y\rangle : z \in F\}$ and $\{\langle x,w\rangle : w \in G\}$ to be $\mathcal{U}$-precompact for each $F \in c(A)$, $G \in c(B)$, $x \in spA$, $y \in spB$. But then $\langle A[\mathcal{V}], B[\mathcal{W}]\rangle$ is a locally uniform duality over $E[\mathcal{U}]$. Now apply Corollary 5.

Chapter 4. ALMOST PERIODIC FUNCTIONS AND LINEAR FORMS

§1. Synopsis

The intent of this chapter is to delineate a generalized theory of almost periodic functions and linear forms and to relate it to the appropriate notions of compactly covered reflections.

The material presented in this chapter will constitute one of the two major applications of the more abstract theories developed in this monograph to a more specialized situation. The other application will be the theory of weakly almost periodic functions and linear forms developed in Chapters 5 and 6. In both of these applications, the results of Section 3.4 will figure importantly. However, these results will play more of a background role than a prominent role. In this chapter, the prominent role will be played by the Ascoli Theorems of Section 3.5. In the other application, the prominent role will be played by extension theorems and double sequence properties. It is worth remembering that the two theories share many striking similarities and that this difference in which general theorems play the prominent role in their development constitutes their essential difference.

Sections 2 and 3 are comprised for the most part of a listing of the various notational tricks we need to make life easy. However, Section 3 does contain one of the most important Theorems of the chapter, Theorem 3.5 in which the Ascoli Theorem is used quite heavily.

Section 4 is the section where most of the work of the chapter is done. However, the way in which the results of this section are expressed, being general enough to dispose of the interesting special cases with one blow, makes them more interesting for their consequences than of intrinsic interest.

In Section 5, a general theory of almost periodic functions on a covered uniform monoid is developed and related to a certain compactly covered reflection which is called a Bohr compactly covered reflection.

Section 6 is quite analogous to Section 5. So analogous in fact that the main results are stated with no more proof than a reference to Section 5. In this section, a general theory of almost periodic linear forms on a covered locally convex algebra is developed and is related to a certain kind of compactly covered reflection for a covered locally convex algebra which again, is called a Bohr compactly covered reflection.

§2. Action of a Monoid on a Duality

We recall the notion of the action of a monoid on the left (right, both sides) of a set introduced in the preliminaries. Since an action of M on the right (both-sides) of X was defined to be an action of M^o $(M \times M^o)$ on the left of X, any theorem or definition we state in general about left action automatically carries an analogue for right (two-sided) action. Because of this, we shall only state definitions and results concerning left action and will simply assume the analogues.

1. Definition: Let $\mathcal{C}$ be a category of covered objects, let A be an object of $\mathcal{C}$, and let M be a monoid.

We say M acts on the left of A if M acts on the left of spA in such a way that each map

$$\begin{aligned} spA &\to spA \\ x &\to a \cdot x \quad (a \in M) \end{aligned}$$

is in Mor(A,A).

We denote the pair (A,·) where A is an object of $\mathcal{C}$ and where · is an action of M on the left of A, by ${}_MA$.

We denote by ${}_M\mathcal{C}$ the category whose objects are all objects ${}_MA$ where A is an object of $\mathcal{C}$ and whose set of morphisms

$$Mor({}_MA, {}_MB)$$

is the subset of Mor(A,B) consisting precisely of the action homomorphisms in Mor(A,B).

If ${}_MA$ is an object of ${}_M\mathcal{C}$, then by a subobject ${}_MB$ of ${}_MA$ we mean a subobject B of A such that $a \cdot c(B)$ refines $c(B)$ for each $a \in M$, together with the action of M on the left of B induced by that on the left of A.

When we say M acts on a uniform space, or on a covered locally convex space, etc., we shall mean by this that M acts on an object in the category of uniform spaces, or of covered locally convex spaces, etc.

2. Proposition: Suppose a monoid M acts on the left of a covered uniform space $A[\mathcal{U}]$. Suppose that ${}_MB$ is a subobject of ${}_MA$.

We consider the duality

$$M \times spA \to spA$$
$$(a, x) \to a \cdot x$$

over $A[\mathcal{U}]$. The uniform structure $\mathcal{N}(B,\mathcal{U})$ on M makes the multiplication of M separately uniformly continuous.

In particular, the uniform structures $\sigma(A,\mathcal{U})$ and $\mathcal{N}(A,\mathcal{U})$ make the multiplication of M separately uniformly continuous.

Proof: Fix $a \in M$, $F \in c(B)$, $U \in \mathcal{U}$. We have $(ba, ca) \in N(F,U) \leftrightarrow (b,c) \in N(a \cdot F, U)$.

Now choose $V \in \mathcal{U}$ s.t. $(x,y) \in V \to (a \cdot x, a \cdot y) \in U$. Then $(b,c) \in N(F,V) \leftrightarrow (b \cdot x, c \cdot x) \in V \ \forall\ x \in F \to (a \cdot (b \cdot x), a \cdot (c \cdot x)) \in U \ \forall\ x \in F \leftrightarrow (ab, ac) \in N(F,U)$.

3. Definition: Let $\mathcal{C}$ be a category of covered objects, let A, E be objects of $\mathcal{C}$, let M be a monoid and suppose that M acts on the left of A.

The relation

$$\phi \cdot a(x) = \phi(a \cdot x)$$

where $x \in spA$, $\phi \in Mor(A,E)$, $a \in M$ defines an action of M on the right of Mor(A,E), called the canonical action of M on the right of Mor(A,E). (This is a special case of the notion of transpose map introduced in §2.6.)

If $\mathcal{C}$ is a Cartesian category, then the relation

$$\phi \cdot a(x) = \phi(a \cdot x)$$

where $x \in spA$, $\phi \in sp(E^A)$, $a \in M$, defines an action of M or the right of any given product object E^A, called *the canonical action of M on the right of E^A*. (This is a special case of the notion of transpose map introduced in §3.3.)

If $\emptyset \neq X$ is a set, if a monoid M acts on the left of X, and if E is any other non-empty set, then we have a duality

$$\langle , \rangle : \quad E^X \times X \to E$$

$$(f, x) \to f(x)$$

and, for $f \in E^X$, $x \in X$, $a \in M$, we have

$$\langle f \cdot a, x\rangle = \langle f, a \cdot x\rangle \quad .$$

4. *Definition*: Let $\mathcal{C}$ be a category of covered objects and let $\langle A,B\rangle$ be a duality over E in $\mathcal{C}$. *A monoid M is said to act on the duality $\langle A, B\rangle$* if

(1) M acts on the right of A.

(2) M acts on the left of B.

(3) $\langle x \cdot a, y\rangle = \langle x, a \cdot y\rangle$ for all $x \in spA$, $y \in spB$, $a \in M$.

We shall in the next few sections deal with quite a few examples of the above type. If we are given a uniform structure $\mathcal{U}$ on spE, a duality $\langle A, B\rangle$ over E on which M acts may then induce a number of other dualities and uniform structures. For instance, the original duality induces $\mathcal{N}(B,\mathcal{U})$ on A and then A and M are in natural duality over $A[\mathcal{N}(B,\mathcal{U})]$. This duality in turn induces $\mathcal{N}(A, \mathcal{N}(B,\mathcal{U}))$ on M. *In the future, uniform structures of this kind will be written down and dealt with without any unnecessary words of explanation as to just what dualities are involved*.

5. *Proposition*: *Let $\mathcal{C}$ be a category of covered objects and let $\langle A, B\rangle$ be a duality over E in $\mathcal{C}$. Let $\mathcal{U}$ be a uniform structure on spE*.

Suppose a monoid M acts on this duality

(1) *Each map*

$$spA \to spA$$

$$x \to x \cdot a \ (a \in M)$$

is $\mathcal{N}(B,\mathcal{U})$-uniformly continuous.

(2) *Each map*

$$spB \to spB$$

$$x \to a \cdot x \ (a \in M)$$

is $\mathcal{N}(A,\mathcal{U})$-uniformly continuous.

(3) *We have*

$$\mathcal{N}(A,\mathcal{N}(B,\mathcal{U})) = \mathcal{N}(B,\mathcal{N}(A,\mathcal{U}))$$

on M. This uniform structure makes the multiplication of M separately uniformly continuous.

Proof: The only thing that really deserves any comment is the equality $\mathcal{N}(A,\mathcal{N}(B,\mathcal{U})) = \mathcal{N}(B,\mathcal{N}(A,\mathcal{U}))$.

Let $F \in c(A)$, $G \in c(B)$, $U \in \mathcal{U}$. Then we have $(a,b) \in N(F,N(G,U)) \leftrightarrow (x \cdot a, x \cdot b) \in N(G,U) \forall x \in F \leftrightarrow (<x \cdot a, y>, <x \cdot b, y>) \in U \forall x \in F, y \in G \leftrightarrow (<x, a \cdot y>, <x, b \cdot y>) \in U \forall x \in F, y \in G \leftrightarrow (a \cdot y, b \cdot y)$ $N(F,U) \ \forall y \in G \leftrightarrow (a,b) \in N(G,N(F,U))$.

§3. *Action of a Covered Monoid on a Duality*

Convention: Throughout this section, $S = (M,\mathcal{M})$ will denote a fixed covered monoid.

1. *Definition*: Let $\mathcal{C}$ be a category of covered objects and let A be an object of $\mathcal{C}$.

We say *S acts on the left of A if* we are given an action of M on the left of A.

The symbols ${}_SA$ and ${}_S\mathcal{C}$ are defined as in 2.1, as is the notion of a subobject ${}_SB$ of ${}_SA$.

We say the action of S on A is orbit-stable if the family of sets

$$\{a \cdot x:\ a \in N\}_{N \in \mathcal{M},\ x \in spA} = \mathcal{M} \cdot spA$$

refines c(A).

We say the action of S on A is fully stable if the family of sets

$$\{a \cdot x:\ a \in N,\ x \in F\}_{N \in \mathcal{M},\ F \in c(A)} = \mathcal{M} \cdot c(A)$$

refines c(A).

If we are simply given an action of a monoid N on an object A, then we will say the action of N on A is orbit-stable or fully stable if this is true of the action of (N, {N}) on A.

2. Proposition: Suppose S acts on the left of a covered uniform space A[$\mathcal{U}$]. Suppose that ${}_S B$ is a subobject of ${}_S A$.

(1) If the action of S on B is fully stable, then, for each $P \in \mathcal{M}$, the family of maps

$$M \to M$$

$$a \to ab \quad (b \in P)$$

is uniformly equicontinuous with respect to $\mathcal{N}(B, \mathcal{U})$.

(2) If each set of $\mathcal{M}$ acts as a set of uniformly equicontinuous transformations on B[$\mathcal{U}$], then, for each $P \in \mathcal{M}$, the family of maps

$$M \to M$$

$$a \to ba \quad (b \in P)$$

is uniformly equicontinuous with respect to $\mathcal{N}(B, \mathcal{U})$.

(3) If the action of S on B is fully stable and if each set of $\mathcal{M}$ acts as a set of locally uniformly equicontinuous transformations on B[$\mathcal{U}$], then, for each pair P, $R \in \mathcal{M}$, the family of maps

$$R \to R$$

$$a \to ba \quad (b \in P)$$

is uniformly equicontinuous with respect to $\mathcal{N}(B, \mathcal{U})$.

Proof: (1) $(ab, cb) \in N(F,U)\ \forall\ b \in P \leftrightarrow (a,c) \in N(B \cdot F, U)$. (2) Let $U \in \mathcal{U}$ be given and choose $V \in \mathcal{U} \ni (x,y) \in V \to (b \cdot x, b \cdot y) \in U\ \forall b \in P$. Then $(a,c) \in N(F,V) \to (ba, bc) \in N(F,U)\ \forall\ b \in P$. (3) Same proof as (2) except that we must choose V s.t. $(x,y) \in V$, $x,y \in R \cdot F \to (b \cdot x, b \cdot y) \in U\ \forall\ b \in P$.

3. Definition: Let $\mathcal{C}$ be a category of covered objects and let <A,B> be a duality over E in $\mathcal{C}$. We say that S acts on this duality <A, B> if we are given an action of M on this duality.

We say the action of S on <A, B> is orbit-stable, resp. fully stable, if this is true of the action of S on both A and B.

4. Proposition: Let $\mathcal{C}$ be a category of covered objects, let <A, B> be a duality over E in $\mathcal{C}$, and let $\mathcal{U}$ be a uniform structure on spE.

Suppose S acts on this duality with fully stable action. Then, for each $P \in \mathcal{M}$, the family of maps

$$M \to M$$

$$a \to bac \quad (b, c \in P)$$

is a uniformly equicontinuous family with respect to $\mathcal{N}(A, \mathcal{N}(B, \mathcal{U}))$.

In particular, if $P \in \mathcal{M}$, the map

$$P \times P \to M$$

$$(a,b) \to ab$$

is jointly uniformly continuous with respect to $\mathcal{N}(A, \mathcal{N}(B, \mathcal{N}))$.

Proof: Apply Proposition 2.5, Proposition 2, and Lemma 3.2.7.

The following theorem is our principal use of Ascoli's theorem in this chapter. It would not be very hard at all to call it the Fundamental Theorem of Almost Periodicity.

5. Theorem: Let $\mathcal{C}$ be a category of covered objects, let <A,B> be a duality over E in $\mathcal{C}$, let $\mathcal{U}$ be a uniform structure on spE and suppose that $A[\sigma(B,\mathcal{U})]$ and $B[\sigma(A,\mathcal{U})]$ are precompactly covered.

Suppose that S acts on this duality with fully stable action.

Finally, we suppose that $A[\mathcal{N}(B,\mathcal{U})]$ *is precompactly covered.*

The following uniform structures are all locally equivalent on S

(1) $\mathcal{N}(A,\mathcal{N}(B,\mathcal{U})) = \mathcal{N}(B,\mathcal{N}(A,\mathcal{U}))$

(2) $\mathcal{N}(A,\sigma(B,\mathcal{U})) = \sigma(B,\mathcal{N}(A,\mathcal{U}))$

(3) $\sigma(A,\mathcal{N}(B,\mathcal{U})) = \mathcal{N}(B,\sigma(A,\mathcal{U}))$

(4) $\sigma(A,\sigma(B,\mathcal{U})) = \sigma(B,\sigma(A,\mathcal{U}))$

Therefore, each of these uniform structures has the following properties:

(a) *It makes the multiplication of M separately uniformly continuous*.

(b) *It makes each set of* $\mathcal{M}$ *precompact*.

(c) *For each* $P \in \mathcal{M}$, *it makes the map*

$$P \times P \to M$$

$$(a,b) \to ab$$

jointly uniformly continuous.

Proof: The only thing that really needs any proof is the statement about local equivalence.

First, notice that the action

$$\text{spA} \times M \to \text{spA}$$

$$(x, a) \to x \cdot a$$

defines a bounded duality <csp(A), csp(S)> over csp(A) in the category of covered sets, since the action of S on A is fully stable. Also, by hypothesis, $\text{csp}(A)[\mathcal{N}(B,\mathcal{U})]$ is precompactly covered. However, since if $P \in \mathcal{M}$, $G \in c(B)$ and $U \in \mathcal{U}$ we have

$$N(P, N(G,U)) = N(P \cdot G, U)$$

$$N(1, N(G,U)) = N(G, U)$$

the fact that the action of S on B is fully stable implies that $\mathcal{N}(B,\mathcal{U}) = \mathcal{N}(S,\mathcal{N}(B,\mathcal{U}))$ on csp(A). Hence, $\text{csp}(A)[\mathcal{N}(\text{csp}(S),\mathcal{N}(B,\mathcal{U}))]$ is precompactly covered. Therefore, by Ascoli's Theorem (3.5.1), the uniform structures $\mathcal{N}(A,\mathcal{N}(B,\mathcal{U}))$ and $\sigma(A,\mathcal{N}(B,\mathcal{U}))$ are locally equivalent on S.

By 3.5.6, $B[\mathcal{N}(A,\mathcal{U})]$ is also precompactly covered, and so, by symmetry, $\mathcal{N}(B,\mathcal{N}(A,\mathcal{U}))$ and $\sigma(B,\mathcal{N}(A,\mathcal{U}))$ are locally equivalent on S.

All that remains is to show the local equivalence of $\sigma(A,\mathcal{N}(B,\mathcal{U}))$ and $\sigma(A,\sigma(B,\mathcal{U}))$. Let $P \in \mathcal{M}$, $G \in c(B)$ and $U \in \mathcal{U}$ be given. Let F be a finite subset of spA. Since the action of S on A is fully stable, F. P is contained in some set of c(A). Therefore, by the symmetric form of the Ascoli Theorem (3.5.6), there is a finite set $H \subset spB$ and an entourage V of $\mathcal{U}$ such that $N(G,U)|_{F \cdot P} \supset N(H,V)|_{F \cdot P}$. But then it is clear that we have

$$N(F,N(G,U))|_P \supset N(F,\ N(H,V))|_P$$

Hence, we have

$$\sigma(A,\mathcal{N}(B,\mathcal{U}))|_P = \sigma(A,\sigma(B,\mathcal{U}))|_P$$

This completes the proof.

§4. Almost Periodic Elements in a Duality

1. Convention: Throughout this section, S = $(M,\mathcal{M})$ will denote a fixed covered monoid.

2. Definition: Let $\mathcal{C}$ be a category of covered objects. By a duality $\langle S,\ {}_SA\rangle$ of S and an object ${}_SA$ of ${}_S\mathcal{C}$ over an object E of $\mathcal{C}$, we mean a duality $\langle csp(S),\ csp(A)\rangle$ over csp(E) in the category of covered sets with the following properties

(1) For each $a \in M$, the map

$$spA \to spE$$
$$x \to \langle a,\ x\rangle$$

is in Mor(A,E)

(2) For a, $b \in M$, $x \in spA$, we have

$$\langle ab,\ x\rangle = \langle a,\ b \cdot x\rangle$$

We call the duality *fully stable* or *orbit stable* if this is true of the action of S on A.

3. *Definition*: Let $\mathcal{C}$ be a category of covered objects and let $\langle S, {}_SA\rangle$ be a duality of S and an object ${}_SA$ of ${}_S\mathcal{C}$ over an object E of $\mathcal{C}$. Let $\mathcal{U}$ be a uniform structure on spE.

An element $x \in$ spA is said to be almost periodic (with respect to this duality and this choice of $\mathcal{U}$) if, for each $P \in \mathcal{M}$, $P \cdot x$ is $\mathcal{N}(S,\mathcal{U})$-precompact.

4. *Proposition*: *Let $\mathcal{C}$ be a category of covered objects and let $\langle S, {}_SA\rangle$ be a duality of S and an object ${}_SA$ of ${}_S\mathcal{C}$ over an object E of $\mathcal{C}$. Let $\mathcal{U}$ be a uniform structure on spE*.

An element $x \in$ spA is almost periodic if and only if for every entourage $U \in \mathcal{U}$ and every set $P \in \mathcal{M}$, there is a finite covering $P = \bigcup_{i=1}^{n} P_i$ of P such that if $(a,b) \in \bigcup_{i=1}^{n} P_i \times P_i$, then $(\langle ac, x\rangle, \langle bc, x\rangle) \in U$ for all $c \in P$.

Proof: We may assume that A and E are covered sets and that $c(A) = \{P \cdot x\colon P \in \mathcal{M}, x \in A\}$. Also, since if x satisfies either of the two statements, then so does every $a \cdot x (a \in M)$ and since also every set $\{\langle a,x\rangle\colon a \in P\}$ where $P \in \mathcal{M}$ must then be precompact, we may assume that $S[\sigma(A,\mathcal{U})]$ and $A[\sigma(S,\mathcal{U})]$ are precompact and that every point of spA satisfies some fixed one of the two statements. But then 3.5.6 implies that every point of spA also satisfies the other.

5. *Definition*: Let $\mathcal{C}$ be a category of covered objects and let $\langle S, {}_SA\rangle$ be a fully stable duality of S and an object ${}_SA$ of ${}_S\mathcal{C}$ over an object E of $\mathcal{C}$. Let $\mathcal{U}$ be a uniform structure on spE.

By the almost periodic subobject of A (defined with respect to this duality and this choice of $\mathcal{U}$), we mean the covered set, *denoted* A_{ap}, whose space is all almost periodic elements of spA and whose covering family is the largest family of subsets of spA which refines c(A) and has the property that for each of its sets F and each $P \in \mathcal{M}$, $P \cdot F$ is $\mathcal{N}(S,\mathcal{U})$-precompact.

6. Theorem: Let $\mathcal{C}$ be a category of covered objects, let $\langle S, {}_SA\rangle$ be a fully stable duality of S and an object ${}_SA$ of ${}_S\mathcal{C}$ over an object E of $\mathcal{C}$, and let $\mathcal{U}$ be a uniform structure on spE.

(1) A_{ap} is a subobject of ${}_SA$ and the action of S on A_{ap} is fully stable.

(2) $\mathcal{N}(A_{ap}, \mathcal{U})$ is locally equivalent to $\sigma(A_{ap}, \mathcal{U})$ on S.

(3) $\mathcal{N}(S, \mathcal{U})$ is locally equivalent to $\sigma(S, \mathcal{U})$ on A_{ap}.

The following statements about $\sigma(A_{ap}, \mathcal{U})$ and uniform equicontinuity are true:

(4) A_{ap} is locally $\sigma(A_{ap}, \mathcal{U})$-$\mathcal{U}$ uniformly equicontinuous on S.

(5) If P, $Q \in \mathcal{M}$, then the family of maps

$$Q \to M$$

$$a \to ab \quad (b \in P)$$

is $\sigma(A_{ap}, \mathcal{U})$-uniformly equicontinuous.

Finally, we have the following characterization of the almost periodic elements of spA.

(6) An element $x \in$ spA is almost periodic if and only if x is locally $\sigma(A_{ap}, \mathcal{U})$-$\mathcal{U}$ uniformly continuous on S.

Proof: (1) is an easy consequence of the fact that the action of S on A is fully stable.

To prove (2) through (4), notice that $S[\sigma(A_{ap}, \mathcal{U})]$ and $A_{ap}[\mathcal{N}(S, \mathcal{U})]$ are precompactly covered and then apply 3.5.5.

(5) is an easy consequence of (4).

Finally, if $x \in$ spA is locally $\sigma(A_{ap}, \mathcal{U})$-$\mathcal{U}$ uniformly continuous on S, then, for each $P \in \mathcal{M}$, (5) implies that $P \cdot x$ is locally $\sigma(A_{ap}, \mathcal{U})$-$\mathcal{U}$ uniformly equicontinuous on S. But this clearly implies the condition of Proposition 4, since $S[\sigma(A_{ap}, \mathcal{U})]$ is precompactly covered.

Using Theorem 3.5 as a model for the kind of conclusions we are trying to force about the uniform structures on S which we obtain from duality situations, Theorem 6 is a bit disappointing. The disappointment comes from the fact that the conclusion in part (5) is just half of what we want. Happily, in the really important cases, this difficulty disappears.

7. Lemma: Let $\mathcal{C}$ be a category of covered objects, let $\langle S, {}_SA\rangle$ be a duality of S and an object ${}_SA$ of ${}_S\mathcal{C}$ over an object E of $\mathcal{C}$, and let $\mathcal{U}$ be a uniform structure on spE.

Suppose we are actually in one of the following special cases:

(I) $E = A$, $\langle a,x\rangle = a \cdot x$ for $x \in spA$, and each function

$$spA \to spA$$
$$x \to a \cdot x \ (a \in M)$$

is $\mathcal{U}$-uniformly continuous.

(II) S acts on both sides of A and we have

$$\langle a, b \cdot x \cdot c\rangle = \langle cab, x\rangle$$

for all $x \in spA$, a, b, $c \in M$.

Then we have

$$\sigma(A,\mathcal{U}) = \sigma(A, \sigma(S,\mathcal{U}))$$
$$\mathcal{N}(A,\mathcal{U}) = \mathcal{N}(A, \sigma(S,\mathcal{U}))$$

In case we additionally assume either

(I') Each family of maps

$$spA \to spA$$
$$x \to a \cdot x \ (a \in P)$$

where $P \in \mathcal{M}$ is uniformly equicontinuous with respect to $\mathcal{U}$ or

(II') S acts on both sides of A with fully stable action.

Then we have

$$\mathcal{N}(A,\mathcal{U}) = \mathcal{N}(A, \mathcal{N}(S,\mathcal{U}))$$

Proof: We will prove only the last equality, since the other proofs are similar and easier.

For all $F \subset spA$, $U \in \mathcal{U}$, we have

$$N(F, U) = N(F, N(1, U))$$

which implies $\mathcal{N}(A,\mathcal{U})$ is weaker than $\mathcal{N}(A,\mathcal{N}(S,\mathcal{U}))$.

Conversely, let $F \in c(A)$, $P \in \mathcal{M}$, $U \in \mathcal{U}$ be given. We must find an entourage of $\mathcal{N}(A,\mathcal{U})$ which is contained in $N(F, N(P, U))$.

(Case I'). Choose $V \in \mathcal{U}$ s.t. $(y,z) \in V \to (a \cdot y, a \cdot z) \in U \ \forall a \in P$. Then we have $(b,c) \in N(F,V) \to (b \cdot x, c \cdot x) \in V \ \forall x \in F \to (a \cdot (b \cdot x), a \cdot (c \cdot x)) \in U \ \forall x \in F, a \in P \to (b \cdot x, c \cdot x)$ $N(P, U) \ \forall x \in X \to (b,c) \in N(F,N(P,U))$.

(Case II'). $(b,c) \in N(F \cdot P, U) \to (\langle b, x \cdot a\rangle, \langle c, x \cdot a\rangle) \in U \ \forall x \in F, a \in P \to (\langle a, b \cdot x\rangle, \langle a, c \cdot x\rangle) \in U \ \forall x \in F, a \in P \to (b \cdot x, c \cdot x) \in N(P, U) \ \forall x \in F \to (b,c) \in N(F,N(P,U))$.

8. <u>Theorem</u>: <u>Let $\mathcal{C}$ be a category of covered objects, let $\langle S, {}_SA\rangle$ be a fully stable duality of S and an object ${}_SA$ of ${}_S\mathcal{C}$ over an object E of $\mathcal{C}$, and let $\mathcal{U}$ be a uniform structure on spE</u>.

Suppose that we are in one of the following two special cases:

(I) $E=A$, $\langle a,x\rangle = a \cdot x$ for $a \in M$, $x \in spA$ and each mapping

$$spA \to spA$$
$$x \to a \cdot x \quad (a \in M)$$

is uniformly continuous with respect to $\mathcal{U}$.

(II) S acts on both sides of A and we have

$$\langle a, b \cdot x \cdot c\rangle = \langle cab, x\rangle$$

for all $a, b, c \in M$, $x \in spA$.

Then the following statements are true:

(1) <u>$\sigma(A_{ap},\mathcal{U})$ makes the multiplication of M separately uniformly continuous</u>.

(2) <u>$S[\sigma(A_{ap},\mathcal{U})]$ is precompactly covered</u>.

(3) For each $P \in M$, the map

$$P \times P \to M$$

$$(a,b) \to ab$$

is jointly $\sigma(A_{ap}, \mathcal{U})$-uniformly continuous.

Proof: Notice that, in case II, we have $A_{ap} \cdot M = A_{ap}$. But then we can apply Lemma 7 in either case to $\langle S, {}_S A_{ap} \rangle$. Since the hypotheses of Theorem 3.5 are satisfied and since we have $\sigma(A_{ap}, \mathcal{U}) = \sigma(A_{ap}, \sigma(S,\mathcal{U}))$ by Lemma 7, the conclusion follows from Theorem 3.5.

We are now in a position to prove that two possibilities for confusion which come to mind in connection with the concepts of this section actually present no difficulty at all. These occur when S acts on both sides of an object A of a category of covered objects, when we are given a fully stable duality $\langle S, {}_S A \rangle$ of S and ${}_S A$ over an object E of that category, and when $\langle a, b \cdot x \cdot c \rangle = \langle cab, x \rangle$ for all $a, b, c \in M$, $x \in spA$. If $\mathcal{U}$ is a uniform structure on spE, this duality induces an almost periodic subobject A_{ap} of A and a uniform structure $\sigma(A_{ap}, \mathcal{U})$ on M which, by Theorem 8, has very desirable properties. But we can also consider this duality as a duality $\langle A_S, S \rangle_0$ over E by putting $\langle x,a \rangle_0 = \langle a,x \rangle$. We have $\langle b \cdot x \cdot c, a \rangle_0 = \langle a, b \cdot x \cdot c \rangle = \langle cab, x \rangle = \langle x, cab \rangle_0$. So we can apply the analogue of Theorem 8 and we get an almost periodic subobject $(A_{ap})_r$ of A and a uniform structure $\sigma((A_{ap})_r, \mathcal{U})$ on M which has the same desirable properties as does $\sigma(A_{ap}, \mathcal{U})$. In other words, we obtain two theories, a left theory and a right theory, both with good results. The following proposition will show that $sp(A_{ap}) = sp((A_{ap})_r)$ and so $\sigma(A_{ap},\mathcal{U}) = \sigma((A_{ap})_r,\mathcal{U})$.

Another potential source of confusion is the following: Our given duality induces a duality of S and A over $A[\mathcal{N}(S, \mathcal{U})]$ and in this new duality the hypotheses of case I of Theorem 8 are satisfied. So we obtain another almost periodic subobject, denote it B, of A and another uniform structure $\sigma(B,\mathcal{N}(S,\mathcal{U}))$ on S, which, by Theorem 8, again has very desirable properties.

So, by following two ostensibly different procedures, we get two sets of desirable results. The following proposition will show that $sp(B) = sp(A_{ap})$, that $N(A_{ap}, U) = N(A_{ap}, N(S,U))$ and that $\sigma(A_{ap}, U)$ is locally equivalent to $\sigma(A_{ap}, N(S,U))$.

9. Proposition: Let C be a category of covered objects, let A be an object of C and suppose S acts on both sides of A. Suppose that we are given a fully stable duality $\langle S, {}_SA\rangle$ of S and ${}_SA$ over an object E of C and that U is a uniform structure on spE. Suppose moreover that we have

$$\langle a, b \cdot x \cdot c\rangle = \langle cab, x\rangle$$

for all a, b, $c \in M$, $x \in spA$.

The following statements about an element $x \in spA$ are equivalent

(1) x is almost periodic.

(2) $x \cdot P$ is $N(S,U)$-precompact for each $P \in M$.

(3) $P \cdot x \cdot P$ is $N(S,U)$-precompact for each $P \in M$.

(4) x is locally $\sigma(A_{ap}, U)$-U uniformly continuous on S.

(5) $P \cdot x \cdot P$ is locally $\sigma(A_{ap}, U)$-U uniformly equicontinuous on S for each $P \in M$.

We now consider also the duality $[S, {}_SA]$ over $A[N(S,U)]$ given by

$$[a, x] = a \cdot x \quad (a \in M,\ x \in spA)$$

Then statement (1) is also equivalent to

(6) x is almost periodic with respect to the duality $[S, {}_SA]$ and the uniform structure $N(S,U)$ on spA.

Finally, we have

(7) $N(A_{ap}, U) = N(A_{ap}, N(S,U))$.

(8) $\sigma(A_{ap}, U)$ is locally equivalent to $\sigma(A_{ap}, N(S,U))$ on S.

Proof: The equivalence of (1) and (4) was proved in Theorem 6. But statement (3) of Theorem 8 forces (4) to imply (5). It is an easy consequence of 3.5.5 that (5) and (3) are equivalent and clearly (3) → (1). So we have (1) ↔ (3) ↔ (4) ↔ (5). Clearly (3) → (2). We claim now that the argument can be completed by appealing to the action of M^o on the left of A.

Clearly (6) → (1). So we need only show that every point of A_{ap} satisfies (6). To this end, we consider the duality $[S, A_{ap}]$ over $A[N(S,U)]$. Now, in the duality $\langle S, A_{ap}\rangle$, we can apply Theorem 3.5 and we get that $\sigma(A_{ap}, N(S,U))$ is locally equivalent to $\sigma(A_{ap}, \sigma(S,U))$ which, by Lemma 7, is just $\sigma(A_{ap}, U)$. This proves (8). (7) also follows from Lemma 7 and allows us to apply 3.5.5 to $[S, A_{ap}]$ and conclude that $A_{ap}[N(S,N(S,U))]$ is precompactly covered. So (1) → (6).

Proposition 9 serves as our justification for turning our attention to case I of Theorem 8. This will occupy us in the next section. For now, we content ourselves with one corollary:

10. Corollary: Let C be a category of covered objects and let $_SA$ be an object of $_SC$. Suppose the action of S on A is fully stable. Let U be a uniform structure on spA and suppose that each map

$$\text{spA} \to \text{spA}$$
$$x \to a \cdot x \quad (a \in M)$$

is U-uniformly continuous.

Then $sp(A_{ap})$ is $N(S,U)$-closed in spA.

Proof: Use part (6) of Theorem 6 and use Proposition 3.4.2.

§5. Almost Periodic Functions on a Covered Uniform Monoid

1. Definition: Let C be a category of covered objects, let A be an object of C and let U be a uniform structure on spA.

We denote by $E(A[U])$ the monoid of all U-uniformly continuous morphisms in Mor(A,A). We agree to consider $E(A[U])$ as a covered monoid by taking as our covering family all bounded uniformly equicontinuous subsets of $E(A[U])$.

2. Convention: For the rest of this section $S = (M,\mathcal{M})$ will denote a fixed covered monoid and $\mathcal{U}$ will denote a fixed uniform structure on M making the multiplication of M separately uniformly continuous, i.e., making $S[\mathcal{U}]$ a covered uniform monoid (see 2.5.4).

Let A be an object in a category of covered objects $\mathcal{C}$. To give an action of S on the left of A is equivalent to giving a monoid homomorphism of M into Mor(A,A). To demand that the action be fully stable is equivalent to demanding that this homomorphism be a covered monoid morphism of S into $\mathcal{D}(A,A)$. To further demand that each set of $\mathcal{M}$ act as a family of $\mathcal{V}$-uniformly equicontinuous mappings of spA, where $\mathcal{V}$ is some uniform structure on spA is to demand that this actually be a covered monoid morphism of S into $\mathcal{E}(A[\mathcal{V}])$. The question is now how to use this "representation" of S in such a way as to define uniform structures on M which bear some sensible relation to $\mathcal{U}$. Since the simplest uniform structure on $\mathcal{E}(A[\mathcal{V}])$ is that of simple convergence, and since this does give $\mathcal{E}(A[\mathcal{V}])$ a separately uniformly continuous multiplication (Prop. 2.2), it certainly is reasonable to demand that our morphism be locally uniformly continuous with respect to this structure on $\mathcal{E}(A[\mathcal{V}])$.

However, our interest now is in uniform structures on M which make the multiplication of M separately uniformly continuous, make each set of $\mathcal{M}$ precompact, and make each map $(P \in \mathcal{M})$

$$P \times P \to M$$

$$(a,b) \to ab$$

jointly uniformly continuous. Neither $\mathcal{U}$ nor the structure of simple convergence on $\mathcal{E}(A[\mathcal{V}])$ need fill this bill. We desire to use this representation to define uniform structures on M which do. Actually, we solved this problem in §4. All that remains is to write down the solution.

3. Convention: We will denote by e the uniformizing rule for the category of covered monoids which assigns to each covered monoid $T = (N,\mathcal{N})$ the family e(T) of all uniform structures on N

separately uniformly continuous and make each map

$$P \times P \to N$$

$$(a,b) \to ab$$

jointly uniformly continuous, ($P \in \mathcal{N}$).

(i, T[$\mathcal{V}$]) will denote an inductive compactly covered reflection (§2.7) of S[$\mathcal{U}$] with respect to e. We agree to write T = (N,$\mathcal{N}$). By Proposition 2.8.6, $i^{-1}(\mathcal{V})$ is the strongest structure in e(S) which makes S precompactly covered and which is locally weaker than $\mathcal{U}$.

4. Theorem: Let $\mathcal{C}$ be a category of covered objects, let A be an object of $\mathcal{C}$ and let $\mathcal{W}$ be a uniform structure on spA.

Let ϕ be a covered monoid morphism of S into $\mathcal{E}$(A[$\mathcal{W}$]) which is locally uniformly continuous with respect to $\mathcal{U}$ and the structure of simple convergence on $\mathcal{E}$(A[$\mathcal{W}$]).

If $a \in M$, $x \in spA$, we write $a \cdot x = \phi(a)(x)$.

The following statements about an element $x \in spA$ are equivalent:

(1) x is almost periodic.

(2) $P \cdot x$ is $\mathcal{W}$-precompact for each $P \in \mathcal{M}$.

(3) The function

$$M \to A$$

$$a \to a \cdot x$$

is $i^{-1}(\mathcal{V})$ -$\mathcal{W}$ uniformly continuous.

Now let A_{ap} denote the almost periodic subobject of A (this is just a covered set, and so $\mathcal{E}(A_{ap}[\mathcal{W}])$ is defined with respect to the category of covered sets).

(4) $\mathcal{N}(A_{ap},\mathcal{W}) \in e(S)$, $\mathcal{N}(A_{ap},\mathcal{W})$ is locally weaker than $\mathcal{U}$ and $S[\mathcal{N}(A_{ap},\mathcal{W})]$ is precompactly covered.

(5) $\sigma(A_{ap},\mathcal{W}) \in e(S)$, $\sigma(A_{ap}, \mathcal{W})$ is locally weaker than $\mathcal{U}$ and $S[\sigma(A_{ap},\mathcal{W})]$ is precompactly covered.

Now suppose that $A[\mathcal{W}]$ is complete and separated.

(6) $\underline{A}_{ap}[\mathcal{W}]$ is complete and separated.

(7) There is a unique covered monoid morphism

$$\psi: \quad T[\mathcal{V}] \to \mathcal{E}(A_{ap}[\mathcal{W}])$$

which is uniformly continuous with respect to the structure of simple convergence on $\mathcal{E}(A_{ap}[\mathcal{W}])$ and which satisfies the condition

$$\phi = \psi i$$

(8) The morphism ψ of part (7) is uniformly continuous with respect to the structure $\mathcal{N}(A_{ap},\mathcal{W})$ on $\mathcal{E}(A_{ap}, [\mathcal{W}])$.

Proof: Since each set of $\mathcal{M}$ acts as a family of uniformly equicontinuous transformations of spA, it is clear that $\mathcal{N}(S,\mathcal{W}) = \mathcal{W}$. So (1) $\leftrightarrow$ (2).

By Proposition 3.2 and Theorems 4.6 and 4.8, (4) and (5) follow.

But then Theorem 4.6 implies that we have (1) $\to$ (3) since $\sigma(A_{ap},\mathcal{W})$ is weaker than $i^{-1}(\mathcal{V})$. On the other hand, if (3) holds, since the map $a \to a \cdot x$ is uniformly continuous and since each $P \in \mathcal{M}$ is $i^{-1}(\mathcal{V})$-precompact, (2) holds.

(6) follows from 4.10 and the equality $\mathcal{N}(S,\mathcal{W}) = \mathcal{W}$.

Now let $P \in \mathcal{M}$. Then by 3.2.7, the $\sigma(A_{ap},\mathcal{W})$-closure of $\phi(P)$ in A_{ap} is a $\mathcal{W}$-uniformly equicontinuous set of maps. It is bounded since $\phi(P)$ is bounded. It is $\sigma(A_{ap},\mathcal{W})$-compact since $P \cdot x$ is relatively compact in $A_{ap}[\mathcal{W}]$ for each $x \in sp(A_{ap})$. Finally, the fact that each such set is a $\mathcal{W}$-uniformly equicontinuous set of maps (and is bounded) forces $\sigma(A_{ap},\mathcal{W})$ and $\mathcal{N}(A_{ap},\mathcal{W})$ to coincide on the $\sigma(A_{ap},\mathcal{W})$-closure of $\phi(P)$ $(P \in \mathcal{M})$ by 3.5.5. But now, by the definition of an inductive compactly covered reflection, there is a unique morphism

$$\psi: \quad T \to \mathcal{E}(A_{ap}, [\mathcal{W}])$$

which is $\mathcal{V}$-$\mathcal{N}(A_{ap},\mathcal{W})$ uniformly continuous and satisfies the condition $\phi = \psi i$. This completes the proof.

5. Definition: We denote by

$$C(S[\mathcal{U}])$$

the space of all K-valued functions on M which are locally uniformly continuous with respect to $\mathcal{U}$ and are bounded on each set of $\mathcal{M}$.

Since we have a natural action of S on both sides of itself, we have, after Definition 2.3, a natural action of S on both sides of $C(S[\mathcal{U}])$.

We agree always to consider $C(S[\mathcal{U}])$ as a covered vector space with its balanced, convex, $\mathcal{T}_{\mathcal{M}}$-bounded sets as its covering family, $\mathcal{T}_{\mathcal{M}}$ denoting (from now on) the locally convex topology on $C(S[\mathcal{U}])$ of uniform convergence on sets of $\mathcal{M}$. (With this topology, $C(S[\mathcal{U}])$ is complete.)

By 4.9, a function of $C(S[\mathcal{U}])$ is an almost periodic element with respect to any of the natural dualities if and only if it is almost periodic with respect to the others. Any such function will be called an almost periodic function on $S[\mathcal{U}]$.

6. Corollary: Let E denote the space of all almost periodic functions on $S[\mathcal{U}]$. We denote by $\mathcal{T}_{\mathcal{M}}$ the topology $\mathcal{T}_{\mathcal{M}E}$.

Associated with the morphism

$$i: S \to T$$

there is a transpose morphism

$$t_i: C(T[\mathcal{V}]) \to C(S[\mathcal{U}])$$

which is a $\mathcal{T}_{\mathcal{N}}$-$\mathcal{T}_{\mathcal{M}}$ embedding.

The following statements about a function $\phi \in C(S[\mathcal{U}])$ are equivalent:

(1) $\phi \in E$

(2) $\phi \in {}^t i(C(T[\mathcal{V}]))$

(3) ϕ is $i^{-1}(\mathcal{V})$-uniformly continuous.

The space $E[\mathcal{T}_{\mathcal{M}}]$ is complete and the following statements about a subset $F \subset E$ are equivalent:

(4) *F is* $\mathcal{T}_M$*-precompact*.

(5) $P \cdot F \cdot P$ *is* $\mathcal{T}_M$*-precompact for every* $P \in \mathcal{M}$.

Therefore, if we consider E as a covered vector space by taking the balanced, convex, $\mathcal{T}_M$*-precompact sets of E as the covering family, if follows that*

(6) *E is equivalent, as a covered set, to the almost periodic subobject of* $C(S[\mathcal{U}])$.

Finally, there is a unique covered monoid morphism

$$\psi : \quad T \to \mathcal{L}(E[\mathcal{T}_M])$$

(where $\mathcal{L}(E[\mathcal{T}_M])$ *denotes the algebra of all* $\mathcal{T}_M$*-continuous linear operators on E) which is uniformly continuous with respect to* $\mathcal{V}$ *and simple convergence on E with respect to* $\mathcal{T}_M$*, and which satisfies the relation*

$$a \cdot \phi = \psi \circ i(a)\ [\phi]$$

for all $a \in M$ *and* $\phi \in E$.

(7) ψ *is a uniform embedding with respect to* $\mathcal{V}$ *and the topology on* $\mathcal{L}(E[\mathcal{T}_M])$ *of uniform convergence on compact sets, i.e.,* $\underline{N}(E, \mathcal{T}_M)$.

(8) ψ *is a local embedding with respect to* $\mathcal{V}$ *and* $\mathcal{T}_M$*-simple convergence*.

Proof: The fact that T is the cover-closed envelope of i(S) in $T[\mathcal{V}]$ clearly forces ${}^t i$ to be a $\mathcal{T}_N$-$\mathcal{T}_M$ embedding.

If $\phi \in E$, then, by Theorem 4, the map

$$a \to a \cdot \phi$$

is $i^{-1}(\mathcal{V})$-uniformly continuous. If this latter statement is true, then it is easy to see that we have $\phi = \psi^\circ\ i$ for some $\psi \in C(T[\mathcal{V}])$, i.e., that $\phi \in {}^t i(C(T[\mathcal{V}]))$.

Now, if $\psi \in C(T[\mathcal{V}])$ then the map

$$P \times P \to K$$

$$(a,b) \to \psi(ab)$$

is $V \times V$ uniformly continuous for each $P \in N$ and so, since ψ is bounded on each set of N, ψ is almost periodic on $T[V]$. So, if $P \in M$, ${}^t i(i(P) \cdot \psi) = P \cdot {}^t i(\psi)$ is T_M-precompact. This proves (1) $\leftrightarrow$ (2) $\leftrightarrow$ (3).

Suppose (4) holds. Then, by 3.5.2, F is locally uniformly equicontinuous on S with respect to simple convergence on E. But then, by Theorem 4.8, this statement is also true of $P \cdot F \cdot P$ for $P \in M$. But since F is T_M-precompact, it is T_M-bounded. This implies that $P \cdot F \cdot P$ is also T_M-bounded if $P \in M$. But now 3.5.4 implies that $P \cdot F \cdot P$ is T_M-precompact if $P \in M$. So (4) $\leftrightarrow$ (5).

(6) is clear.

By (7) of Theorem 4, there is a unique covered monoid morphism

$$\psi: \quad T \to E(E[T_M])$$

(considering E as a covered set) which is uniformly continuous with respect to V and T_M-simple convergence, and which satisfies

$$a \cdot \phi = \psi \circ i(a)[\phi]$$

for all $a \in M$, $\phi \in E$. It is clear that these conditions also force $\psi(N) \subset L(E[T_M])$.

The Ascoli Theorems force the two topologies mentioned on $L(E[T_M])$ to be equivalent on compact sets. So, by part (8) of Theorem 4, it remains only to show that ψ is a uniform embedding with respect to V and the uniform structure on $L(E[T_M])$ of T_M-uniform convergence on compact sets. This is equivalent to showing that if we consider the duality

$$\langle T,\ C(T[V])\rangle$$

over $C(T[V])$ given by $\langle a,\phi\rangle = a \cdot \phi$, then V is precisely the uniform structure of T_N-uniform convergence on the precompact subsets of $C(T[V])$. Moreover, since every function of $C(T[V])$ is almost periodic on $T[V]$, it is an easy consequence of part (8) of Theorem 4 that V is the stronger of the two uniform structures. But the other uniform structure is stronger than the uniform structure of uniform convergence on compact sets induced by the duality

$$(a,\phi) \to \phi(a) \ .$$

So it remains to show that this uniform structure is stronger than $\mathcal{V}$.

Let U be any entourage of $\mathcal{V}$. There is a <u>bounded</u>, $\mathcal{V}$-uniformly continuous pseudo-metric g on N with the property that

$$g(x,y) \leq 1 \to (x,y) \in U.$$

For each $x \in N$, we define

$$h_x\colon\ N \to K$$
$$y \to g(x,y)$$

Then, since $|h_x(y) - h_x(z)| \leq g(y,z)$ for all y, z, $x \in N$, the family $F = \{h_x\colon\ x \in N\}$ is a uniformly bounded, $\mathcal{V}$-uniformly equicontinuous subset of $C(T[\mathcal{V}])$.

By the Ascoli Theorems, F is $\mathcal{T}_N$-precompact. But if y, $z \in N$ and if $|h_x(y) - h_x(z)| \leq 1$ for all $x \in N$, then $g(y,z) = |h_y(y) - h_y(z)| \leq 1$ and so $(y,z) \in U$. That is, $N(F, 1) \subset U$. This completes the proof.

7. <u>Definition</u>: Any inductive compactly covered reflection (i, $T[\mathcal{V}]$) of $S[\mathcal{U}]$ with respect to e will be called <u>a Bohr compactly covered reflection of $S[\mathcal{U}]$</u>.

The above corollary gives a realization of a Bohr compactly covered reflection of $S[\mathcal{U}]$ as a compactly covered monoid of operators on the space of almost periodic functions with the uniform structure of uniform convergence on compact sets. In the case where $\{M\} = \mathcal{M}$, this is a well known representation of the Bohr compact reflection.

§6. Almost Periodic Linear Forms on a Covered Locally Convex Algebra

1. Recall: (2.5.8) By a covered locally convex algebra (over K), we mean a covered algebra $E = (A,\mathcal{A})$ (see 2.3.8) together with a locally convex topology $\mathcal{T}$ on A which makes the multiplication of A separately continuous and makes each set of $\mathcal{A}$ bounded.

2. Convention: In this section, e will denote the uniformizing rule for the category of covered algebras which assigns to each covered algebra $E = (A,\mathcal{A})$ the family e(E) of all locally convex topologies on A which make each set of $\mathcal{A}$ bounded, make the multiplication of A separately continuous, and make each map

$$P \times P \to A$$

$$(a,b) \to ab \ ,$$

where $P \in \mathcal{A}$, jointly uniformly continuous.

3. Convention: For the rest of this section, $E = (A,\mathcal{A})$ will denote a given covered algebra. $\mathcal{T}$ will denote a given locally convex topology on A making $E[\mathcal{T}]$ a covered locally convex algebra.

(i, $F[\mathcal{S}]$) will denote an inductive compactly covered reflection of $E[\mathcal{T}]$ with respect to the rule e. We will agree to write $F = (B,\mathcal{B})$.

It is an easy application of Proposition 2.8.6 and of the fact that a precompactly covered locally convex space is compactifiable that $i^{-1}(\mathcal{S})$ is the strongest structure in e(E) which makes E precompactly covered and is locally weaker than $\mathcal{T}$.

4. Definition: Let $G[\mathcal{U}]$ be a locally convex space. We denote by

$$L(G[\mathcal{U}])$$

the algebra of all $\mathcal{U}$-continuous linear operators on G.

We will call the topology on $L(G[\mathcal{U}])$ of $\mathcal{U}$-simple convergence the $\mathcal{U}$-operator topology.

We will call the topology on $L(G[\mathcal{U}])$ of $\sigma(G, G')$-simple convergence the weak operator topology.

We will agree to consider $L(G[\mathcal{U}])$ always as a covered algebra by taking the balanced, convex, equicontinuous sets of $L(G[\mathcal{U}])$ to be its covering family.

As such, either the $\mathcal{U}$-operator topology or the weak operator topology makes $L(G[\mathcal{U}])$ a covered locally convex algebra. (See Schaefer [1], III.4.1.)

If $G[\mathcal{U}]$ is a locally convex space and if we consider it as a covered locally convex space by taking the balanced, convex, bounded sets of G as the covering family, then $L(G[\mathcal{U}])$ acts on $G[\mathcal{U}]$ with fully stable action. (See Schaefer [1], III.4.1.) The following theorem is an obvious analogue of Theorem 5.4 and its proof will be omitted.

5. Theorem: Let $G[\mathcal{U}]$ be a locally convex space.

Let ϕ be a covered algebra morphism from E to $L(G[\mathcal{U}])$ which is locally uniformly continuous with respect to $\mathcal{T}$ and the $\mathcal{U}$-operator topology on $L(G[\mathcal{U}])$.

If $a \in A$, $x \in G$, we denote

$$a \cdot x = \phi(a)(x)$$

The following statements about an element $x \in spA$ are equivalent:

(1) x is almost periodic.

(2) $P \cdot x$ is $\mathcal{U}$-precompact for each $P \in \mathcal{A}$.

(3) The function

$$A \to G$$

$$a \to a \cdot x$$

is $i^{-1}(\mathcal{S})$-$\mathcal{U}$ uniformly continuous.

Now let G_{ap} *denote the almost periodic subobject of G.* G_{ap} *is, in the natural way, equivalent to a covered vector space.*

(4) $N(G_{ap},\mathcal{U}) \in e(E)$ *.* $N(G_{ap},\mathcal{U})$ *is locally weaker than* T *and* $E[N(G_{ap},\mathcal{U})]$ *is precompactly covered.*

(5) $\sigma(G_{ap},\mathcal{U}) \in e(E)$, $\sigma(G_{ap},\mathcal{U})$ *is locally weaker than* T*, and* $E[\sigma(G_{ap},\mathcal{U})]$ *is precompactly covered.*

Now suppose that $G[\mathcal{U}]$ *is complete and separated.*

(6) $G_{ap}[\mathcal{U}]$ *is complete and separated.*

(7) *There is a unique covered algebra morphism*

$$\psi: \ F[S] \to L(G_{ap}[\mathcal{U}])$$

which is (uniformly) continuous with respect to S *and the* $\mathcal{U}$*-operator topology, and which satisfies the condition*

$$\phi = \psi i$$

(8) *The morphism* ψ *of part 7 is continuous with respect to* S *and the structure* $N(G_{ap},\mathcal{U})$ *on* $L(G_{ap}[\mathcal{U}])$.

6. *Definition*: T_A will denote the topology on A', the dual of $A[T]$, of uniform convergence on sets of A. *$\tilde{A}'$ will denote the particular completion of $A'[T_A]$ which consists of all linear forms on A which are locally continuous with respect to $\sigma(A,A')$* or with respect to T (see 3.4.5 and 3.4.8). T_A will again denote the topology on $\tilde{A}'$ of uniform convergence on sets of A.

There is a canonical action of A on both sides of $\tilde{A}'$, defined by the obvious action of A on both sides of itself (see Definition 2.3).

$\tilde{A}'$ will play the same role in this section that $C(S[\mathcal{U}])$ played in Section 5. Accordingly, we introduce the following definition, which, by Corollary 4.9 is independent of the duality we use to make the definition.

7. Definition: An almost periodic element of $\tilde{A}'[\mathcal{T}_A]$ will be called an almost periodic linear form on $E[\mathcal{T}]$.

The following result stands in the same relation to Theorem 5 that Corollary 5.6 did to Theorem 5.4. The resemblance being a good deal more than superficial, we omit the proof.

8. Corollary: Let C denote the space of all almost periodic linear forms on $E[\mathcal{T}]$.

Associated with the morphism

$$i: \; E \to F$$

there is a transpose morphism

$$^{t}i: \; \tilde{B}' \to \tilde{A}'$$

which is a $\mathcal{T}_B$-$\mathcal{T}_A$ embedding. (We note that $B' = \tilde{B}'$).

The following statements about a form $\phi \in \tilde{A}'$ are equivalent:

(1) $\phi \in C$

(2) $\phi \in {}^{t}i(B')$

(3) ϕ is $i^{-1}(\mathcal{S})$-continuous.

The space $C[\mathcal{T}_A]$ is complete and separated and the following statements about a subset $D \subset C$ are equivalent.

(4) D is $\mathcal{T}_A$-precompact.

(5) $P \cdot D \cdot P$ is $\mathcal{T}_A$-precompact for ever $P \in A$.

Therefore, if we consider C as a covered vector space by taking the balanced, convex, $\mathcal{T}_A$-precompact sets of C as the covering family, it follows that

(6) C is equivalent, as a covered set, to the almost periodic subobject of $\tilde{A}'[\mathcal{T}_A]$.

Finally, there is a unique covered algebra morphism

$$\psi: \; F \to L(C[\mathcal{T}_A])$$

which is continuous with respect to $\mathcal{S}$ and the $\mathcal{T}_A$-operator topology and which satisfies the relation

$$a \cdot \phi = \psi \circ i\,(a)[\phi]$$

For all $a \in A$, $\phi \in C$.

(7) ψ is an embedding with respect to S and the compact-open topology on $L(C[T_A])$.

(8) ψ is a local embedding with respect to S and the T_A-operator topology.

9. Definition: Any inductive compactly covered reflection (i, $F[S]$) of $E[T]$ will be called a Bohr compactly covered reflection of $E[T]$.

We now recall the uniformizing rule "$\mathcal{W}e$", introduced in 2.5.8. ($\mathcal{W}e(E)$ is all weak topologies in e(E)). By Proposition 2.8.8, if (i, $F[S]$) is a Bohr compactly covered reflection of $E[T]$ and if $F = (B,\mathcal{B})$, then (i, $F[\sigma(B,B')]$ is an inductive compactly covered reflection of $E[T]$ w.r.t. the rule $\mathcal{W}e$.

10. Definition: Any compactly covered reflection of $E[T]$ with respect to the rule $\mathcal{W}e$ will be called a weak Bohr compactly covered reflection of $E[T]$.

11. Recall: If $S[\mathcal{U}]$ is a covered uniform monoid, then it has inductive reflections in the category of covered locally convex algebras. (See 2.4.7.) In fact, it is rather easy to construct a reflection for S in the category of covered algebras. (It is just the familiar "semi-group algebra" with the obvious covering family.) Having done this, 2.4.8 gives an explicit way of obtaining the reflection mentioned above.

12. Proposition: Let $S[\mathcal{U}]$ be a covered uniform monoid and let (γ, $C[\mathcal{R}]$) be an inductive reflection for $S[U]$ in the category of covered locally convex algebras, where $C = (D,\mathcal{D})$.

There is a natural transpose map

$$^t\gamma: \quad D' \to C(S[\mathcal{U}])$$

(We note that $D' = \tilde{D}'$.) If $S = (M,\mathcal{M})$, then $^t\gamma$ is a linear and topological isomorphism with respect to $T_{\mathcal{D}}$ and $T_{\mathcal{M}}$.

<u>Proof</u>: That $D' = \tilde{D}'$ follows from Corollary 3.4.8 and the fact that $C[\sigma(D, \tilde{D}')]$ is a covered locally convex algebra. That ${}^t\gamma$ is a topological and linear embedding follows from the fact that every set of $\mathcal{D}$ is contained in the balanced, convex hull of some set of $\gamma(\mathcal{M})$.

Finally, since (γ, C) is a reflection for csp(S) in the category of covered vector spaces, if D^b represents the space of all linear forms on D which are bounded on each set of $\mathcal{D}$, then ${}^t\gamma$ maps D^b bijectively onto the space of all K-valued functions on M which are bounded on each set of $\mathcal{M}$. Since we have

$$D^b \supset {}^t\gamma^{-1}(C(S[\mathcal{U}])) \supset D'$$

the proof will be complete if we show

$${}^t\gamma^{-1}(C(S[\mathcal{U}])) \subset D'$$

Let $G = {}^t\gamma^{-1}(C(S[\mathcal{U}]))$.

Then if $\phi \in D^b$, we have $\phi \in G \leftrightarrow \phi o \gamma$ is locally uniformly continuous on $S[\mathcal{U}]$. Hence γ is locally uniformly continuous with respect to $\mathcal{U}$ and $\sigma(D,G)$.

We claim that if $\phi \in G$ and $x \in M$, then $\gamma(x) \cdot \phi$ and $\phi \cdot \gamma(x)$ are also in G. For if $\psi = \phi \cdot \gamma(x)$, then we have

$$\begin{aligned} \psi o \gamma: \quad y \to \phi &\cdot \gamma(x)(\gamma(y)) \\ &= \phi(\gamma(x)\gamma(y))) \\ &= \phi(\gamma(xy)) \\ &= \phi o \gamma(xy) \end{aligned}$$

that is, $\psi o \gamma = (\phi o \gamma) \cdot x \in C(S[\mathcal{U}])$. Likewise, $(\gamma(x) \cdot \phi) o \gamma \in C(S[\mathcal{U}])$. Since G is a linear space, and since $\gamma(M)$ spans D, we have proved that

$$D \cdot G = G = G \cdot D$$

This proves that the multiplication of D is separately continuous with respect to $\sigma(D,G)$.

We have proved that $C[\sigma(D,G)]$ is a covered locally convex algebra and that

$$\gamma: \quad S[\mathcal{U}] \to C[\sigma(D,G)]$$

is locally uniformly continuous. Therefore, we have

$$\sigma(D,G) \subset \mathcal{R}$$

Therefore, we have $G \subset D'$.

13. Theorem: Let $S[\mathcal{U}]$ be a covered uniform monoid and let $(\gamma, C[\mathcal{R}])$ be an inductive reflection for $S[\mathcal{U}]$ in the category of covered locally convex algebras. Let $(g, G[\mathcal{V}])$ be a Bohr compactly covered reflection, resp. a weak Bohr compactly covered reflection, for $C[\mathcal{R}]$.

(1) $(g\gamma, G[\mathcal{V}])$ is an inductive compactly covered reflection for $S[\mathcal{U}]$ in the category of covered algebras with respect to the rule e, resp. the rule $\mathcal{W}$e. (See 2.7.7.)

(2) If $(j, T[\mathcal{P}])$ is a Bohr compactly covered reflection of $S[\mathcal{U}]$. then the unique uniformly continuous covered monoid morphism

$$\ell: \quad T[\mathcal{P}] \to G[\mathcal{V}]$$

such that $\ell j = g\gamma$ is a uniform embedding.

Proof: (1) See 2.8.8. (2) This follows from Proposition 12, Corollary 8 and Corollary 5.6.

14. Definition: Let $S[\mathcal{U}]$ be a covered uniform monoid. Any inductive compactly covered reflection for $S[\mathcal{U}]$ in the category of covered algebras with respect to the rule e, resp. the rule $\mathcal{W}$e, will be called a Bohr compactly covered algebra reflection for $S[\mathcal{U}]$, resp. a weak Bohr compactly covered algebra reflection for $S[\mathcal{U}]$.

15. Corollary: Let $S[\mathcal{U}]$ be a covered uniform monoid and let $(j, G[\mathcal{V}])$ be a Bohr compactly covered algebra reflection for $S[\mathcal{U}]$ where $G = (C, \mathcal{C})$.

Then $(j, G[\sigma(C,C')])$ is a weak Bohr compactly covered algebra reflection for $S[\mathcal{U}]$.

Chapter 5. EXTENSION OF UNIFORM DUALITIES

§1. Synopsis

Roughly speaking, this chapter concerns itself with the problem of trying to "extend" a locally uniform duality in a Cartesian category to a locally uniform duality involving compactly covered local reflections of the various objects involved.

The problem is first approached internally, within the duality itself and without appealing to the notion of a compactly covered local reflection, by means of "extension contexts" which are introduced in Sections 2, 3 and 4. Here it is seen that the problem of extension breaks naturally into two steps, the second step of which cannot even be attempted unless the first step can be successfully taken.

In Section 5, the principal tool that is used in dealing with our problem is introduced: The notion of the double sequence property. This is an analogue of the double limit property used so extensively by Grothendieck (Grothendieck, [1]), which seems more suitable when the duality is not over a metric space.

In Section 6, it is shown that if the first step in the extension process can be taken, then the presence of the double sequence property will force the second step also. This particular part of the process is perhaps less deep than that of trying to take the first step, but the results obtained are powerful enough to allow an interesting application. This is given in Section 7 and concerns itself with Arens multiplication in the bidual of a bornological algebra.

In Section 8, the first step in the extension process is finally handled by means of the double sequence property. The crucial theorem involved turns out to be a generalization of the Eberlein-Grothendieck Theorem in the theory of locally convex spaces. In order to make this fact clear, the latter theorem is proved as a corollary.

In Section 9, the two steps are put together and the extension theorems are stated and proved.

In Section 10, the application of Section 7 is generalized by using the results of Sections 8 and 9, and a theory is defined and developed of weakly almost periodic linear forms on a covered locally convex algebra.

§2. Extension Contexts in a Duality of Sets

1. Convention: Throughout this section E will denote a fixed non-empty set.

Given any non-empty set S, we have (relative to E) a natural way of mapping S into a set of functions, namely the "evaluation map"

$$e_S: \quad S \to E^{(E^S)}$$

defined by

$$e_S(a): \quad f \to f(a)$$

We shall use this terminology and notation quite freely from now on.

Given a set T and a subset S of T (or given an object T in a category of covered objects and a subobject S of T), we hereafter agree to denote by

$$i_{ST}: \quad S \to T$$

the inclusion map of S into T.

2. Convention: For the rest of this section, <X, Y> will denote a fixed duality over E in the category of sets.

Recall that we denote by

$$r_X: \quad X \to E^Y$$

$$r_Y: \quad Y \to E^X$$

the functions defined by

$$r_X(x)(y) = \langle x,y \rangle = r_Y(y)(x)$$

for $x \in X$, $y \in Y$.

3. <u>Definition</u>: By an <u>extension context</u> in this duality, we mean the following:

(1) A non-empty subset m of X and a non-empty subset n of Y.

(2) A non-empty subset M of E^n such that for each $x \in m$, we have $r_X(x)|_n \in M$.

(3) A non-empty subset N of E^m such that for each $y \in n$, we have $r_Y(y)|_m \in N$.

If we recall our definition of transpose maps given in §2.6 and §3.3, it is quite apparent that if S and T are non-empty sets and S is a subset of T, then

$$t_{i_{ST}} : E^T \to E^S$$

is just the "<u>restriction map</u>". i.e., if $f \in E^T$, then $t_{i_{ST}}(f) = f|_S$. Therefore, the conditions given in (2) and (3) of the above definition can be rephrased as follows:

(2') $t_{i_{nY}} \circ r_X(m) \subset M$

(3') $t_{i_{mX}} \circ r_Y(n) \subset N$

Therefore, there exist unique maps

$$j_{mM}: \quad m \to M$$

$$j_{nN}: \quad n \to N$$

which make the following diagram commutative:

$$\begin{array}{ccccccc}
m & \xrightarrow{i_{mX}} & X & & Y & \xleftarrow{i_{nY}} & n \\
 & & \downarrow r_X & & r_Y \downarrow & & \\
j_{mM} \downarrow & & E^Y & & E^X & & \downarrow j_{nN} \\
 & & \downarrow & & t_{i_{mX}} \downarrow & & \\
M & \xrightarrow{i_{ME^n}} & E^n & & E^m & \xleftarrow{i_{NE^m}} & N
\end{array}$$

We agree, given such an extension context, always to use this notation. We further agree to denote the extension context by by the diagram

$$\begin{array}{ccc} m & \longrightarrow & X \\ \downarrow & & \downarrow \\ M & \longrightarrow & E^n \end{array} \qquad \begin{array}{ccc} Y & \longleftarrow & n \\ \downarrow & & \downarrow \\ E^m & \longleftarrow & N \end{array}$$

Given this convention, expressions like "Suppose we are given an extension context

$$\begin{array}{ccc} m & \longrightarrow & X \\ \downarrow & & \downarrow \\ M & \longrightarrow & E^n \end{array} \qquad \begin{array}{ccc} Y & \longleftarrow & n \\ \downarrow & & \downarrow \\ E^m & \longleftarrow & N \end{array} \text{"}$$

have the obvious meaning.

4. *Lemma*: Suppose we are given an extension context

$$\begin{array}{ccc} m & \longrightarrow & X \\ \downarrow & & \downarrow \\ M & \longrightarrow & E^n \end{array} \qquad \begin{array}{ccc} Y & \longleftarrow & n \\ \downarrow & & \downarrow \\ E^m & \longleftarrow & N \end{array}$$

The following diagram is commutative.

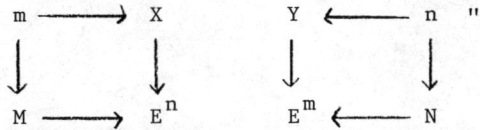

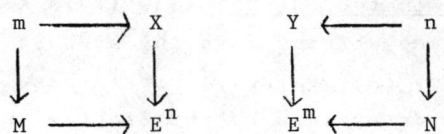

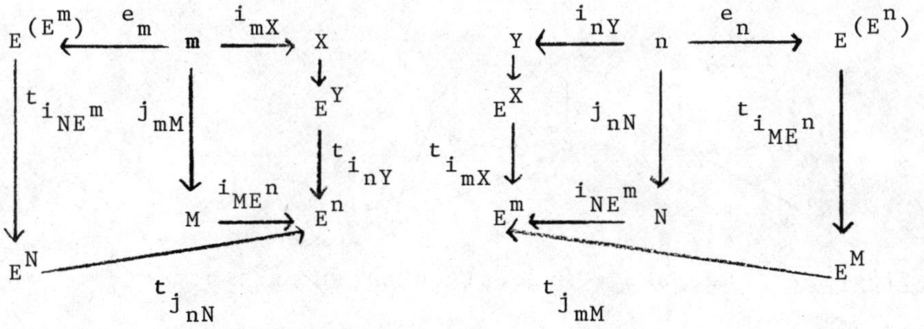

Let S be a non-empty set and let N be a non-empty subset of E^S. *We agree to denote by*

$$e_{SN}: \quad S \to E^N$$

the map ${}^t i_{NE^S} \circ e_S$. *This will also be called an evaluation map.*

If we are given an extension context

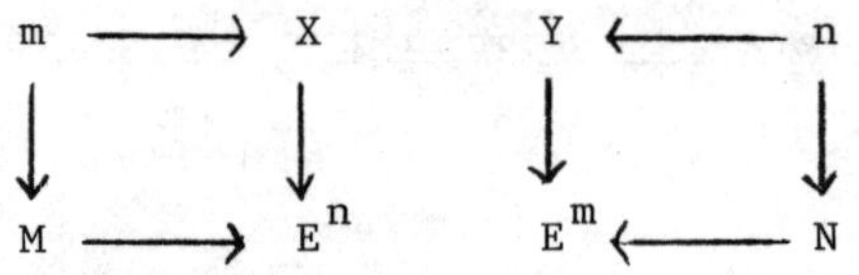

then our diagram fills out to a commutative diagram

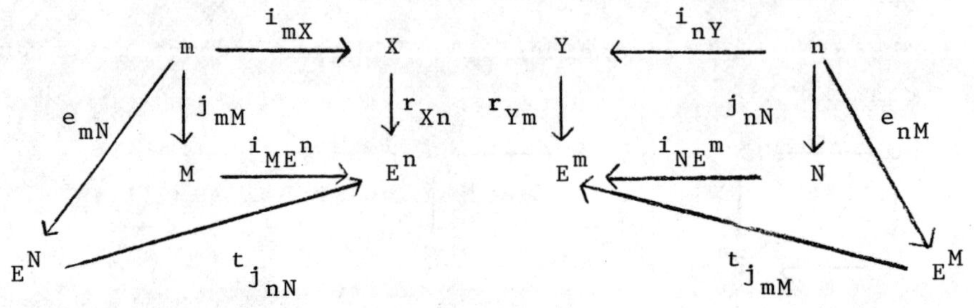

<u>Where</u> $r_{Xn} = {}^{t}i_{nY} \circ r_X$ <u>and</u> $r_{Ym} = {}^{t}i_{mX} \circ r_Y$, <u>notation which we</u> <u>will use without comment in the future</u>. Now it is a rather clear inconvenience to keep writing down the symbols for the maps in the above diagram. Accordingly, since these symbols are, by our conventions, determined by the diagram anyway, <u>we</u> <u>shall often hereafter suppress the symbols and write the diagram</u> <u>simply as</u>

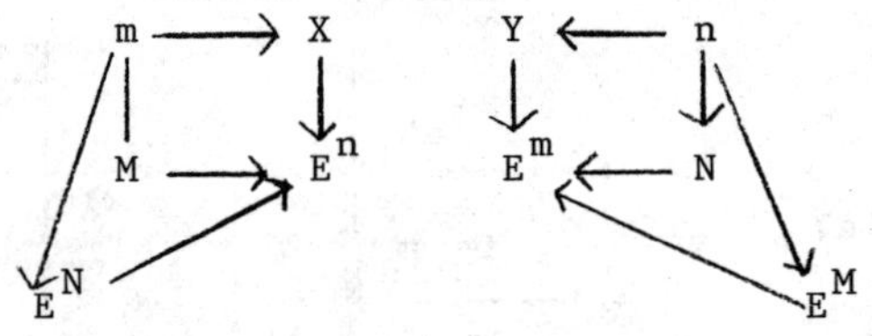

5. <u>Definition</u>: Suppose we are given an extension context

$$
\begin{array}{ccccc}
m & \longrightarrow & X & Y & \longleftarrow & n \\
\downarrow & & \downarrow & \downarrow & & \downarrow \\
M & \longrightarrow & E^n & E^m & \longleftarrow & N
\end{array}
$$

Let $\Phi \subseteq E^N$ and let $\psi \subseteq E^M$.

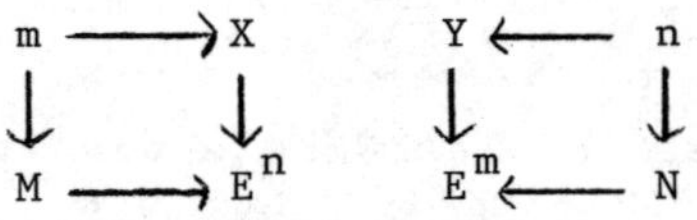

By the Φ-Ψ extension problem, we mean the following two questions:

(1) Is it true that we have ${}^t j_{nN}(\Phi) \subset M$ and ${}^t j_{mM}(\Psi) \subset N$?

(2) If this is true, is it true that for each $\phi \in \Phi$ and each $\psi \in \Phi$, we have

$$\phi({}^t j_{mM}\psi) = \psi({}^t j_{nN}\phi)?$$

If question (1) has an affirmative answer, we say that *Φ and Ψ are compatible in this context*.

If both question (1) and question (2) have affirmative answers, we say that the *Φ-Ψ extension problem has an affirmative solution*.

6. *Lemma*: Suppose we are given an extension context

$$\begin{array}{ccc} m & \longrightarrow & X \\ \downarrow & & \downarrow \\ M & \longrightarrow & E^n \end{array} \qquad \begin{array}{ccc} Y & \longleftarrow & n \\ \downarrow & & \downarrow \\ E^m & \longleftarrow & N \end{array}$$

Let $\Phi = e_{mN}(m) \subset E^N$

$\Psi = e_{nM}(n) \subset E^M$

$\pi = {}^t j_{nN}{}^{-1}(M) \subset E^N$

$\Sigma = {}^t j_{mM}{}^{-1}(N) \subset E^M$

(1) $\Phi \subset \pi$ and $\Psi \subset \Sigma$

(2) Both the Φ-Σ extension problem and the π-Ψ extension problem have affirmative solutions.

(3) If $x \in m$, $y \in n$, we have

$$e_{mN}x\ ({}^t j_{mM}\ e_{nM}y) = \langle x,y \rangle$$

$$e_{nM}y\ ({}^t j_{nN}\ e_{mN}x) = \langle x,y \rangle$$

The above lemma should serve as a justification for the constant use of the word "extension". For if we are given an extension context

$$\begin{array}{ccc} m & \longrightarrow & X \\ \downarrow & & \downarrow \\ M & \longrightarrow & E^n \end{array} \qquad \begin{array}{ccc} Y & \longleftarrow & n \\ \downarrow & & \downarrow \\ E^m & \longleftarrow & N \end{array}$$

and if we are given $\Phi \subset E^N$, $\Psi \subset E^M$ such that $e_{mN}(m) \subset \Phi$ and $e_{nM}(n) \subset \Psi$, and if Φ and Ψ are compatible, then we obtain two dualities

$$<,>_1 : \quad \Phi \times \Psi \to E$$

$$(\phi,\psi) \to \phi({}^t j_{mM}\psi)$$

$$<,>_2 : \quad \Phi \times \Psi \to E$$

$$(\phi,\psi) \to \psi({}^t j_{nN}\phi)$$

and for $x \in X$, $y \in Y$, we have

$$<e_{mN}(x), e_{nM}(y)>_1 = <x,y> = <e_{mN}(x), e_{nM}(y)>_2$$

That is, we have two "extensions" of the duality $<m,n>$ over E. If the Φ-Ψ extension problem has an affirmative solution, the two extensions are the same.

Let us list one trivial special case which points out that at least the questions we are dealing with are not vacuous. (We shall later show that Fubini Theorems and Krein's Theorem fall within their scope.)

Suppose E contains more than one point. Let m=X, n=Y, $M=E^Y$, $N=E^X$. We are now interested in the diagram

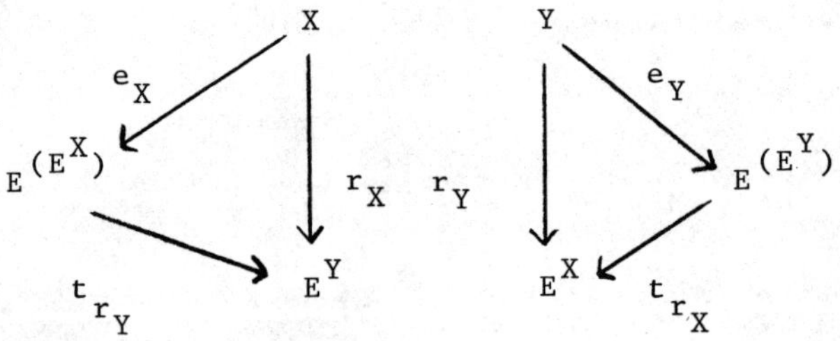

Let $\psi \in E^{(E^Y)}$ be a constant map. Let Im ψ = {z}. Whatever choice we make of $\phi \in E^{(E^X)}$, we have

$$\psi({}^t r_Y \phi) = z.$$

But we can choose $\phi \in E^{(E^X)}$ such that

$$\phi({}^t r_X \psi) \neq z.$$

So $E^{(E^X)}$ and $E^{(E^Y)}$ are compatible, but the extension problem does not have an affirmative solution.

§3. Extension Contexts in a Duality in a Cartesian Category

1. Convention: Throughout this section, $\mathcal{C}$ will denote a fixed Cartesian category. <A,B> will denote a fixed duality over an object E in $\mathcal{C}$.

2. Definition: By an extension context in this duality, we mean the following:

(1) A subobject C of A and a subobject D of B.

(2) A non-empty subset M of Mor(D,E) such that, for each $x \in spC$, $r_A(x)|_{spD} \in M$.

(3) A non-empty subset N of Mor(C,E) such that, for each $y \in spD$, $r_B(y)|_{spC} \in N$.

I mentioned in the paragraph after 3.3.4 that one of the more important properties of a Cartesian category is that transpose maps can be handled in the same way as they are handled in the category of sets. In doing so, there tends to be a certain amount of procedural abbreviation, but the results are no less valid for it. The only alternative to the abbreviated procedure would be to use Lemma 3.3.2 repeatedly in the obvious way, a process which would be most tedious.

We recall the notational conventions introduced in 3.3.3 and 3.3.4.

Let E^D, E^C, E^N and E^M be choices of the appropriate products in C.

By the extension context of sets associated with our given context, we mean the context

$$\begin{array}{ccc} spC & \longrightarrow & spA \\ \downarrow & & \downarrow \\ M & \longrightarrow & spE^{spD} \end{array} \qquad \begin{array}{ccc} spB & \longleftarrow & spD \\ \downarrow & & \downarrow \\ spE^{spC} & \longleftarrow & N \end{array}$$

We agree to let M, resp. N, denote both itself and its canonical image in $sp(E^D)$, resp. $sp(E^C)$.

We obtain a diagram

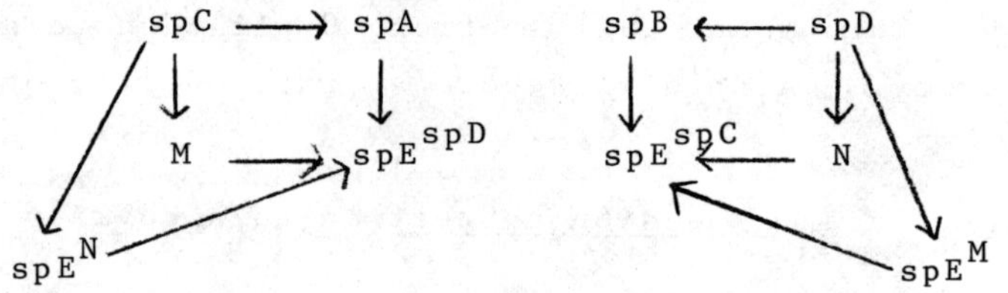

and a corresponding commutative diagram

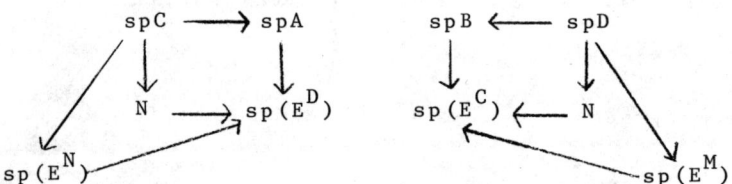

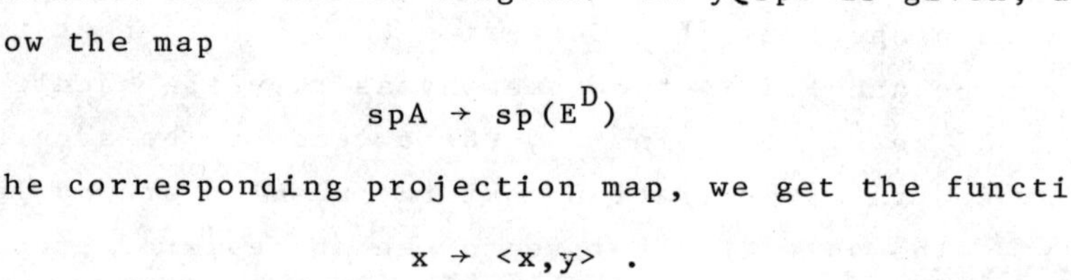

We consider this latter diagram. If $y \in spD$ is given, and if we follow the map

$$spA \to sp(E^D)$$

by the corresponding projection map, we get the function

$$x \to \langle x,y \rangle \ .$$

Likewise, if $x \in spC$ is given and if we follow the map

$$spB \to sp(E^C)$$

by the corresponding projection map, we get the function

$$y \to \langle x,y \rangle \ .$$

If $f \in N$ is given and if we follow the map

$$spC \to sp(E^N)$$

by the corresponding projection map, we get

$$x \to f(x).$$

If $g \in M$ is given and if we follow the map

$$spD \to sp(E^M)$$

by the corresponding projection map, we get

$$y \to g(y).$$

<u>We now agree to label the various maps in the diagram as follows</u>:

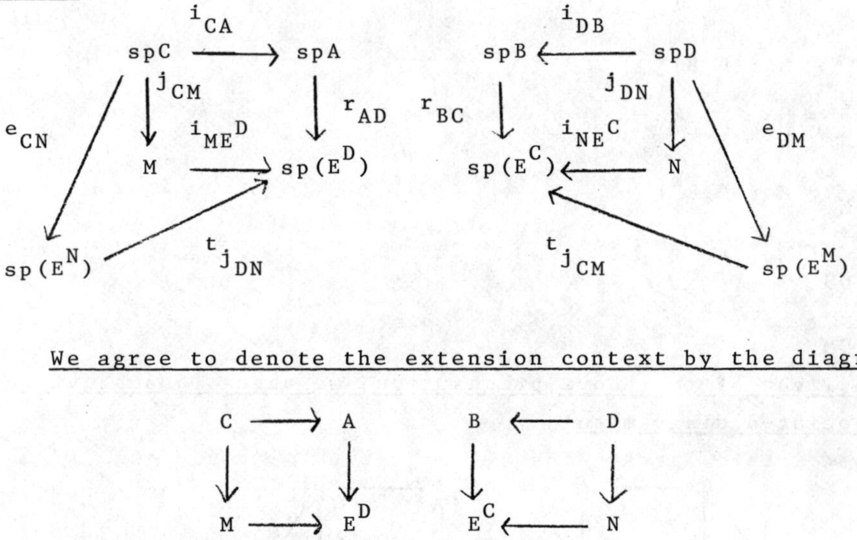

<u>We agree to denote the extension context by the diagram</u>:

$$\begin{array}{ccc} C & \longrightarrow & A \\ \downarrow & & \downarrow \\ M & \longrightarrow & E^D \end{array} \qquad \begin{array}{ccc} B & \longleftarrow & D \\ \downarrow & & \downarrow \\ E^C & \longleftarrow & N \end{array}$$

We have proved the following proposition:

3. <u>Proposition</u>: <u>Suppose we are given an extension context</u>

$$\begin{array}{ccc} C & \longrightarrow & A \\ \downarrow & & \downarrow \\ M & \longrightarrow & E^D \end{array} \qquad \begin{array}{ccc} B & \longleftarrow & D \\ \downarrow & & \downarrow \\ E^C & \longleftarrow & N \end{array}$$

Suppose E^D, E^C, E^N, E^M *are choices of the appropriate products in* $\mathcal{C}$. *We have a commutative diagram*

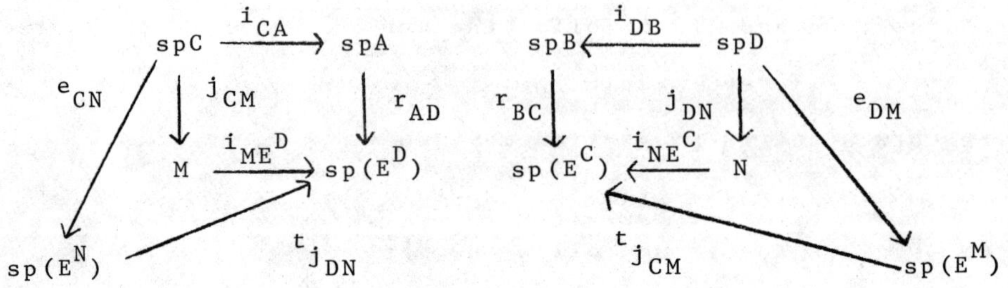

Moreover, we have

$r_{AD} \in Mor(A, E^D)$

$r_{BC} \in Mor(B, E^C)$

$i_{CA} \in Mor(C, A)$

$i_{DB} \in Mor(D, B)$

$e_{CN} \in Mor(C, E^N)$

$e_{DM} \in Mor(D, E^M)$

$t_{j_{DN}} \in Mor(E^N, E^D)$

$t_{j_{CM}} \in Mor(E^M, E^C)$

In light of the above proposition, we agree to abbreviate the associated diagram to

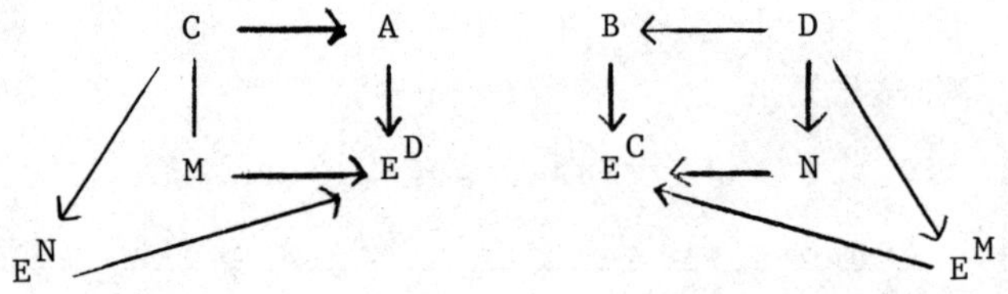

with a warning note that, of course, M and N are not objects of $\mathcal{C}$ and that the maps to and from these sets (albeit only these maps) are simply functions.

Also, since it makes no difference which choices we make of the products E^D, E^C, E^M, E^N, as long as after this choice the argument proceeds canonically, we agree to suppress any mention of the choice of these products in the future.

4. Proposition: Suppose we are given an extension context

$$\begin{array}{ccccccc} C & \longrightarrow & A & \quad & B & \longrightarrow & D \\ \downarrow & & \downarrow & & \downarrow & & \downarrow \\ M & \longrightarrow & E^D & & E^C & \longrightarrow & N \end{array}$$

Let Φ be a subobject of E^N which has $e_{CN}(C)$ as a subobject. Let Ψ be a subobject of E^M which has $e_{DM}(D)$ as a subobject.

(1) Suppose ${}^t j_{CM}(\Psi) \subset N$.

We obtain a duality

$$<,>_1: \quad sp\Phi \times sp\Psi \to spE$$

$$(\phi, \psi) \to \phi({}^t j_{CM}(\psi))$$

For each fixed $\psi \in \Psi$, the map

$$sp\Phi \to spE$$

$$\phi \to <\phi, \psi>_1$$

is in $Mor(\Phi, E)$.

If $x \in spC$, $y \in spD$, we have

$$<x, y> = <e_{CN}(x), e_{DM}(y)>_1$$

(2) Suppose ${}^t j_{DN}(\Phi) \subset M$.

We obtain a duality

$$<,>_2: \quad sp\Phi \times sp\Psi \to spE$$

$$(\phi, \psi) \to \psi({}^t j_{DN}(\phi))$$

For each fixed $\phi \in \Phi$, the map

$$\mathrm{sp}\Psi \to \mathrm{sp}E$$

$$\psi \to \langle \phi, \psi \rangle_2$$

is in $\mathrm{Mor}(\Psi, E)$.

If $x \in \mathrm{sp}C$, $y \in \mathrm{sp}D$, we have

$$\langle x, y \rangle = \langle e_{CN}(x),\ e_{DM}(y) \rangle_2$$

Proof: Both follow from the fact that a coordinate projection on a product is a morphism.

5. Definition: Suppose we are given an extension context

$$\begin{array}{ccc} C & \longrightarrow & A \\ \downarrow & & \downarrow \\ M & \longrightarrow & E^D \end{array} \qquad \begin{array}{ccc} B & \longleftarrow & D \\ \downarrow & & \downarrow \\ E^C & \longleftarrow & N \end{array}$$

Let Φ be a subobject of E^N containing $e_{CN}(C)$ as a subobject and let Ψ be a subobject of E^M containing $e_{DM}(D)$ as a subobject.

(1) We say Φ and Ψ are compatible in this context if this is true of (the canonical image of) $\mathrm{sp}\Phi$ and $\mathrm{sp}\Psi$ in the associated duality of sets.

(2) We say the Φ-Ψ extension problem has an affirmative solution, if this is true of the $\mathrm{sp}\Phi$ - $\mathrm{sp}\Psi$ extension problem in the associated duality of sets.

6. Corollary: Suppose we are given an extension context

$$\begin{array}{ccc} C & \longrightarrow & A \\ \downarrow & & \downarrow \\ M & \longrightarrow & E^D \end{array} \qquad \begin{array}{ccc} B & \longleftarrow & D \\ \downarrow & & \downarrow \\ E^C & \longleftarrow & N \end{array}$$

Let Φ be a subobject of E^N having $e_{CN}(C)$ as a subobject. Let Ψ be a subobject of E^M having $e_{DM}(D)$ as a subobject.

If the Φ-Ψ extension problem has an affirmative solution, then we have a duality

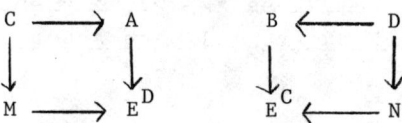

$$<\,,\,>:\ \Phi \times \Psi \to E$$

$$(\phi,\psi) \to \phi({}^t j_{CM}\psi)$$

$$= \psi({}^t j_{DN}\phi)$$

in $\mathcal{C}$.

Moreover, if $x \in spC$, $y \in spD$, we have

$$<x,\ y> = <e_{CN}(x),\ e_{DM}(y)>$$

7. *Definition*: Suppose we are given an extension context

$$\begin{array}{ccc} C & \longrightarrow & A \\ \downarrow & & \downarrow \\ M & \longrightarrow & E^D \end{array} \qquad \begin{array}{ccc} B & \longleftarrow & D \\ \downarrow & & \downarrow \\ E^C & \longleftarrow & N \end{array}$$

Let Φ be a subobject of E^N which contains $e_{CN}(C)$ as a subobject. Let Ψ be a subobject of E^M which contains $e_{DM}(D)$ as a subobject.

Suppose the Φ-Ψ extension problem has an affirmative solution.

By *the extended duality $<\Phi,\ \Psi>$ over E in $\mathcal{C}$*, we mean the duality,

$$<\,,\,>:\ sp\Phi \times sp\Psi \to spE$$

$$(\phi,\psi) \to \phi({}^t j_{MC}\psi)$$

§4. Extension Contexts over a Uniformized Object

1. *Convention*: Throughout this section, $\mathcal{C}$ will denote a fixed Cartesian category. u will denote a fixed uniformizing rule for $\mathcal{C}$.

Let <A,B> be a duality over E in $\mathcal{C}$. We have a natural duality <csp(A), csp(B)> over csp(E) in the category of covered sets which is associated with our given duality. We call this *the associated duality of covered sets*.

2. *Definition*: *By a duality <A,B> in $\mathcal{C}$ over a uniformized object $E[\mathcal{U}]$ in $\mathcal{C}_u$*, we mean a duality <A,B> over E in $\mathcal{C}$ together with a uniform structure $\mathcal{U} \in u(E)$.

By *the associated duality over a covered uniform space*, we mean the associated duality of covered sets, together with the uniform structure $\mathcal{U}$.

3. *Definition*: Let $\langle A,B \rangle$ be a duality in $\mathcal{C}$ over a *cover-closed* uniformized object $E[\mathcal{U}]$ in $\mathcal{C}_u$. (i.e., we assume that each set of $c(E)$ is contained in a $\mathcal{U}$-closed set of $c(E)$; see §2.4).

Suppose we are given an extension context

$$\begin{array}{ccc} C & \longrightarrow & A \\ \downarrow & & \downarrow \\ M & \longrightarrow & E^D \end{array} \qquad\qquad \begin{array}{ccc} B & \longleftarrow & D \\ \downarrow & & \downarrow \\ E^C & \longleftarrow & N \end{array}$$

If $F \in c(C)$, we denote by $\overline{e_{CN}(F)}$ the closure of $e_{CN}(F)$ in the product space $E[\mathcal{U}]^N$. *We denote by* $\overline{e_{CN}(C)}$ *the cover-closed envelope of the object (not set)* $e_{CN}(C)$ *in* $E[\mathcal{U}]^N$. Similarly, $\overline{e_{DM}(G)}$ (for G in $c(D)$) and $\overline{e_{DM}(D)}$ denote closure and cover-closed envelope in $E[\mathcal{U}]^M$. In terms of $\Phi = \overline{e_{CN}(C)}$ and $\Psi = \overline{e_{DM}(D)}$, we say that *C and D are compatible in this context* if Φ and Ψ are, that *C and D have the extension property in this context* if the Φ-Ψ extension problem has an affirmative solution, and, if this is the case, by *the extended uniform duality over* $E[\mathcal{U}]$ *in* $\mathcal{C}$ *obtained from this context*, we mean the extended duality $\langle \Phi, \Psi \rangle$ over E in $\mathcal{C}$, together with $\mathcal{U}$ and the induced product structures on Φ and Ψ. (These induced product structures will be in $u(\Phi)$ and $u(\Psi)$.)

4. *Proposition*: *Let* $\langle A,B \rangle$ *be a duality in* $\mathcal{C}$ *over a cover-closed uniformized object* $E[\mathcal{U}]$ *in* $\mathcal{C}_u$.

Suppose we are given an extension context

$$\begin{array}{ccc} C & \longrightarrow & A \\ \downarrow & & \downarrow \\ M & \longrightarrow & E^D \end{array} \qquad\qquad \begin{array}{ccc} B & \longleftarrow & D \\ \downarrow & & \downarrow \\ E^C & \longleftarrow & N \end{array}$$

Suppose moreover that C and D have the extension property in this context.

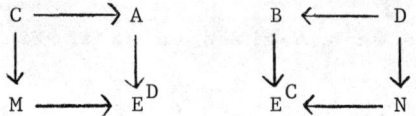

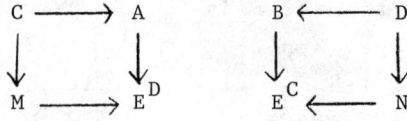

Then if $\phi \in sp\ \overline{e_{CN}(C)}$ *and* $\psi \in sp\ \overline{e_{DM}(D)}$, the *maps*

$$sp\ \overline{e_{DM}(D)} \to spE$$

$$\pi \to \langle \phi, \pi \rangle$$

$$sp\ \overline{e_{CN}(C)} \to spE$$

$$\theta \to \langle \theta, \psi \rangle$$

are both uniformly continuous with respect to the product uniform structures.

That is, the extended uniform duality over $E[\mathcal{U}]$ *in* $\mathcal{C}$ *obtained from this context is indeed a uniform duality in* $\mathcal{C}$.

Now suppose we are given a duality $\langle A,B \rangle$ in $\mathcal{C}$ over a uniformized object $E[\mathcal{U}]$ in $\mathcal{C}_u$. Suppose moreover that we are given an extension context

$$\begin{array}{ccccccc} C & \longrightarrow & A & \qquad & B & \longleftarrow & D \\ \downarrow & & \downarrow & & \downarrow & & \downarrow \\ M & \longrightarrow & E^D & & E^C & \longleftarrow & N \end{array}$$

Associated with this is a canonically defined context

$$\begin{array}{ccccccc} csp(C) & \longrightarrow & csp(A) & \qquad & csp(B) & \longleftarrow & csp(D) \\ \downarrow & & \downarrow & & \downarrow & & \downarrow \\ M & \longrightarrow & csp(E)^D & & csp(E)^C & \longleftarrow & N \end{array}$$

which will be called *the associated context of covered sets*.

5. *Proposition*: *Let* $\langle A, B \rangle$ *be a duality in* $\mathcal{C}$ *over a cover-closed uniformized object* $E[\mathcal{U}]$ *in* $\mathcal{C}_u$.

Suppose we are given an extension context

$$\begin{array}{ccccccc} C & \longrightarrow & A & \qquad & B & \longleftarrow & D \\ \downarrow & & \downarrow & & \downarrow & & \downarrow \\ M & \longrightarrow & E^D & & E^C & \longleftarrow & N \end{array}$$

(1) *C and D are compatible in this context if and only if csp(C) and csp(D) are compatible in the associated context*

of covered sets.

(2) C and D have the extension property in this context if and only if csp(C) and csp(D) have the extension property in the associated context of covered sets.

6. Proposition: Let <A,B> be a duality in $\mathcal{C}$ over a cover-closed, separated, uniformized object $E[\mathcal{U}]$ in $\mathcal{C}_u$.

Suppose we are given an extension context

$$\begin{array}{ccccccc} C & \longrightarrow & A & \qquad & B & \longleftarrow & D \\ \downarrow & & \downarrow & & \downarrow & & \downarrow \\ M & \longrightarrow & E^D & & E^C & \longleftarrow & N \end{array}$$

and suppose that C and D are compatible in this context.

The following statements are equivalent:

(1) C and D have the extension property in this context.

(2) If $\psi \in sp\ (\overline{e_{DM}(D)})$, then the function

$$sp(\overline{e_{CN}(C)}) \to spE$$

$$\phi \to \psi({}^t j_{DN}\phi)$$

is locally continuous with respect to the product uniform structure and $\mathcal{U}$.

(3) If $\psi \in sp(\overline{e_{DM}(D)})$, then the function

$$sp(\overline{e_{CN}(C)}) \to spE$$

$$\phi \to \psi({}^t j_{DN}\phi)$$

is uniformly continuous with respect to the product uniform structure and $\mathcal{U}$.

(4) ${}^t j_{DN}$ is uniformly continuous on $\overline{e_{CN}(C)}$ with respect to the product structure on $\overline{e_{CN}(C)}$ and the structure $\sigma(\overline{e_{DM}(D)},\mathcal{U})$ on M.

(5) If $\phi \in sp(\overline{e_{CN}(C)})$, then the function

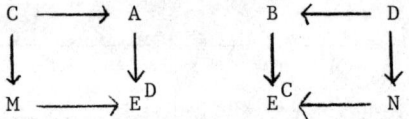

$$\mathrm{sp}(\overline{e_{DM}(D)}) \to \mathrm{sp}E$$

$$\psi \to \phi({}^t j_{CM}\psi)$$

is locally continuous with respect to the product uniform structure and $\mathcal{U}$.

(6) *If* $\phi \in \mathrm{sp}(\overline{e_{CN}(C)})$, *then the function*

$$\mathrm{sp}(\overline{e_{DM}(D)}) \to \mathrm{sp}E$$

$$\psi \to \phi({}^t j_{CM}\psi)$$

is uniformly continuous with respect to the product uniform structure and $\mathcal{U}$.

(7) ${}^t j_{CM}$ *is uniformly continuous on* $\overline{e_{DM}(D)}$ *with respect to the product structure on* $\overline{e_{DM}(D)}$ *and the structure* $\sigma(\overline{e_{CN}(C)}, \mathcal{U})$ on N.

Proof: Clearly (1) → (3) → (2), (3) ↔ (4), (1) → (6) → (5) and (6) ↔ (7). So it suffices to show (2) → (1) and (5) → (1). We will show (5) → (1), the other case following by symmetry.

Suppose (5) holds and that $\phi \in \mathrm{sp}(\overline{e_{CN}(C)})$, $\psi \in \overline{e_{DM}(G)}$ where $G \in c(D)$. We have two maps

$$\overline{e_{DM}(G)} \to \mathrm{sp}E$$

$$\theta \to \theta({}^t j_{DN}\phi)$$

$$\theta \to \phi({}^t j_{CM}\theta)$$

which agree on $e_{DM}(G)$. The first is uniformly continuous in any case and the second is, by (5), assumed to be continuous. Since $\mathcal{U}$ is separated, it follows that the two maps are the same. So

$$\psi({}^t j_{DN}\phi) = \phi({}^t j_{CM}\psi) \ .$$

Since this is true for any $\phi \in \mathrm{sp}(\overline{e_{CN}(C)})$ and any $\psi \in \mathrm{sp}(\overline{e_{DM}(D)})$, (1) follows.

7. Definition: Suppose $\langle A,B\rangle$ is a duality in $\mathcal{C}$ over a cover-closed uniformized object $E[\mathcal{U}]$ in $\mathcal{C}_u$.

Let C be a subobject of A, D a subobject of B. If $F \in c(C)$, we denote by $\overline{r_{AD}(F)}$ the closure of $r_{AD}(F)$ in the product space $E[\mathcal{U}]^D$. We denote by $\overline{\overline{r_{AD}(C)}}$ the cover-closed envelope of the object $r_{AD}(C)$ in $E[\mathcal{U}]^D$.

8. Proposition: Let $\langle A,B\rangle$ be a duality in $\mathcal{C}$ over a closed uniformized object $E[\mathcal{U}]$ in $\mathcal{C}_u$.

Suppose we are given an extension context

$$\begin{array}{ccc} C & \longrightarrow & A \\ \downarrow & & \downarrow \\ M & \longrightarrow & E^D \end{array} \qquad\qquad \begin{array}{ccc} B & \longleftarrow & D \\ | & & \downarrow \\ E^C & \longleftarrow & N \end{array}$$

(1) ${}^t j_{DN}(\overline{\overline{e_{CN}(C)}})$ is a subobject of $\overline{\overline{r_{AD}(C)}}$. If $E[\mathcal{U}]$ is compactly covered, $\overline{\overline{r_{AD}(C)}}$ is a subobject of ${}^t j_{DN}(\overline{\overline{e_{CN}(C)}})$.

(2) ${}^t j_{CM}(\overline{\overline{e_{DM}(D)}})$ is a subobject of $\overline{\overline{r_{BC}(D)}}$. If $E[\mathcal{U}]$ is compactly covered, $\overline{\overline{r_{BC}(D)}}$ is a subobject of ${}^t j_{CM}(\overline{\overline{e_{DM}(D)}})$.

(3) A sufficient condition that C and D be compatible in this context is that we have

$$sp(\overline{\overline{r_{AD}(C)}}) \subset M$$

$$sp(\overline{\overline{r_{BC}(D)}}) \subset N$$

If $E[\mathcal{U}]$ is compactly covered, this condition is also necessary.

Proof: This is a trivial application of the continuity of transpose maps on products.

The following proposition is the first of many we shall see of its kind: It shows that under certain circumstances the extension property is equivalent to a kind of "weak compactness".

9. Proposition: Let $\langle A,B\rangle$ be a duality in $\mathcal{C}$ over a compactly covered uniformized object $E[\mathcal{U}]$ in $\mathcal{C}_u$.

Suppose we are given an extension context

$$\begin{array}{ccc} C & \longrightarrow & A \\ \downarrow & & \downarrow \\ M & \longrightarrow & E^D \end{array} \qquad\qquad \begin{array}{ccc} B & \longleftarrow & D \\ \downarrow & & \downarrow \\ E^C & \longleftarrow & N \end{array}$$

in which C and D are compatible.

The following statements are equivalent:

(1) *C and D have the extension property in this context.*

(2) $\overline{r_{AD}(C)}$ *is compactly covered with respect to* $\sigma(\overline{e_{DM}(D)},\mathcal{U})$.

(3) $\overline{r_{BC}(D)}$ *is compactly covered with respect to* $\sigma(\overline{e_{CN}(C)},\mathcal{U})$.

Proof: By Proposition 8, we have

$$sp(\overline{r_{AD}(C)} \subset M$$

$$sp(\overline{r_{BC}(D)} \subset N$$

and so statements (2) and (3) make sense.

But, by compactness, we can restate (2) and (3) as follows.

(2') $\sigma(\overline{e_{DM}(D)}\ ,\mathcal{U})$ is locally equivalent to the product structure on $\overline{r_{AD}(C)}$.

(3') $\sigma(\overline{e_{CN}(C)}\ ,\mathcal{U})$ is locally equivalent to the product structure on $\overline{r_{BC}(D)}$.

But it is clear that (2') implies statement (2) of Proposition 6 and (3') implies statement (5) of Proposition 6. And, clearly, statement (4) of Proposition 6 implies (2) and statement (7) of Proposition 6 implies (3).

§5. *The Double Sequence Property*

Let $X[\mathcal{U}]$ be a uniform space. If a filter base $\mathcal{F}$ on X converges with respect to $\mathcal{U}$ to a point $x \in X$, *we write* $x = \ell im\ \mathcal{F}$ *even though $\mathcal{F}$ may converge to two distinct points of X.* Note that, if $x = \ell im\ \mathcal{F}$ and $y = \ell im\ \mathcal{F}$, we can state that $(x,y) \in \bigcap \mathcal{U}$.

Now let X be a set. By *a double sequence in X*, we mean a function from N × N into X where N = {1, 2,...,}. *We denote such a function by* $\{a_{ij}\}$ *where* a_{ij} *is the value of the function* at (i,j). By <u>a subsequence of</u> $\{a_{ij}\}$, we mean a double sequence in X whose general term is of the form $a_{m_i n_j}$, where $\{m_i\}$ and $\{n_j\}$ are strictly increasing.

If $X[\mathcal{U}]$ is a uniform space and $\{a_{ij}\}$ is a double sequence in X, we say the <u>double limit</u>

$$\lim_i \lim_j a_{ij}$$

<u>exists in</u> $X[\mathcal{U}]$ <u>and that</u>

$$x = \lim_i \lim_j a_{ij}$$

if $\lim_j a_{ij}$ exists for all but finitely many i and these limits converge to x. $\lim_j \lim_i a_{ij}$ is defined analogously.

If X is a set, Y is a subset of X and $\mathcal{F}$ is a filter base on X, we say <u>$\mathcal{F}$ is eventually in Y</u> if Y contains a set of $\mathcal{F}$.

1. <u>Definition</u>: Let $X[\mathcal{U}]$ be a uniform space and let $\{a_{ij}\}$ be a double sequence in X.

We say <u>the double sequence property holds for</u> $\{a_{ij}\}$ <u>in</u> $X[\mathcal{U}]$ if for every entourage $U \in \mathcal{U}$, every pair of non-empty sets C, $D \subset X$ such that $(C \times D) \cap U = \emptyset$, and every subsequence $\{a_{m_i n_j}\}$ of $\{a_{ij}\}$, one of the following statements is false.

(a) For each $i \geq 1$, the sequence $\{a_{m_i n_j}\}_j$ is eventually in C.

(b) For each $j \geq 1$, the sequence $\{a_{m_i n_j}\}_i$ is eventually in D.

We say <u>the double limit property holds for</u> $\{a_{ij}\}$ <u>in</u> $X[\mathcal{U}]$ <u>if for</u> every subsequence $\{a_{m_i n_j}\}$ of $\{a_{ij}\}$ such that both double limits

$$x = \lim_i \lim_j a_{m_i n_j}$$

$$y = \lim_j \lim_i a_{m_i n_j}$$

exist, we have $(x,y) \in \cap\mathcal{U}$.

2. Definition: Let $E[\mathcal{U}]$ be a covered uniform space and let $\{a_{ij}\}$ be a double sequence in spE.

We say the double sequence property holds for $\{a_{ij}\}$ in $E[\mathcal{U}]$ if there is a set $X \in c(E)$ such that $a_{ij} \in X$ for all $i,j \geq 1$ and such that the double sequence property holds for $\{a_{ij}\}$ in $X[\mathcal{U}|_X]$.

We say the double limit property holds for $\{a_{ij}\}$ in $E[\mathcal{U}]$ if there is a set $X \in c(E)$ such that $a_{ij} \in X$ for all $i,j \geq 1$ and such that the double limit property holds for $\{a_{ij}\}$ in $X[\mathcal{U}|_X]$.

The next proposition is a kind of catch-all for useful facts concerning double sequences. It is stated in terms of covered uniform spaces, though the point could be made that it might as well have been stated in terms of uniform spaces. If it had had any intrinsic interest, it would have been stated in terms of uniform spaces. But since its only interest is basically as a lemma and since it will be used on covered uniform spaces, it is stated for them.

3. Proposition: Let $E[\mathcal{U}]$ be a covered uniform space. Let $F[\mathcal{V}]$ be a compactly covered uniform space and let

$$\phi: \quad E \rightarrow F$$

be a locally $\mathcal{U}$-$\mathcal{V}$ uniformly continuous morphism.

Let $\{a_{ij}\}$ be a double sequence in some set of $c(E)$.
The following three statements are equivalent:

(I) The double sequence property holds for $\{a_{ij}\}$ in $E[\mathcal{U}]$.

(II) For every $\mathcal{U}$-uniformly continuous function ψ from spE to K which is bounded on spE, the double limit property holds for $\{\psi(a_{ij})\}$ in K.

(III) For every function ψ from spE to K which is bounded and $\mathcal{U}$-uniformly continuous on each set of $c(E)$, the double limit property holds for $\{\psi(a_{ij})\}$ in K.

Any of these statements implies the following statement, and, if $\phi^{-1}(\mathcal{V})|_H = \mathcal{U}|_H$ for each $H \in c(E)$, the converse is also true.

(IV) If G is any compact set in $c(F)$ which contains each term of the double sequence $\{\phi(a_{ij})\}$, if C and D are disjoint, closed subsets of G, and if $\{a_{m_i m_j}\}$ is any subsequence of $\{a_{ij}\}$, then one of the following statements is false.

(a) For each $i \geq 1$, the sequence $\{\phi(a_{m_i n_j})\}_j$ is eventually in C.

(b) For each $j \geq 1$, the sequence $\{\phi(a_{m_i n_j})\}_i$ is eventually in D.

<u>Any of the statements (I) through (III) implies the following statement, and, if some countably compact set of c(E) contains each term of</u> $\{a_{ij}\}$, <u>then the converse is also true</u>.

(V) If g is any $\mathcal{U}$-uniformly continuous pseudo-metric on spE, then the double limit property holds for $\{a_{ij}\}$ in $E[g]$.

<u>This statement in turn implies the following statement</u>.

(VI) The double limit property holds for $\{a_{ij}\}$ in $E[\mathcal{U}]$.

<u>In case some sequentially compact set of c(E) contains each term of</u> $\{a_{ij}\}$, <u>then statement (VI) implies statement (I)</u>.

<u>Proof</u>: (I) $\rightarrow$ (III) $\rightarrow$ (II) is reasonably clear. Suppose (I) fails. Then there exist sets $C, D \subset spE$, an entourage $U \in \mathcal{U}$ and a subsequence $\{a_{m_i n_j}\}$ of $\{a_{ij}\}$ such that $(C \times D) \cap U = \emptyset$ and such that for each $i \geq 1$, the sequence $\{a_{m_k n_j}\}_j$ is eventually in C and for each $j \geq 1$, the sequence $\{a_{m_i n_j}\}_i$ is eventually in D. Choose a uniformly continuous pseudo-metric g on spE such that $g(x,y) < 1$ implies $(x,y) \in U$. We define

$$\psi(x) = \inf\{1, g(x,y): y \in C\}.$$

Then ψ is bounded, uniformly continuous, and we have

$$\lim_i \lim_j \psi(a_{m_i n_j}) = 0 \neq 1 = \lim_j \lim_i \psi(a_{m_i n_j})$$

So (II) $\rightarrow$ (I).

Suppose (IV) fails for some choice of G, C, D and $\{a_{m_i n_j}\}$. Choose $H \in c(E)$ s.t. $a_{ij} \in H \ \forall_{i,j \geq 1}$. We may assume $G \supset \overline{\phi(H)}$. But

$\exists\, V \in \mathcal{V}$ s.t. $(C \times D) \cap V = \emptyset$, since G is compact. But then we have $(\phi(x), \phi(y)) \notin V$ whenever $x \in H \cap \phi^{-1}(C)$, $y \in H \cap \phi^{-1}(D)$. So, if $C' = H \cap \phi^{-1}(C)$, $D' = H \cap \phi^{-1}(D)$, the local uniform continuity of ϕ forces the existence of some $U \in \mathcal{U}$ s.t. $(C' \times D') \cap U = \emptyset$. But now, for each $i \geq 1$, $\{a_{m_i n_j}\}_j$ is eventually in C' and for each $j \geq 1$, $\{a_{m_i n_j}\}_i$ is eventually in D'. So (I) → (IV).

That (I) → (V) → (VI) is reasonably clear.

Now suppose that $\phi^{-1}(\mathcal{V})|_H = \mathcal{U}_H$ for each $H \in c(E)$. Suppose moreover that (I) fails. Then $\exists\, H \in c(E)$, $U \in \mathcal{U}$, $C, D \subset H$ s.t. $(C \times D) \cap U = \emptyset$, and a subsequence $\{a_{m_i n_j}\}$ of $\{a_{ij}\}$ s.t. $\forall i \geq 1$, $\{a_{m_i n_j}\}_j$ is eventually in C and $\forall j \geq 1$ $\{a_{m_i m_j}\}_i$ is eventually in D. Choose G in c(F) s.t. G is compact and $\phi(H) \subset G$. $\exists\, V \in \mathcal{V}$ s.t. $x, y \in H$ and $(\phi(x), \phi(y)) \in V \rightarrow (x,y) \in U$. Therefore $V \cap (\phi(C) \times \phi(D)) = \emptyset$. Therefore $\overline{\phi(C)} \cap \overline{\phi(D)} = \emptyset$. But then (IV) fails for G, $\overline{\phi(C)}$, $\overline{\phi(D)}$ and $\{a_{m_i n_j}\}$.

Now suppose that there is a sequentially compact set $H \in c(E)$ which contains each term of $\{a_{ij}\}$. Suppose (I) fails. Then there exist sets $C, D \subset H$, an entourage $U \in \mathcal{U}$ and a subsequence $\{a_{m_i n_j}\}$ of $\{a_{ij}\}$ such that $(C \times D) \cap U = \emptyset$ and such that $\forall_{i \geq 1}$, $\{a_{m_i n_j}\}_j$ is eventually in C, $\forall_{j \geq 1}$, $\{a_{m_i n_j}\}_i$ is eventually in D. Since H is sequentially compact, we can choose strictly increasing sequences $\{r_\ell\}$, $\{s_k\}$ of integers such that $\forall i \geq 1$, $j \geq 1$, the sequences $\{a_{m_i n_{s_k}}\}_k$ and $\{a_{m_{r_\ell} n_j}\}_\ell$ converge in H. (Use a diagonal process.) But then, by taking subsequences if necessary, we may assume that the double limits

$$\lim_i \lim_j a_{m_{r_i} n_{s_j}} = x$$

$$\lim_j \lim_i a_{m_{r_i} n_{s_j}} = y$$

exist. But if $V^2 \subset U$, we must have $(x,y) \notin V$. So (VI) fails.

Finally suppose that there is a countably compact set $H \in c(E)$ which contains each term of $\{a_{ij}\}$. Suppose (I) fails. Then $\exists C, D \subset H$, $U \in \mathcal{U}$ and a subsequence $\{a_{m_i n_j}\}$ of $\{a_{ij}\}$ such that $\forall i \geq 1$, $\{a_{m_i n_j}\}_j$ is eventually in C and $\forall j \geq 1$, $\{a_{m_i n_j}\}_i$ is eventually in D. Choose a uniformly continuous pseudo-metric g on E such that $g(x,y) < 1 \rightarrow (x,y) \in U$. Since H is $\mathcal{U}$-countably compact, H is g-sequentially compact. But (I) still fails with respect to g in place of $\mathcal{U}$. So, by what we just proved, (VI) fails with respect to g in place of $\mathcal{U}$. But this means that (V) fails.

Some of the parts of the above proposition which we commented were obvious are included in the following, equally obvious, lemma.

4. Lemma: Let $E[\mathcal{U}]$ and $F[\mathcal{U}]$ be covered uniform spaces and let

$$\phi: \quad E \rightarrow F$$

be a locally $\mathcal{U}$-$\mathcal{V}$ uniformly continuous morphism.

Suppose the double sequence property holds in $E[\mathcal{U}]$ for a double sequence $\{a_{ij}\}$ in spE. Then the double sequence property holds for $\{\phi(a_{ij})\}$ in $F[\mathcal{V}]$.

§6. The Double Sequence Property and Extension Contexts

1. Convention: Throughout this section, $\mathcal{C}$ will denote a fixed Cartesian category and u will denote a fixed uniformizing rule for $\mathcal{C}$.

<A,B> will denote a fixed, bounded (see 3.2.1) duality in $\mathcal{C}$ over a fixed object $E[\mathcal{U}]$ in $\mathcal{C}_u$.

2. Definition: Let C be a subobject of A and let D be a subobject of B.

We say that C and D have the double sequence property (with respect to this duality) if for every set $F \in c(C)$, every sequence $\{x_i\}$ in F, every set $G \in c(D)$ and every sequence $\{y_i\}$ in G, the double sequence property holds for $\{<x_i, y_j>\}$ in the covered uniform space $csp(E)[\mathcal{U}]$. We shall often abbreviate this by saying that C and D have the DSP.

We say that <u>C and D have the double limit property (with respect to this duality)</u> if for every set $F \in c(C)$, every sequence $\{x_i\}$ in F, every set $G \in c(D)$ and every sequence $\{y_i\}$ in G, the double limit property holds for $\{<x_i, y_i>\}$ in the covered uniform space $csp(E)[\mathcal{U}]$. We shall often abbreviate this by saying that <u>C and D have the DLP</u>.

3. <u>Proposition</u>: <u>Let C be a subobject of A and let D be a subobject of B.</u>

<u>If each set of c(D) is contained in a $\sigma(C,\mathcal{U})$-countably compact set of c(D) and if each set of c(C) is contained in a $\sigma(D,\mathcal{U})$-countably compact set of c(C), then C and D have the DSP</u>.

<u>Proof</u>: This is an easy consequence of the following lemma.

4. <u>Lemma</u>: Let $<X, Y>$ be a duality of sets over a uniform space $Z[\mathcal{V}]$.

Let $\{x_i\}$ be a sequence in X and let $\{y_i\}$ be a sequence in Y.

Let x_o be a $\sigma(Y,\mathcal{V})$-adherent point of $\{x_i\}$ in X and let y_o be a $\sigma(X,\mathcal{V})$-adherent point of $\{y_j\}$ in Y. Let O be any neighborhood of $<x_o, y_o>$ in Z.

There is a subsequence $\{x_{m_i}\}$ of $\{x_i\}$ and a subsequence $\{y_{n_j}\}$ of $\{y_j\}$ such that

(1) For each $i \geq 1$, the sequence $\{<x_{m_i}, y_{n_j}>\}_j$ is eventually in O.

(2) For each $j \geq 1$, the sequence $\{<x_{m_i}, y_{n_j}>\}_i$ is eventually in O.

<u>Proof</u>: Let g be a uniformly continuous pseudo-metric on Z such that $g(z, <x_o, y_o>) \leq 1$, implies $z \in O$. Let $M = \{x_o, x_1, x_2, \ldots\} \subset X$, $N = \{y_o, y_1, y_2, \ldots\} \subset Y$. Then we have

$$\sigma(M,g) \subset \sigma(X,\mathcal{V})$$

$$\sigma(N,g) \subset \sigma(Y,\mathcal{V})$$

Moreover, $\sigma(M,g)$ and $\sigma(N,g)$ are pseudo-metrizable. So we may choose subsequences $\{x_{m_i}\}$ of $\{x_i\}$ and $\{y_{n_j}\}$ of $\{y_j\}$ such that

$$x_o = \ell im_i \, x_{m_i} \quad \text{w.r.t. } \sigma(N,g)$$

$$y_o = \ell im_j \, y_{n_j} \quad \text{w.r.t. } \sigma(M,g)$$

But then, with respect to g, we have

$$\ell im_i \, \ell im_j \, \langle x_{m_i}, y_{n_j} \rangle = \ell im_i \, \langle x_{m_i}, y_o \rangle = \langle x_o, y_o \rangle$$

$$\ell im_j \, \ell im_i \, \langle x_{m_i}, y_{n_j} \rangle = \ell im_j \, \langle x_o, y_{n_j} \rangle = \langle x_o, y_o \rangle$$

Also, we may assume

$$g(\langle x_{m_i}, y_o \rangle, \langle x_o, y_o \rangle) < \tfrac{1}{2} \quad (i \geq 1)$$

$$g(\langle x_o, y_{n_j} \rangle, \langle x_o, y_o \rangle) < \tfrac{1}{2} \quad (j \geq 1)$$

These subsequences $\{x_{m_i}\}$ and $\{y_{n_j}\}$ satisfy conditions (1) and (2).

5. _Convention_: _For the rest of this section, we assume that $E[\mathcal{U}]$ is separated and cover-closed_.

6. _Theorem_: _Let C be a subobject of A and let D be a subobject of B._

Suppose we are given an extension context

$$\begin{array}{ccc} C & \longrightarrow & A \\ \downarrow & & \downarrow \\ M & \longrightarrow & E^D \end{array} \qquad \begin{array}{ccc} B & \longleftarrow & D \\ \downarrow & & \downarrow \\ E^C & \longleftarrow & N \end{array}$$

and suppose that C and D are compatible in this context.

A sufficient condition for C and D to have the extension property in this context is that C and D have the DSP. In case $E[\mathcal{U}]$ is compactly covered this condition is also necessary.

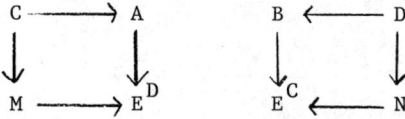

Proof: Suppose that $E[\mathcal{U}]$ is compactly covered and that C and D have the extension property in this context. Then, since $\overline{e_{CN}(C)}$ and $\overline{e_{DM}(D)}$ are compactly covered with respect to their product uniform structures, and since the extended uniform duality over $E[\mathcal{U}]$ in $\mathcal{C}$ obtained from this context is a uniform duality in $\mathcal{C}$, the conditions of Proposition 3 are satisfied in the extended duality. Then Proposition 3 forces C and D to have the DSP.

Now suppose, in the general case, that C and D have the DSP. Let $F\in c(C)$, $G\in c(D)$, $\phi\in\overline{e_{CN}(F)}$, $\psi\in\overline{e_{DM}(G)}$ and let g be a uniformly continuous pseudo-metric on spE. It suffices to show that

$$g(\phi({}^t j_{CM}\psi),\ \psi({}^t j_{DN}\phi)) = 0 .$$

If we now utilize the definition of the product uniform structures on E^N and E^M, a simple recursion argument allows us to select sequences $\{x_i\}$ in F and $\{y_j\}$ in G such that

(1) $g(\phi({}^t j_{CM}\psi),\ e_{CN}x_i({}^t j_{CM}\psi)) \le \frac{1}{i}$ $(i\ge 1)$

(2) $g(\phi(r_{BC}y_j),\ e_{CN}x_i(r_{BC}y_j)) \le \frac{1}{i}$ $(i\le j<i)$

(3) $g(\psi({}^t j_{DN}\phi),\ e_{DM}y_j({}^t j_{DN}\phi)) \le \frac{1}{j}$ $(j\ge 1)$

(4) $g(\psi(r_{AD}x_i),\ e_{DM}y_j(r_{AD}x_i)) \le \frac{1}{j}$ $(1\le i\le j)$

(The recursion proceeds by choosing x_i to satisfy (1) and (2) and then choosing y_i to satisfy (3) and (4).)

But then, with respect to g, we have

$$\begin{aligned}\lim_i \lim_j \langle x_i, y_j\rangle &= \lim_i \lim_j e_{DM}y_j(r_{AD}x_i)\\ &= \lim_i \psi(r_{AD}x_i)\\ &= \lim_i e_{CN}x_i({}^t j_{CM}\psi)\\ &= \phi({}^t j_{CM}\psi)\end{aligned}$$

and, likewise,

$$\lim_j \lim_i \langle x_i, y_j\rangle = \psi({}^t j_{DN}\phi) .$$

But now, by Propostion 5.3 (the part that says (I) $\to$ (V)) it follows by the DSP that we have

$$g(\phi({}^t j_{CM}\psi),\ \psi({}^t j_{DN}\phi)) = 0 .$$

This concludes the proof.

We now recall a notion we introduced in Section 2.6: u is said to give $\mathcal{C}$ cover-closed dual objects if for each pair of objects C, F of $\mathcal{C}$ and each $\mathcal{V} \in u(F)$ making $F[\mathcal{V}]$ separated and cover-closed, $\mathcal{D}(C,F)$ is a cover-closed subobject of the product covered uniform space $csp(F)[\mathcal{V}]^{spC}$. We noted at the beginning of Section 3.2 that the fact that our duality <A,B> is bounded implies that r_A is actually a covered set morphism from csp(A) to $\mathcal{D}(B,E)$ and r_B is actually a covered set morphism from csp(B) to $\mathcal{D}(A,E)$. If we put this fact together with the above-mentioned notion and then use Proposition 4.8, we can easily prove the following corollary to Theorem 6.

7. Corollary: Suppose that u gives $\mathcal{C}$ cover-closed dual objects and that $E[\mathcal{U}]$ is compactly covered.

Let C be a subobject of A and let D be a subobject of B. The following statements are equivalent:

(1) C and D have the DSP

(2) In the extension context

$$\begin{array}{ccc} C & \longrightarrow & A \\ \downarrow & & \downarrow \\ M & \longrightarrow & E^D \end{array} \qquad \begin{array}{ccc} B & \longleftarrow & D \\ \downarrow & & \downarrow \\ E^C & \longleftarrow & M \end{array}$$

Where M = Mor(D,E) and N = Mor(C,E), C and D have the extension property.

(3) In the extension context

$$\begin{array}{ccc} C & \longrightarrow & A \\ \downarrow & & \downarrow \\ M & \longrightarrow & E^D \end{array} \qquad \begin{array}{ccc} B & \longleftarrow & D \\ \downarrow & & \downarrow \\ E^C & \longleftarrow & N \end{array}$$

where $M = sp(\overline{r_{AD}(C)})$ and $N = sp(\overline{r_{BC}(D)})$, C and D have the extension property.

(4) In any extension context

$$\begin{array}{ccc} C & \longrightarrow & A \\ \downarrow & & \downarrow \\ M & \longrightarrow & E^D \end{array} \qquad \begin{array}{ccc} B & \longleftarrow & D \\ \downarrow & & \downarrow \\ E^C & \longleftarrow & N \end{array}$$

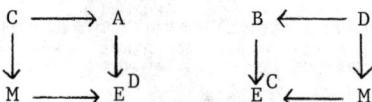

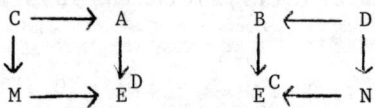

for which we have $M \supset sp(\overline{r_{AD}(C)})$ *and* $N \supset sp(\overline{r_{BC}(D)})$, *C and D have the extension property*.

(5) *In any extension context*

$$\begin{array}{ccc} C & \longrightarrow & A \\ \downarrow & & \downarrow \\ M & \longrightarrow & E^D \end{array} \qquad \begin{array}{ccc} B & \longleftarrow & D \\ \downarrow & & \downarrow \\ E^C & \longleftarrow & N \end{array}$$

in which C and D are compatible, $\overline{r_{AD}(C)}$ *is compactly covered with respect to* $\sigma(\overline{e_{DM}(D)}, \mathcal{U})$.

(6) *In any extension context*

$$\begin{array}{ccc} C & \longrightarrow & A \\ \downarrow & & \downarrow \\ M & \longrightarrow & E^D \end{array} \qquad \begin{array}{ccc} B & \longleftarrow & D \\ \downarrow & & \downarrow \\ E^C & \longleftarrow & N \end{array}$$

in which C and D are compatible, $\overline{r_{BC}(D)}$ *is compactly covered with respect to* $\sigma(\overline{e_{CN}(C)}, \mathcal{U})$.

Proof: See Propositions 4.8 and 4.9.

While the above corollary may seem to be quite ample in some respects, it is lacking in a very important respect: It does not allow us to make choices of M and N in an extension context

$$\begin{array}{ccc} C & \longrightarrow & A \\ \downarrow & & \downarrow \\ M & \longrightarrow & E^D \end{array} \qquad \begin{array}{ccc} B & \longleftarrow & D \\ \downarrow & & \downarrow \\ E^C & \longleftarrow & N \end{array}$$

in such a way as to force the morphisms to respect given uniform structures in u(A) and u(B). In other words, if we are going to look at locally uniform dualities in $\mathcal{C}$, the question of when C and D are compatible in many natural extension contexts is still very much unresolved. We turn our attention to this problem in the section after the next. In the next section, however, we will examine one particular case where the limitations we just mentioned do not trouble us.

§7. An Application: Arens Multiplication in the Bidual of a Bornological Algebra

Recall that, by standing convention, K-algebras are assumed to have identities.

In two papers (Arens, R. [1] and [2]) Arens introduced a way--in fact two ways--to extend the multiplication in a normed algebra to its bidual. One can show that in this case each of the multiplications will each make the bidual a normed algebra. However, unless the two coincide, the multiplication will not be separately continuous with respect to simple convergence on the dual. In case this happens, the algebra is called regular. Our aim is to utilize Section 6 in order to state theorems as to when this is the case.

We shall begin by approaching the problem entirely without any topology and then apply the results we get to the case where the topology is entirely determined by the algebraic setting: the case of a bornological algebra. The general setting we will begin with is that of covered algebras (see 2.3.8). We will denote also by K the covered algebra $(K,\mathcal{K})$ where K is the scalar field and $\mathcal{K}$ is all subsets of K of the form $\{\alpha: |\alpha| \le \beta\}$ where $\beta \ge 0$. (See §2.6.)

We will investigate covered algebras by first considering them via a forgetful functor as objects in the category of covered vector spaces (See 2.3.6.). Then, if $E = (A,\mathcal{A})$ is a covered algebra, the dual object of E over K in the category of covered vector spaces (See §2.6.) is the covered set $\mathcal{D}(E,K)$ whose space is the set of all linear forms on A which are bounded on each set of $\mathcal{A}$ and whose covering family is all sets of such forms which are uniformly bounded on each set of $\mathcal{A}$. The space $\mathcal{D}(E,K)$ admits a natural linear structure as a subspace of A^* and we denote the resulting vector space by A^b. The family, denoted $\mathcal{A}^b$, of all balanced, convex subsets of A^b which are uniformly bounded on each set of $\mathcal{A}$ is equivalent to (i.e., is refined by and refines) the covering family of $\mathcal{D}(E,K)$ and so the covered set which underlies the covered vector space $(A^b,\mathcal{A}^b)$ (denoted by E^b)

is equivalent to $\mathcal{D}(E,K)$. By a similar process, we obtain a third covered vector space $(A^{bb},\mathcal{A}^{bb})$ *(denoted by E^{bb})* where A^{bb} is all forms in A^{b*} which are bounded on each set of $\mathcal{A}^{b}$ and $\mathcal{A}^{bb}$ is all balanced convex sets in A^{bb} which are uniformly bounded on each set of $\mathcal{A}^{b}$. $(A^{bb},\mathcal{A}^{bb})$ (as a covered set) is equivalent to $\mathcal{D}(E^{b},K)$.

It is a triviality to check that the covered vector space E^{b} is cover-closed in the product covered locally convex space K^{A} and that E^{bb} is cover-closed in the product covered locally convex space $K^{A^{b}}$. Therefore, *$E^{b}[\sigma(A^{b},A)]$ and $E^{bb}[\sigma(A^{bb},A^{b})]$ are both compactly covered locally convex spaces*.

Now we must agree to fix some notation:

We have canonical linear dualities:

$$\langle , \rangle : \quad A \times A^{b} \to K$$
$$(x,x^{b}) \to x^{b}(x)$$
$$\langle , \rangle : \quad A^{bb} \times A^{b} \to K$$
$$(x^{bb},x^{b}) \to x^{bb}(x^{b})$$

We can define actions (see 4.2.3)

$$A \times A^{b} \to A^{b}$$
$$(x,x^{b}) \to x \cdot x^{b}$$
$$A^{b} \times A \to A^{b}$$
$$(x^{b},x) \to x^{b} \cdot x$$

via the relations

$$\langle xy,\ x^{b}\rangle = \langle x, y \cdot x^{b}\rangle = \langle y,\ x^{b} \cdot x\rangle$$

for $x,y \in A$, $x^{b} \in A^{b}$. The maps which constitute these actions are easily seen to be bilinear.

1. *Proposition*: *Each of the actions*

$$A \times A^{b} \to A^{b}$$
$$(x,x^{b}) \to x \cdot x^{b}$$
$$A^{b} \times A \to A^{b}$$
$$(x^{b},x) \to x^{b} \cdot x$$

defines a bounded duality in the category of covered vector spaces.

Proof: We must show that if $F \in A$, $G \in A^b$, then
$F \cdot G = \{x \cdot x^b: x \in F, x^b \in G\}$ and $G \cdot F = \{x^b \cdot x: x \in F, x^b \in G\}$
are contained in some set of A^b. For instance, if $H \in A$, we must show

$$\sup\{|\langle y, x^b \cdot x\rangle|: y \in H, x \in F, x^b \in G\} < \infty$$

But this is just

$$\sup\{|\langle xy, x^b\rangle|: y \in H, x \in F, x^b \in G\}$$

which is finite since A is stable under multiplication.

2. Corollary: Let $x \in A$, $x^{bb} \in A^b$. The linear forms

$$x^b \to \langle x^{bb}, x^b \cdot x\rangle$$

$$x^b \to \langle x^{bb}, x \cdot x^b\rangle$$

on A^b are again in A^{bb}.

In light of the above corollary, we can define actions

$$A \times A^{bb} \to A^{bb}$$

$$(x, x^{bb}) \to x \cdot x^{bb}$$

$$A^{bb} \times A \to A^{bb}$$

$$(x^{bb}, x) \to x^{bb} \cdot x$$

via the relations

$$\langle x \cdot x^{bb}, x^b\rangle = \langle x^{bb}, x^b \cdot x\rangle$$

$$\langle x^{bb} \cdot x, x^b\rangle = \langle x^{bb}, x \cdot x^b\rangle$$

for $x \in A$, $x^b \in A^b$, $x^{bb} \in A^{bb}$. The maps which constitute these actions are easily seen to be bilinear.

3. Proposition: Each of the actions

$$A \times A^{bb} \to A^{bb}$$

$$(x, x^{bb}) \to x \cdot x^{bb}$$

$$A^{bb} \times A \to A^{bb}$$

$$(x^{bb}, x) \to x^{bb} \cdot x$$

defines a bounded duality in the category of covered vector spaces.

Proof: This is an easy consequence of Proposition 1.

4. Corollary: Let $x^b \in A^b$, $x^{bb} \in A^{bb}$. The linear forms

$$x \to \langle x^{bb} \cdot x, x^b \rangle = \langle x^{bb}, x \cdot x^b \rangle$$

$$x \to \langle x \cdot x^{bb}, x^b \rangle = \langle x^{bb}, x^b \cdot x \rangle$$

on A are again in A^b.

In light of the above corollary, we can define actions

$$A^{bb} \times A^b \to A^b$$

$$(x^{bb}, x^b) \to x^{bb} \cdot x^b$$

$$A^b \times A^{bb} \to A^b$$

$$(x^b, x^{bb}) \to x^b \cdot x^{bb}$$

by the relations

$$\langle x, x^{bb} \cdot x^b \rangle = \langle x \cdot x^{bb}, x^b \rangle = \langle x^{bb}, x^b \cdot x \rangle$$

$$\langle x, x^b \cdot x^{bb} \rangle = \langle x^{bb} \cdot x, x^b \rangle = \langle x^{bb}, x \cdot x^b \rangle$$

for $x \in A$, $x^b \in A^b$, $x^{bb} \in A^{bb}$.

The evaluation map e_{AA^b} of A into K^{A^b} actually takes A to A^{bb}. We shall abbreviate our notation for this map to simply

$$e: \; A \to A^{bb}$$

e is a covered vector space morphism from E to E^{bb}. If $x \in A$, $y \in A$, $x^b \in A^b$, we have

$$\langle x, e(y) \cdot x^b \rangle = \langle e(y), x^b \cdot x \rangle = \langle y, x^b \cdot x \rangle$$

$$= \langle xy, x^b \rangle = \langle x, y \cdot x^b \rangle$$

and so

$$e(y) \cdot x^b = y \cdot x^b$$

and likewise

$$x^b \cdot e(y) = x^b \cdot y$$

if $y \in A$, $x^b \in A^b$.

5. Proposition: Each of the actions

$$A^{bb} \times A^b \to A^b$$
$$(x^{bb}, x^b) \to x^{bb} \cdot x^b$$
$$A^b \times A^{bb} \to A^b$$
$$(x^b, x^{bb}) \to x^b \cdot x^{bb}$$

defines a bounded duality in the category of covered vector spaces.

Proof: This is an easy consequence of Proposition 3.

6. Corollary: Let x^{bb}, $y^{bb} \in A^{bb}$. The two linear forms

$$z^b \to \langle x^{bb}, y^{bb} \cdot z^b \rangle$$
$$z^b \to \langle y^{bb}, z^b \cdot x^{bb} \rangle$$

on A^b are again in A^{bb}.

7. Definition: Let x^{bb}, $y^{bb} \in A^{bb}$. We define

$$x^{bb} \lambda y^{bb}, \ x^{bb} \rho y^{bb} \in A^{bb}$$

by the relations

$$\langle x^{bb} \lambda y^{bb}, z^b \rangle = \langle x^{bb}, y^{bb} \cdot z^b \rangle$$
$$\langle x^{bb} \rho y^{bb}, z^b \rangle = \langle y^{bb}, z^b \cdot x^{bb} \rangle$$

for $x^b \in A^b$.

The map

$$A^{bb} \times A^{bb} \to A^{bb}$$
$$(x^{bb}, y^{bb}) \to x^{bb} \lambda y^{bb}$$

is bilinear and is called the left Arens multiplication on A^{bb}.

<u>The map</u>

$$A^{bb} \times A^{bb} \to A^{bb}$$

$$(x^{bb}, y^{bb}) \to x^{bb} \rho y^{bb}$$

<u>is bilinear and is called the right Arens multiplication on A^{bb}</u>.

We now denote by $L(A^b)$ the K-algebra of all linear transformations of A^b into itself which map sets of A^b to sets of A^b. We denote by $L(E^b)$ the covered algebra whose K-algebra is $L(A^b)$ and whose covering family consists of all balanced, convex subsets $S \subset L(A^b)$ which have the property that for each $F \in A^b$, $\{\phi(x^b): \phi \in S, x^b \in F\}$ is contained in some set of A^b. Then the covered set underlying $L(E^b)$ is isomorphic to the covered set $\mathcal{D}(E^b, E^b)$.

We now define maps

$$\ell: A \to L(A^b)$$

$$r: A \to L(A^b)$$

$$L: A^{bb} \to L(A^b)$$

$$R: A^{bb} \to L(A^b)$$

as follows: If $x \in A$, $x^{bb} \in A^{bb}$, then

$$\ell(x): x^b \to x \cdot x^b$$

$$r(x): x^b \to x^b \cdot x$$

$$L(x^{bb}): x^b \to x^{bb} \cdot x$$

$$R(x^{bb}): x^b \to x \cdot x^{bb}$$

Now if B and C are K-algebras, we define the opposite algebra of C to be the algebra C° whose underlying vector space is the same as that of C, but whose multiplication is the opposite multiplication to that of C. A linear map ϕ: B → C is called a K-algebra antihomomorphism if it is a K-algebra homomorphism to C°. If $(B,\mathcal{B})$ and $(C,\mathcal{C})$ are covered algebras, then a linear map ϕ: B → C is called a covered algebra pair antimorphism if it is a morphism from $(B,\mathcal{B})$ to $(C°,\mathcal{C})$. We denote $(C°,\mathcal{C})$ by $(C,\mathcal{C})°$.

8. Theorem:

1. ℓ is a covered algebra morphism from E to $L(E^b)$.

2. r is a covered algebra anti-morphism from E to $L(E^b)$.

3. L is an injective covered vector space morphism from E^{bb} to $L(E^b)$ and $\ell = Le$.

4. R is an injective covered vector space morphism from E^{bb} to $L(E^b)$ and $r = Re$.

5. If $x^{bb}, y^{bb} \in A^{bb}$, then we have

$$L(x^{bb} \lambda y^{bb}) = L(x^{bb})L(y^{bb})$$

$$R(x^{bb} \rho y^{bb}) = R(y^{bb})R(x^{bb})$$

6. Therefore, left Arens multiplication makes E^{bb} into a covered algebra $E^{bb}\lambda$ and L is an injective covered algebra morphism from $E^{bb}\lambda$ to $L(E^b)$. e is a covered algebra morphism from E to $E^{bb}\lambda$.

7. Likewise, right Arens multiplication makes E^{bb} into a covered algebra $E^{bb}\rho$ and R is an injective covered algebra anti-morphism from $E^{bb}\rho$ to $L(E^b)$. e is a covered algebra morphism from E to $E^{bb}\rho$.

Proof: The statements about the behavior of the respective covering families under the various maps follows easily from the propositions we established. The only thing that is worth checking formally is 5.

Before we do this we establish a lemma.

9. Lemma: Let $x \in A$, $x^b \in A^b$, $x^{bb} \in A^{bb}$. We have

$$x \cdot (x^b \cdot x^{bb}) = (x \cdot x^b) \cdot x^{bb}$$

$$(x^{bb} \cdot x^b) \cdot x = x^{bb} \cdot (x^b \cdot x)$$

Proof: Let $y \in A$. We have

$$\begin{aligned} \langle y, x \cdot (x^b \cdot x^{bb})\rangle &= \langle yx, x^b \cdot x^{bb}\rangle \\ &= \langle x^{bb} \cdot (yx), x^b\rangle \\ &= \langle (x^{bb} \cdot y) \cdot x, x^b\rangle \end{aligned}$$

$$= \langle x^{bb} \cdot y, x \cdot x^b \rangle$$

$$= \langle y, (x \cdot x^b) \cdot x^{bb} \rangle$$

The other half of the proof is entirely similar.

We can now prove (5). Let x^{bb}, $y^{bb} \in A^{bb}$, $z^b \in A^b$, $w \in A$. We have

$$\langle w, L(x^{bb})L(y^{bb})z^b \rangle = \langle w, x^{bb} \cdot (y^{bb} \cdot z^b) \rangle$$

$$= \langle w \cdot x^{bb}, y^{bb} \cdot z^b \rangle$$

$$= \langle x^{bb}, (y^{bb} \cdot z^b) \cdot w \rangle$$

$$= \langle x^{bb}, y^{bb} \cdot (z^b \cdot w) \rangle$$

$$= \langle x^{bb} \lambda y^{bb}, z^b \cdot w) \rangle$$

$$= \langle 1, (x^{bb} \lambda y^{bb}) \cdot (z^b \cdot w) \rangle$$

$$= \langle 1, ((x^{bb} \lambda y^{bb}) \cdot z^b) \cdot w \rangle$$

$$= \langle w, L(x^{bb} \lambda y^{bb}) z^b \rangle$$

So $L(x^{bb})L(y^{bb}) = L(x^{bb} \lambda y^{bb})$. The proof that $R(x^{bb} \rho y^{bb}) = R(y^{bb})R(x^{bb})$ is quite similar.

Lemma 9 is interesting for more reasons than its use in proving Theorem 8. The reason for its interest is that if x^{bb}, $y^{bb} \in A^{bb}$ and $z^b \in A$, we need not have $x^{bb} \cdot (z^b \cdot y^{bb}) = (x^{bb} \cdot z^b) \cdot y^{bb}$, that is, we need not have $L(x^{bb})R(y^{bb}) = R(y^{bb})L(x^{bb})$. Aside from the fact that this makes our notation cumbersome, it is disappointing for more important reasons: For suppose we had $L(x^{bb})R(y^{bb}) = R(y^{bb}) L(x^{bb})$ for all x^{bb}, $y^{bb} \in A^{bb}$. Then, if x^{bb}, $y^{bb} \in A^{bb}$ and $z^b \in A^b$, we would have

$$\langle x^{bb} \lambda y^{bb}, z^b \rangle = \langle x^{bb}, y^{bb} \cdot z^b \rangle$$

$$= \langle 1, (y^{bb} \cdot z^b) \cdot x^{bb} \rangle = \langle 1, y^{bb} \cdot (z^b \cdot x^{bb}) \rangle$$

$$= \langle y^{bb}, z^b \cdot x^{bb} \rangle = \langle x^{bb} \rho y^{bb}, z^b \rangle .$$

That is, we would have

$$x^{bb} \lambda y^{bb} = x^{bb} \rho y^{bb}$$

for all x^{bb}, $y^{bb} \in A^{bb}$. Conversely, if this condition held, we would have, for x^{bb}, $y^{bb} \in A$, $z^{b} \in A^{b}$, $w \in A$,

$$<w, (y^{bb} \cdot z^{b}) \cdot x^{bb}> = <x^{bb} \cdot w, y^{bb} \cdot z^{b}>$$

$$= <x^{bb} \lambda e(w), y^{bb} \cdot z^{b}> = <x^{bb} \lambda e(w) \lambda y^{bb}, z^{b}>$$

$$= <x^{bb} \rho e(w) \rho y^{bb}, z^{b}> = <e(w) \rho y^{bb}, z^{b} \cdot x^{bb}>$$

$$= <w \cdot y^{bb}, z^{b} \cdot x^{bb}> = <w, y^{bb} \cdot (z^{b} \cdot x^{bb})> .$$

That is, we would have

$$x^{bb} \cdot (z^{b} \cdot y^{bb}) = (x^{bb} \cdot z^{b}) \cdot y^{bb}$$

For all x^{bb}, $y^{bb} \in A^{bb}$, $z^{b} \in A^{b}$.

The above line of reasoning can be carried out in a slightly more general context. If one does so, one has part of the proposition we are about to state.

10. Proposition: Let B be a linear subspace of A^{bb} which contains e(A) and is stable under both λ and ρ.

(1) If $y^{bb} \in B$, the map

$$B \to B$$
$$x^{bb} \to x^{bb} \lambda y^{bb}$$

is $\sigma(B,A^{b})$-continuous.

(2) If $x^{bb} \in B$, the map

$$B \to B$$
$$y^{bb} \to x^{bb} \rho y^{bb}$$

is $\sigma(B,A^{b})$-continuous.

(3) L maps B onto an algebra of $\sigma(A^{b},B)$-continuous linear transformations of A^{b} into itself.

(4) R maps B onto an algebra of $\sigma(A^{b},B)$-continuous linear transformations of A^{b} into itself.

We denote by C the algebra of all $\sigma(A^{b},B)$-continuous linear transformations of A^{b} into itself and by T the $\sigma(A^{b},B)$-operator topology on C. (See 4.6.4.)

The following statements about B are equivalent:

(5) If x^{bb}, $y^{bb} \in B$, then

$$x^{bb} \lambda y^{bb} = x^{bb} \rho y^{bb}$$

(6) If x^{bb}, $y^{bb} \in B$ and $z^b \in A^b$, then

$$x^{bb} \cdot (z^b \cdot y^{bb}) = (x^{bb} \cdot z^b) \cdot y^{bb}$$

that is,

$$L(x^{bb})R(y^{bb}) = R(y^{bb})L(x^{bb})$$

(7) The multiplication λ is separately $\sigma(B,A^b)$-continuous on B.

(8) The multiplication ρ is separately $\sigma(B,A^b)$-continuous on B.

(9) The map L is continuous on B with respect to $\sigma(B,A^b)$ and $\mathcal{T}$.

(10) The map L is a topological embedding of $B[\sigma(B,A^b)]$ into $C[\mathcal{T}]$.

(11) The map R is continuous on B with respect to $\sigma(B,A^b)$ and $\mathcal{T}$.

(12) The map R is a topological embedding of $B[\sigma(B,A^b)]$ into $C°[\mathcal{T}]$.

Proof: (1) Let $z^b \in A^b$. The map

$$x^{bb} \to \langle x^{bb} \lambda y^{bb}, z^b \rangle$$

is simply

$$x^{bb} \to \langle x^{bb}, y^{bb} \cdot z^b \rangle$$

and so is $\sigma(B,A^b)$-continuous. So the map

$$x^{bb} \to x^{bb} \lambda y^{bb}$$

is $\sigma(B,A^b)$-continuous. The proof of (2) is similar.

(3) If x^{bb}, $y^{bb} \in A^{bb}$, the map

$$z^b \to \langle x^{bb}, y^{bb} \cdot z^b \rangle$$

is simply the map

$$z^b \to \langle x^{bb} \lambda y^{bb}, z^b \rangle$$

and so is continuous. So the map

$$z^b \to y^{bb} \cdot z^b$$

is $\sigma(A^b, B)$-continuous. The proof of (4) is similar.

The line of reasoning carried out in the paragraphs preceding this proposition is valid, word by word, for B in place of A^{bb}. So (5) is equivalent to (6).

(5) → (7) and (5) → (8) by (1) and (2).

If $z^b \in A^b$, then we have $\langle x^{bb}, z^b\rangle = \langle 1, x^{bb} \cdot z^b\rangle = \langle 1, z^b \cdot x^{bb}\rangle$ for all $x^{bb} \in A^{bb}$. This means that (9) ↔ (10) and (11) ↔ (12).

By symmetry, it remains to prove that (7) → (9) → (6). **But** if (7) holds and if $x^{bb} \in A^{bb}$, $z^b \in A^b$, the map

$$y^{bb} \to \langle x^{bb}, y^{bb} \cdot z^b\rangle$$

is just

$$y^{bb} \to \langle x^{bb} \lambda y^{bb}, z^b\rangle$$

which, assuming (7), is continuous so (9) holds. If (9) holds, then, given $z^b \in A^b$, $y^{bb} \in A^{bb}$, the two maps

$$x^{bb} \to x^{bb} \cdot (z^b \cdot y^{bb})$$

$$x^{bb} \to (x^{bb} \cdot z^b) \cdot y^{bb}$$

are $\sigma(B, A^b) - \sigma(A^b, B)$ continuous by (4). But, by Lemma 9, these two maps agree on e(A). Since e(A) is $\sigma(B, A^b)$-dense in B, it follows that (6) holds.

We recall that $E^{bb}[\sigma(A^{bb}, A^b)]$ is a compactly covered locally convex space. Therefore, if we denote by $\overline{e(E)}$ the cover-closed envelope of e(E) in E^{bb}, w.r.t. $\sigma(A^{bb}, A^b)$ it follows that $\overline{e(E)}[\sigma(A^{bb}, A^b)]$ is a compactly covered locally convex space. We have the following theorem:

11. Theorem: The following two statements are equivalent:

(1) For each $z^b \in A^b$, E and E have the double limit property in the duality

$$A \times A \to K$$

$$(x,y) \to \langle xy, z^b\rangle$$

over K in the category of covered vector spaces.

(2) *For each $F \in A$ and each $x^b \in A^b$, the set $F \cdot x^b$ is relatively $\sigma(A^b, sp(\overline{e(E)}))$-compact in A^b.*

(3) *For each $F \in A$ and each $x^b \in A^b$, the set $x^b \cdot F$ is relatively $\sigma(A^b, sp(\overline{e(E)}))$-compact in A^b.*

(4) *$sp(\overline{e(E)})$ is closed under both left and right Arens multiplication and they coincide on this algebra.*

(5) *$E[\sigma(A,A^b)]$ is compactifiable in the category covered locally convex algebras.*

Proof: (4) → (5) → (1) is rather clear.

Now, for each $z^b \in A^b$, we have a map

$$A \times A \to K$$

$$(x,y) \to \langle xy, z^b \rangle$$

which defines a duality in the category of covered vector spaces over the uniformized object K. Associated with this particular duality is an extension context

$$\begin{array}{ccc} C & \longrightarrow & E \\ \downarrow & & \downarrow \\ A^b & \longrightarrow & K^A \end{array} \qquad \begin{array}{ccc} E & \longleftarrow & D \\ \downarrow & & \downarrow \\ K^A & \longleftarrow & A^b \end{array}$$

where C = D = E and where

$$j_{CA^b}: \quad x \to z^b \cdot x$$

$$j_{DA^b}: \quad x \to y \cdot z^b$$

Therefore, if $x^{bb} \in A^{bb}$, $y^{bb} \in A^{bb}$, we have

$$^t j_{DA^b}\, x^{bb}: \quad y \to \langle x^{bb}, y \cdot z^b \rangle$$

$$^t j_{CA^b}\, y^{bb}: \quad x \to \langle y^{bb}, z^b \cdot x \rangle$$

That is,

$$ {}^{t}j_{DA}{}^{b}\, x^{bb} = z^{b} \cdot x^{bb} $$

$$ {}^{t}j_{CA}{}^{b}\, y^{bb} = y^{bb} \cdot z^{b} $$

Therefore, C and D are compatible in this context and, by Theorem 6.6 and Proposition 5.3, C and D have the DLP if and only if we have

$$ <x^{bb}, y^{bb} \cdot z^{b}> = <y^{bb}, z^{b} \cdot x^{bb}> $$

for all x^{bb}, $y^{bb} \in \overline{sp(e(E))}$, that is, if and only if

$$ <x^{bb} \lambda y^{bb}, z^{b}> = <x^{bb} \rho y^{bb}, z^{b}> $$

for all x^{bb}, $y^{bb} \in \overline{sp(e(E))}$.

Therefore, statement (1) holds if and only if we have

$$ x^{bb} \lambda y^{bb} = x^{bb} \rho y^{bb} $$

for all x^{bb}, $y^{bb} \in \overline{sp(e(E))}$.

(1) $\leftrightarrow$ (2) $\leftrightarrow$ (3) by Corollary 6.7.

It only remains to show that these statements imply that $\overline{sp(e(E))}$ is closed under λ. But, since the map

$$ x^{bb} \to x^{bb} \lambda e(y) $$

is $\sigma(A^{bb}, A^{b})$-continuous for each $y \in A$, we have

$$ x^{bb} \lambda e(y) \in \overline{sp(e(E))} $$

for all $x^{bb} \in \overline{sp(e(E))}$, $y \in A$. But this implies (since $\lambda = \rho$ on $\overline{sp(e(E))}$) that

$$ x^{bb} \rho e(y) \in \overline{sp(e(E))} $$

For all $x^{bb} \in \overline{sp(e(E))}$, $y \in A$. The continuity of each map

$$ y^{bb} \to x^{bb} \rho y^{bb} $$

now completes the proof.

Perhaps the strongest reason for being interested in the above theorem is the following: We denote by T_A the topology on A^b of uniform convergence on sets of $\mathcal{A}$. $A^b[T_A]$ is a locally convex space and, by 3.4.3, it is complete. The homomorphism ℓ gives a topological embedding of A into the algebra $L(A^b[T_A])$ where A is given the topology $\sigma(A,A^b)$ and $L(A^b[T_A])$ is given the $\sigma(A^b,A^{b'})$-operator topology, $A^{b'}$ denoting the dual of $A^b[T_A]$. This dual is, of course, simply $sp(\overline{e(E)})$ and every equicontinuous set in it is contained in some set of $c(\overline{e(E)})$-every set of which is equicontinuous. If any (hence all) of the statements of Theorem 11 is true, then $c(\overline{e(E)})$ is stable under multiplication and L is a topological embedding of $sp(\overline{e(E)})$ into $L(A^b[T_A])$, where the topologies are $\sigma(A^{b'},A^b)$ and the $\sigma(A^b,A^{b'})$-operator topology. Moreover, if $F\in\mathcal{A}$, $\ell(F)$ is relatively compact in $L(A^b[T_A])$ with respect to the $\sigma(A^b,A^{b'})$-operator topology. Since this latter statement implies statement (5) of Theorem 11, it is therefore equivalent to any of the statements of Theorem 11. We have proved the following corollary.

12. Corollary: The homomorphism

$$\ell: \ A \to L(A^b[T_A])$$

is a topological embedding with respect to $\sigma(A,A^b)$ and the $\sigma(A^b,A^{b'})$-operator topology. Statements (1) through (5) of Theorem 11 hold if and only if $\ell(F)$ is relatively compact in $L(A^b[T_A])$ for each $F\in\mathcal{A}$.

13. Definition: By a bornological algebra we mean a K-algebra A together with a separated, bornological topology on A which makes the bounded sets stable under multiplication.

It is a triviality to check that if A is a bornological algebra then

(1) Each bounded set of A acts as an equicontinuous set of linear maps of A into itself via left or right multiplication.

(2) A linear form on A is continuous if and only if it is bounded on bounded sets.

If F is a locally convex space, then <u>the bidual of F</u> is defined to be the dual of $F'[\beta(F',F)]$.

We can consider a bornological algebra A as a covered vector space by taking the covering family $\mathcal{A}$ to be all balanced, convex, bounded sets. In that case, we have $A' = A^b$ and $\mathcal{A}^b$ is all $\beta(A',A)$-bounded sets of A'. We can then immediately state the following theorem:

14. Theorem: *Let A be a bornological algebra.*

(1) *$A'[\beta(A',A)]$ is a complete locally convex space.*

(2) *The homomorphism*

$$\ell: \quad A \to L(A'[\beta(A',A)])$$

is a topological embedding with respect to $\sigma(A,A')$ and the $\sigma(A',A'')$-operator topology.

The following five statements are equivalent:

(3) *For every pair $\{x_i\}$, $\{y_j\}$ of bounded sequences in A and every form $z \in A'$, the double limit property holds for $\{\langle x_i y_j, z\rangle\}$ in K.*

(4) *A" is closed under both left and right Arens multiplication and these coincide on A".*

(5) *For each bounded set $B \subset A$, $\ell(B)$ is relatively compact in $L(A'[\beta(A',A)])$ with respect to the $\sigma(A',A'')$-operator topology.*

(6) *For each bounded set $B \subset A$ and each form $\phi \in A'$, $B \cdot \phi$ is relatively $\sigma(A',A'')$-compact in A'.*

(7) *For each bounded set $B \subset A$ and each form $\phi \in A'$, $\phi \cdot B$ is relatively $\sigma(A',A'')$-compact in A'.*

We could replace statement (3) in the above theorem with a variant which a simple application of one of the forms of the Hahn-Banach theorem will prove to be equivalent to (3). We say that <u>the convex double sequence property holds for a double sequence</u> $\{a_{ij}\}$ <u>in a locally convex space</u> $E[\mathcal{T}]$ if for every neighborhood U of 0 in E, every pair C, D of convex subsets of E such that $(C+U)\cap D = \emptyset$ and every subsequence $\{a_{m_i n_j}\}$ of $\{a_{ij}\}$, one of the following statements is false:

(a) For every $i \geq 1$, $\{a_{m_i n_j}\}_j$ is eventually in C

(b) For every $j \geq 1$, $\{a_{m_i n_j}\}_i$ is eventually in D

Then statement (3) of the above theorem is equivalent to

(3') For every pair $\{x_i\}$, $\{y_j\}$ of bounded sequences in A, the convex double sequence property holds for $\{x_i y_i\}$ in A.

In the particular case where A is a <u>normed algebra</u>, i.e., a K-algebra together with a norm $||\cdot||$ such that $||1|| = 1$ and $||xy|| \leq ||x||\ ||y||$ for all $x, y \in A$, we will have $A'' = A^{bb}$ and so statement (4) can be simplified somewhat. Statement (1) can be replaced with the well known fact that A' is a Banach space in its strong topology.

§8. <u>A Generalized Eberlein-Grothendieck Theorem</u>

We noted at the end of Section 6 that if <A,B> is a duality in a Cartesian category $\mathcal{C}$ over a uniformized object $E[\mathcal{U}]$ and if C, resp. D, is a subobject of A, resp. B, then we have no way of knowing how to choose an extension context

$$\begin{array}{ccc} C & \longrightarrow & A \\ \downarrow & & \downarrow \\ M & \longrightarrow & E^D \end{array} \qquad \begin{array}{ccc} B & \longleftarrow & D \\ \downarrow & & \downarrow \\ E^C & \longleftarrow & N \end{array}$$

in such a way that

(1) Each map in M, resp. N, satisfies some uniform continuity condition with respect to a given uniform structure on spA, resp. spB.

(2) C and D are compatible in this context.

The following theorem will give us the kind of criteria we need. It is a generalization of the Eberlein-Grothendieck Theorem on weak compactness in the theory of locally convex spaces.

(See Köthe [1] 24.2.) In order to make this clear, we will state and prove this latter theorem as a corollary of the general theorem.

1. Lemma: Let $<X,Y>$ be a duality of sets over a precompact uniform space $E[\mathcal{U}]$.

Suppose that X and Y have the DSP in this duality.

Then every function in $\overline{r_X(X)}$ is $\sigma(X,\mathcal{U})$-$\mathcal{U}$ uniformly continuous on Y and every function in $\overline{r_Y(Y)}$ is $\sigma(Y,\mathcal{U})$-$\mathcal{U}$ uniformly continuous on X.

Proof: It is easy to see that we may assume $E[\mathcal{U}]$ is compact.

We suppose that the conclusion of the lemma is not true. We will show that the DSP does not hold. So we suppose that there is some $v \in \overline{r_Y(Y)}$ which is not $\sigma(Y,\mathcal{U})$-$\mathcal{U}$ uniformly continuous on X.

There is a continuous pseudo-metric g on E with the property that for every finite set $F \subset Y$ and every $V \in \mathcal{U}$ there exists some $(x,z) \in N(F,V)$ such that $g(v(x), v(z)) \geq 1$. Therefore, we can, by recursion, choose sequences $\{x_i\}$ in X, $\{z_i\}$ in X and $\{y_j\}$ in Y such that the following conditions hold:

(1) $g(<x_i,y_j>, <z_i,y_j>) \leq \frac{1}{i}$ for $1 \leq j < 1$

(2) $g(<x_i,y_j>, v(x_i)) \leq \frac{1}{j}$ for $1 \leq i \leq j$

(3) $g(<z_i,y_j>, v(z_i)) \leq \frac{1}{j}$ for $1 \leq i \leq j$

(4) $g(v(x_i), v(z_i)) \geq 1$ for $i \geq 1$.

Now let (ϕ, X^*) denote a completion of the (precompact) uniform space $X[\sigma(Y,\mathcal{U})]$. For each $y \in Y$, there is a unique uniformly continuous function

$$y^*: \quad X^* \to E$$

such that

$$y^*\phi(x) = <x,y> \quad (x \in X)$$

Since, if $N^* = \{y_j^*: \ j \geq 1\}$, the uniform structure $\sigma(N^*,g)$ on X^* is pseudo-metrizable and, being weaker than the original uniform structure on X^*, countably compact, there is a point $w \in X^*$ and a strictly increasing sequence $\{k_i\}$ of integers such that

(5) $$g(<x_{k_i}, y_j>, y_j^*(w)) \overset{i}{\to} 0 \quad (j \geq 1)$$

But then (1) implies

(6) $$g(<z_{k_i}, y_j>, y_j^*(w)) \overset{i}{\to} 0 \quad (j \geq 1).$$

Now, since E[g] is countably compact, we may choose a strictly increasing sequence $\{n_j\}$ of integers and a point $u \in E$ such that

(7) $$g(y_{n_j}^*(w), u) \overset{j}{\to} 0$$

Now, by (4), at least one of the following statements is true:

(4') There is a subsequence $\{x_{r_i}\}$ of $\{x_{k_i}\}$ such that

$$g(v(x_{r_i}), u) \geq \frac{1}{2} \quad (i \geq 1)$$

(4") There is a subsequence $\{z_{s_i}\}$ of $\{z_{k_i}\}$ such that

$$g(v(z_{s_i}), u) \geq \frac{1}{2} \quad (i \geq 1).$$

We may assume that (4') is true. By taking a subsequence if necessary, we may also assume that there is some $e \in E$ such that

(8) $$g(v(x_{r_i}), e) \overset{i}{\to} 0$$

But now, with respect to g, we have

(2') $$\lim_j <x_{r_i}, y_{n_j}> = v(x_{r_i})$$

(8') $$\lim_i \lim_j <x_{r_i}, y_{n_j}> = e$$

(5') $$\lim_i <x_{r_i}, y_{n_j}> = y_{n_j}^*(w)$$

(7') $$\lim_j \lim_i <x_{r_i}, y_{n_j}> = u$$

And, by (4') and (8)

$$g(e,u) \geq \frac{1}{2} \tag{9}$$

Therefore, by Proposition 5.3, the proof is complete.

By rights, the above lemma could be our theorem. But since the corollary of this lemma which we will soon state is the form we want, it will be called the theorem. It is equivalent to the lemma. First, however, let us introduce a definition.

2. Definition: Let $\mathcal{C}$ be a Cartesian category and let u be a uniformizing rule for $\mathcal{C}$. By a local duality in $\mathcal{C}_u$, we mean a duality in $\mathcal{C}_u^{\ell}$. That is, we mean a locally uniform duality $\langle A[\mathcal{V}], B[\mathcal{W}]\rangle$ over $E[\mathcal{U}]$ in $\mathcal{C}$, where $\mathcal{V}\in u(A)$, $\mathcal{W}\in u(B)$, $\mathcal{U}\in u(E)$.

3. Theorem: Let $\mathcal{C}$ be a Cartesian category and let u be a uniformizing rule for $\mathcal{C}$ which gives $\mathcal{C}$ cover-closed dual objects.

Let $\langle A[\mathcal{V}], B[\mathcal{W}]\rangle$ be a bounded local duality in $\mathcal{C}_u$ over a compactly covered object $E[\mathcal{U}]$.

If A and B have the DSP in this duality, then the following statements are true.

(1) $csp(\overline{r_A(A)})$ is a compactly covered subobject of $\mathcal{LD}(B[\mathcal{W}], E[\mathcal{U}])$ with respect to the product structure on $E[\mathcal{U}]^B$.

(2) $csp(\overline{r_B(B)})$ is a compactly covered subobject of $\mathcal{LD}(A[\mathcal{V}], E[\mathcal{U}])$ with respect to the product structure on $E[\mathcal{U}]^A$.

4. Corollary: (The Eberlein-Grothendieck Theorem.) Let $E[\mathcal{T}]$ be a separated, complete locally convex space. Let $\mathcal{B}$ denote the family of all equicontinuous subsets of E'. Let $\mathcal{A}$ be a directed covering of E by bounded sets.

The following statements are equivalent:

(1) Each set of $\mathcal{A}$ is relatively $\sigma(E,E')$-countably compact.

(2) In the canonical duality $\langle E,E'\rangle$ over K, $(E,\mathcal{A})$ and $(E',\mathcal{B})$ have the DLP.

(3) Each set of $\mathcal{A}$ is relatively $\sigma(E,E')$-compact.

Proof: This is a simple matter of applying 3.4.6, Lemma 1, Proposition 6.3, and the fact that $E'^*[\sigma(E'^*,E')]$ is complete.

§9. Extension Theorems

If we apply Corollary 6.7 and Theorem 8.3, the following theorem is almost immediate:

1. *Theorem*: *Let $\mathcal{C}$ be a Cartesian category and let u be a uniformizing rule for $\mathcal{C}$ which gives $\mathcal{C}$ cover-closed dual objects.*

Let $\langle A[\mathcal{V}], B[\mathcal{W}]\rangle$ be a bounded local duality in $\mathcal{C}_u$ over a compactly covered object $E[\mathcal{U}]$.

The following statements are equivalent:

(1) *A and B have the DSP in this duality.*

(2) *In the extension context*

$$\begin{array}{ccc} A & \longrightarrow & A \\ \downarrow & & \downarrow \\ M & \longrightarrow & E^B \end{array} \qquad\qquad \begin{array}{ccc} B & \longleftarrow & B \\ \downarrow & & \downarrow \\ E^A & \longleftarrow & N \end{array}$$

where M is all locally $\mathcal{W}$-$\mathcal{U}$ uniformly continuous morphisms in Mor(B,E) and N is all locally $\mathcal{V}$-$\mathcal{U}$ uniformly continuous morphisms in Mor(A,E), A and B have the extension property.

(3) *In the extension context given in (2), if $F \in c(A)$ then $r_A(F)$ is relatively $\sigma(\overline{e_{BM}(B)},\mathcal{U})$-compact in M.*

(4) *In the extension context given in (2), if $G \in c(B)$ then $r_B(G)$ is relatively $\sigma(\overline{e_{AN}(A)},\mathcal{U})$-compact in N.*

Proof: All that needs to be argued is the fact that either (3) or (4) implies that A and B are compatible in the context of (2). It suffices to show that (3) → (1) and (4) → (1). We will show (3) → (1), the other case being symmetric.

Suppose (3) holds. If we consider the natural duality

$$\langle M, \overline{e_{BM}(B)}\rangle$$

then (1) holds by Lemma 6.4 and compactness.

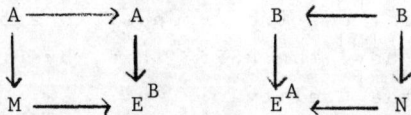

2. Corollary: Let $\mathcal{C}$ be a Cartesian category and let u be a uniformizing rule for $\mathcal{C}$ which gives $\mathcal{C}$ cover-closed dual objects.

Let $\langle A[\mathcal{V}], B[\mathcal{W}]\rangle$ be a bounded local duality in $\mathcal{C}_u$ over an object $E[\mathcal{U}]$.

Let $(i, \tilde{A}[\tilde{\mathcal{V}}])$, resp. $(j, \tilde{B}[\tilde{\mathcal{W}}])$, resp. $(k, \tilde{E}[\tilde{\mathcal{U}}])$, be a compactly covered local reflection of $A[\mathcal{V}]$, resp. $B[\mathcal{W}]$, resp. $E[\mathcal{U}]$ with respect to u.

If A and B have the DSP in this duality, then there is a bounded local duality $\langle \tilde{A}[\tilde{\mathcal{V}}], \tilde{B}[\tilde{\mathcal{W}}]\rangle$ in $\mathcal{C}_u$ over $\tilde{E}[\tilde{\mathcal{U}}]$ such that for all $x \in spA$, $y \in spB$, we have

$$k(\langle x,y\rangle) = \langle i(x), j(y)\rangle$$

If $\tilde{E}[\tilde{\mathcal{U}}]$ is a local compactification of $E[\mathcal{U}]$, then the converse is also true.

Proof: The last remark follows from Propositions 5.3 and 6.3.

Now suppose A and B have the DSP. Then, by Proposition 5.3, A and B have the DSP in the duality

$$(x,y) \to k(\langle x,y\rangle) .$$

So it suffices to assume that $E[\mathcal{U}] = \tilde{E}[\tilde{\mathcal{U}}]$, $k = Id_E$.

Let M be all locally $\mathcal{W}$-$\mathcal{U}$ uniformly continuous morphisms in Mor(B,E), N all locally $\mathcal{V}$-$\mathcal{U}$ uniformly continuous morphisms in Mor(A,E). We consider the extension context

$$\begin{array}{ccccccc} A & \longrightarrow & A & \quad & B & \longleftarrow & B \\ \downarrow & & \downarrow & & \downarrow & & \downarrow \\ M & \longrightarrow & E^B & & E^A & \longleftarrow & N \end{array}$$

By Theorem 1, A and B have the extension property in this context.

By Proposition 4.4, we have a local duality $\langle \overline{e_{AN}(A)}, \overline{e_{BM}(B)}\rangle$ in $\mathcal{C}_u$ over $E[\mathcal{U}]$ with respect to the product uniform structures. Moreover $\langle e_{AN}(x), e_{BM}(y)\rangle = \langle x,y\rangle$ $(x \in spA, y \in spB)$.

But $\overline{e_{AN}(A)}$ and $\overline{e_{BM}(B)}$ are compactly covered and, by the choice of M and N, e_{AN} and e_{BM} are locally uniformly continuous morphisms with respect to $\mathcal{V}$ and $\mathcal{W}$. The proof is now completed by appealing to the definition of a compactly covered local reflection and defining the new duality in the obvious way.

3. Corollary: Let $\mathcal{C}$ be a Cartesian category and let u be a uniformizing rule for $\mathcal{C}$ which gives $\mathcal{C}$ cover-closed dual objects.

Let <A[$\mathcal{V}$], B[$\mathcal{W}$]> be a bounded duality in $\mathcal{C}_u$ over an object E[$\mathcal{U}$].

Let (i, $\tilde{A}[\tilde{\mathcal{V}}]$), resp. (j, $\tilde{B}[\tilde{\mathcal{W}}]$), resp. (k, $\tilde{E}[\tilde{\mathcal{U}}]$) be a compactly covered reflection of A[$\mathcal{V}$], resp. B[$\mathcal{W}$], resp. E[$\mathcal{U}$] with respect to u.

We suppose that each locally $\mathcal{W}$-$\mathcal{U}$ uniformly continuous morphism in Mor(B,E) is uniformly continuous and each locally $\mathcal{V}$-$\mathcal{U}$ uniformly continuous morphism in Mor(A,E) is uniformly continuous.

If A and B have the DSP in this duality, then there is a bounded duality <$\tilde{A}[\tilde{\mathcal{V}}]$, $\tilde{B}[\tilde{\mathcal{W}}]$> in $\mathcal{C}_u$ over $\tilde{E}[\tilde{\mathcal{U}}]$ such that for all $x \in$ spA, $y \in$ spB, we have

$$k(<x,y>) = <i,(x), j(y)>$$

Proof: This proof is an obvious variant of that of Corollary 2 and will be omitted.

The rest of this section will be devoted to briefly treated examples of the above results. The next section will be devoted to one example which will be treated in more detail.

Corollary 2 is a generalization of a result by Pták (Pták, V. [2]) which it implies immediately and which we will now state. We will remark, however, that Pták's result stated more than we will state right now. The rest of his result will be stated in §6.7.

Because of the obvious way in which Corollary 2 generalizes Pták's result, we will call it the Generalized Pták Extension Theorem.

4. Example: (The Pták Extension Theorem.) Let X[$\mathcal{T}$] and Y[$\mathcal{S}$] be topological spaces. Let (i, βX), resp. (j, βY) be a Stone-Čech compact reflection of X[$\mathcal{T}$], resp. Y[$\mathcal{S}$].

Let

$$<,>: \quad X \times Y \to K$$

be a separately continuous map from $X \times Y$ to a bounded subset of K.

The following statements are equivalent:

(1) X and Y have the DLP in this duality.

(2) There is a separately continuous map

$$<,>: \quad \beta X \times \beta Y \to K$$

such that

$$<x,y> = <i(x), j(y)> \quad (x \in X, \; y \in Y).$$

One could, of course, state an obvious variant of Pták's theorem for Samuel compact reflections. We shall refrain from doing so.

5. <u>Example</u>: Let $<(X,\mathcal{A}), (Y,\mathcal{B})>$ be a bounded duality over K in the category of covered vector spaces over K.

We denote by $\tilde{X}$ a completion of $X[\mathcal{N}(\mathcal{B})]$ and by $\tilde{Y}$ a completion of $Y[\mathcal{N}(\mathcal{A})]$. We denote by X' the dual space of $X[\mathcal{N}(\mathcal{B})]$ and by Y' the dual space of $Y[\mathcal{N}(\mathcal{A})]$.

The following two statements are equivalent:

(1) $(X,\mathcal{A})$ and $(Y,\mathcal{B})$ have the DLP in this duality.

(2) There is a bilinear map

$$\phi: \quad Y' \times X' \to K$$

which satisfies the following two conditions:

(a) ϕ is $\sigma(Y', \tilde{Y})$-continuous in the first variable and $\sigma(X', \tilde{X})$-continuous in the second variable.

(b) $\phi(r_X(x), r_Y(y)) = <x,y>$ for all $x \in X$, $y \in Y$.

<u>Proof</u>: Apply Theorem 1 and Corollary 3.4.5.

§10. An Application: Weakly Almost Periodic Linear Forms on a Covered Locally Convex Algebra

Throughout this section, we will be interested in the (Cartesian) category of covered algebras. We will be interested in two uniformizing rules for this category. One rule, denoted u, will assign to each covered algebra $E = (A,\mathcal{A})$ the set $u(E)$ of all locally convex topologies on A which make each set of $\mathcal{A}$ bounded and make the multiplication of A separately continuous. If $E = (A,\mathcal{A})$ is a covered algebra and $\mathcal{U}\in u(E)$, then we will call $E[\mathcal{U}]$ a covered locally convex algebra (see 2.5.8). The other rule, denoted w, will assign to each covered algebra $E = (A,\mathcal{A})$ the set of all weak topologies in $u(E)$. If E is a covered algebra and $\mathcal{U}\in w(E)$, then we will call $E[\mathcal{U}]$ covered weak locally convex algebra (see 2.5.8).

1. Notation: Throughout this section, $E[\mathcal{T}]$ will denote a fixed covered locally convex algebra, where $E = (A,\mathcal{A})$. We adopt also the notation of definition 4.6.6. A" will denote the dual of $A'[\mathcal{T}_{\mathcal{A}}]$ (and also of $\tilde{A}'[\mathcal{T}_{\mathcal{A}}]$).

As in Section 7, we define actions

$$A \times \tilde{A}' \to \tilde{A}'$$

$$(x,\phi) \to x \cdot \phi$$

$$\tilde{A}' \times A \to \tilde{A}'$$

$$(\phi,x) \to \phi \cdot x$$

via the relations

$$\langle xy,\phi\rangle = \langle x,y \cdot \phi\rangle = \langle y, \phi \cdot x\rangle \quad (x, y\in A, \phi\in \tilde{A}') .$$

Since $\mathcal{A}$ is stable under multiplication, the maps

$$\tilde{A}' \to \tilde{A}'$$

$$\phi \to x \cdot \phi$$

$$\phi \to \phi \cdot x$$

are $\mathcal{T}_{\mathcal{A}}$-continuous. In fact it is easy to check that each set of $\mathcal{A}$ acts as an equicontinuous family. For we have, for instance,

$$x \cdot \phi \in F^{o} \forall x \in G \leftrightarrow |\langle yx, \phi\rangle| \leq 1 \forall x \in G,\ y \in F \leftrightarrow \phi \in (FG)^{o}$$

We can define actions

$$A \times A'' \to A''$$

$$(x, \alpha) \to x \cdot \alpha$$

$$A'' \times A \to A''$$

$$(\alpha, x) \to \alpha \cdot x$$

via the relations

$$\langle \alpha, x \cdot \phi\rangle = \langle \alpha \cdot x, \phi\rangle$$

$$\langle \alpha\ \ \phi \cdot x\rangle = \langle x \cdot \alpha, \phi\rangle$$

for $x \in A$, $\alpha \in A''$, $\phi \in \tilde{A}'$. Moreover, since each set of A acts as a T_A-equicontinuous family on $\tilde{A}'$, it follows that <u>if $F \in A$ and if $G \subset A''$ is T_A-equicontinuous then $F \cdot G$ and $G \cdot F$ are T_A-equicontinuous</u>.

Now let $\alpha \in A''$, $\phi \in \tilde{A}'$. Then, as in Section 7, we can define linear forms on A as follows:

$$x \to \langle \alpha \cdot x, \phi\rangle = \langle \alpha, x \cdot \phi\rangle$$

$$x \to \langle x \cdot \alpha, \phi\rangle = \langle \alpha, \phi \cdot x\rangle$$

However, <u>it need not happen that these forms are in $\tilde{A}'$</u>, unlike §7. (It is precisely this difficulty which forced us to wait until after §8 to handle the case for covered algebras other than bornological algebras.) <u>It is true however that these forms are in A^b (See §7.)</u>. So we obtain bilinear maps

$$A'' \times \tilde{A}' \to A^b$$

$$(\alpha, \phi) \to \alpha \cdot \phi$$

$$\tilde{A}' \times A'' \to A^b$$

$$(\phi, \alpha) \to \phi \cdot \alpha$$

via the relations

$$<x, \alpha \cdot \phi> = <x \cdot \alpha, \phi> = <\alpha, \phi \cdot x>$$

$$<x, \phi \cdot \alpha> = <\alpha \cdot x, \phi> = <\alpha, x \cdot \phi>$$

($x \in A$, $\phi \in \tilde{A}'$, $\alpha \in A''$). Moreover, if <u>$G \subset A''$ is $\mathcal{T}_A$-equicontinuous, then each of the families of maps</u>

$$\tilde{A}' \to A^b$$

$$\phi \to \alpha \cdot \phi (\alpha \in G)$$

$$\phi \to \phi \cdot \alpha (\alpha \in G)$$

is $\mathcal{T}_A$-equicontinuous. For instance, if $F \in \mathcal{A}$, we have $\alpha \cdot \phi \in F^o \forall \alpha \in G \leftrightarrow \phi \in (G \cdot F)^o$.

Finally, we notice that if

$$e: \ A \to A''$$

is the natural evaluation map, then, putting $E'' = (A'', \mathcal{A}'')$ where $\mathcal{A}''$ is the balanced, convex $\mathcal{T}_A$-equicontinuous sets of A'', e is a $\sigma(A, A')$-$\sigma(A'', \tilde{A}')$ locally uniformly continuous morphism from E to E'' and, in fact, <u>(e, E'') is a local compactification of $E[\sigma(A, A')]$ in the category of covered weak locally convex spaces (2.5.7)</u>. For if $(F, \mathcal{C})$ is a compactly covered object in that category and if

$$\phi: \ A \to F$$

is a locally $\sigma(A, A')$-$\sigma(F, F')$ continuous linear map, then

$$t_\phi: \ F' \to \tilde{A}'$$

is $\tau(F', F)$-$\mathcal{T}_A$ continuous and so

$$tt_\phi: \ A'' \to F$$

is $\sigma(A'', \tilde{A}')$-$\sigma(F, F')$ continuous (of course, ${}^{tt}\phi e = \phi$.)

Now fix $\phi \in \tilde{A}'$. We have a natural duality

$$<E, E>_\phi$$

over K given by

$$A \times A \to K$$

$$(x,y) \to <xy, \phi> .$$

With respect to this duality, we have an extension context

$$\begin{array}{ccc} C & \longrightarrow & E \\ \downarrow & & \downarrow \\ \tilde{A}' & \longrightarrow & K^D \end{array} \qquad \begin{array}{ccc} E & \longleftarrow & D \\ \downarrow & & \downarrow \\ K^C & \longleftarrow & \tilde{A}' \end{array}$$

where $C = D = E$ and where, just as in Theorem 7.11, we have

$$j_{C\tilde{A}'}: \quad x \to \phi \cdot x$$

$$j_{D\tilde{A}'}: \quad y \to y \cdot \phi$$

Then, by Theorem 9.1, C and D have the DLP with respect to $<, >_\phi$ if and only if C and D have the extension property in this context.

This latter statement--that C and D have the extension property in this context--really consists of two parts: (See 7.11 again.)

(1) If $\alpha \in A''$, then $\phi \cdot \alpha \in \tilde{A}'$ and $\alpha \cdot \phi \in \tilde{A}'$.

(2) If $\alpha, \beta \in A''$, then $<\alpha, \beta \cdot \phi> = <\beta, \phi \cdot \alpha>$

So we have proved the better part of the following theorem.

2. Theorem: The following five statements are equivalent:

(1) For each set $F \in A$, every pair $\{x_i\}$, $\{y_j\}$ of sequences in F, and every form $\phi \in \tilde{A}'$, the double limit property holds for $\{<x_i y_j, \phi>\}$ in K.

(2) For every pair $\alpha, \beta \in A''$ and every $\phi \in \tilde{A}'$, we have $\phi \cdot \alpha \in \tilde{A}'$, $\beta \cdot \phi \in \tilde{A}'$, and

$$<\alpha, \beta \cdot \phi> = <\beta, \phi \cdot \alpha> ,$$

(3) $E[\sigma(A,A')]$ is locally compactifiable with respect to u.

(4) For each set $F \in A$ and each form $\phi \in \tilde{A}'$, $F \cdot \phi$ is relatively $\sigma(\tilde{A}', A'')$-compact in $\tilde{A}'$.

(5) For each set $F \in A$ and each form $\phi \in \tilde{A}'$, $\phi \cdot F$ is relatively $\sigma(\tilde{A}', A'')$-compact in $\tilde{A}'$.

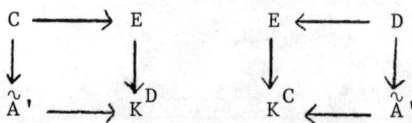

In case these statements hold, then we can define a multiplication in A" by putting

$$\alpha \times \beta: \quad \phi \to \langle \alpha, \beta \cdot \phi \rangle = \langle \beta, \phi \cdot \alpha \rangle .$$

This multiplication makes A" into a K-algebra and is separately $\sigma(A'', \tilde{A}')$-continuous. If F and G are equicontinuous subsets of A", then so is F × G. Hence E" is a covered algebra. (e, E"[$\sigma(A'', \tilde{A}')$]) is a local compactification and an inductive compactly covered reflection of E[$\sigma(A, A')$] with respect to w. It is also an inductive compactly covered reflection of E[$\mathcal{T}$] with respect to w.

Proof: I will comment only on the fact that if G and F are equicontinuous, then so is F × G. This comes from the fact that the family of maps

$$\tilde{A}' \to \tilde{A}'$$

$$\phi \to \beta \cdot \phi \quad (\beta \in G)$$

is equicontinuous. Hence, if it is followed by F, the resulting family is equicontinuous. But this family is just F × G. (The last statement of the theorem comes from Corollary 3.4.8.)

Let us also note that we have a natural homomorphism

$$\ell: \quad A \to L(\tilde{A}'[\mathcal{T}_A])$$

where

$$\ell(x): \quad \phi \to x \cdot \phi$$

and an anti-homomorphism

$$r: \quad A \to L(\tilde{A}'[\mathcal{T}_A])$$

where

$$r(x): \quad \phi \to \phi \cdot x$$

In general, these need not be locally uniformly continuous with respect to the $\sigma(\tilde{A}', A'')$-operator topology and $\sigma(A, A')$. However if the statements of the above theorem are true, then both are locally continuous. Moreover, in this case there is a natural homomorphism

$$L: \quad A'' \to L(\tilde{A}'[T_A])$$

given by

$$L(\alpha): \quad \phi \to \alpha \cdot \phi$$

and an anti-homomorphism

$$R: \quad A'' \to L(\tilde{A}'[T_A])$$

given by

$$R(\alpha): \quad \phi \to \phi \cdot \alpha$$

Both of these maps will be topological embeddings and will map T_A-equicontinuous sets to T_A-equicontinuous sets. We have, of course

$$Re = r \ , \quad Le = \ell \ .$$

3. Definition: If statement (2) of Theorem 2 is true then the multiplication × defined in A" via

$$\langle \alpha \times \beta, \phi \rangle = \langle \alpha, \beta \cdot \phi \rangle = \langle \beta, \phi \cdot \alpha \rangle$$

will be called convolution (or Arens multiplication).

To see the motivation for the name "convolution", let us indulge a little in heuristics: If $\alpha \in A''$, $\phi \in \tilde{A}'$, we write

$$\langle \alpha, \phi \rangle = \int \phi(x) \, d\,\alpha(x)$$

Then statement (2) of the theorem says that the forms

$$\phi \cdot \alpha: \quad y \to \int \phi(xy) \, d\,\alpha(x)$$

$$\beta \cdot \phi: \quad x \to \int \phi(xy) \, d\,\beta(y)$$

are in $\tilde{A}'$ and that we have

$$\iint \phi(xy) \, d\beta(y) d\alpha(x) = \langle \alpha, \beta \cdot \phi \rangle$$

$$= \langle \beta, \phi \cdot \alpha \rangle$$

$$= \iint \phi(xy) \, d\alpha(x) d\beta(y)$$

4. Definition: Let $\phi \in \tilde{A}'$. If, for each pair $\alpha, \beta \in A''$ we have $\phi \cdot \alpha \in \tilde{A}'$, $\beta \cdot \phi \in \tilde{A}'$ and $\langle \alpha, \beta \cdot \phi \rangle = \langle \beta, \phi \cdot \alpha \rangle$, then we say ϕ admits convolutions.

We are going to prove a very striking result about forms $\phi \in \tilde{A}'$ which admit convolutions. But first we will introduce some more notation and some new concepts:

Let $(\psi, F[\sigma(B, B')])$ be an inductive compactly covered reflection of the covered weak locally convex algebra $E[\sigma(A, A')]$ with respect to w, where $F = (B, \beta)$. Since each set of β is contained in the $\sigma(B, B')$-closure of some set of $\psi(\mathcal{A})$, it follows that the transpose map

$$^t\psi: \quad B' \to \tilde{A}'$$

is a $\mathcal{T}_{\mathcal{B}}$-$\mathcal{T}_{\mathcal{A}}$ topological embedding. Moreover, since $F[\sigma(B, \tilde{B}')]$ is also a compactly covered local reflection of $E[\sigma(A, \tilde{A}')]$ with respect to w, it follows that $B' = \tilde{B}'$ and so $B'[\mathcal{T}_{\mathcal{B}}]$ is complete and $^t\psi(B')$ is a closed subspace of $\tilde{A}'[\mathcal{T}_{\mathcal{A}}]$.

5. Definition: A linear form ϕ in $\tilde{A}'$ will be called a locally compactifiable form if $\phi \in {}^t\psi(B')$

Since each set of $\mathcal{B}$ is contained in some $\sigma(B, B')$-compact set of $\mathcal{B}$, it follows that we have $B''=B$. Therefore, if $\phi \in B'$, the maps

$$B \to B'$$

$$x \to x \cdot \phi$$

$$x \to \phi \cdot x$$

are $\sigma(B, B')$-$\sigma(B', B'')$ continuous. Therefore, if $H \in \mathcal{B}$ and $\phi \in B'$ the sets $H \cdot \phi$ and $\phi \cdot H$ are relatively $\sigma(B', B'')$-compact. But since the map $^t\psi$ is $\mathcal{T}_{\mathcal{B}}$-$\mathcal{T}_{\mathcal{A}}$ continuous, it is $\sigma(B', B'')$-$\sigma(\tilde{A}', A'')$ continuous and so the sets $^t\psi(H \cdot \phi)$ and $^t\psi(\phi \cdot H)$ are relatively $\sigma(A', A'')$ compact. But if $G \in \mathcal{A}$ and $\phi \in B'$, we have $G \cdot {}^t\psi(\phi) = {}^t\psi(\psi(G) \cdot \phi)$ and ${}^t\psi(\phi) \cdot G = {}^t\psi(\phi \cdot \psi(G))$. Therefore, it follows that if $G \in \mathcal{A}$ and $\phi \in \mathcal{B}'$, then $G \cdot {}^t\psi(\phi)$ and ${}^t\psi(\phi) \cdot G$ are relatively $\sigma(\tilde{A}', A'')$-compact.

6. Definition: A linear form $\phi \in \tilde{A}'$ will be called left (right) weakly almost periodic if $G \cdot \phi (\phi \cdot G)$ is relatively $\sigma(\tilde{A}', A'')$-compact for each $G \in \mathcal{A}$.

7. Theorem: The following statements about a form $\phi \in \tilde{A}'$ are equivalent.

(1) If $F \in \mathcal{A}$ and if $\{x_i\}$, $\{y_j\}$ are sequences in F, then the the double limit property holds for $\{\langle x_i y_i, \phi\rangle\}$ in K.

(2) ϕ admits convolutions

(3) ϕ is locally compactifiable

(4) ϕ is left weakly almost periodic

(5) ϕ is right weakly almost periodic.

Proof: We have already proved that (1) is equivalent to (2) and that (3) implies (4) and (5). The equivalence of (1), (2), (4) and (5) follows from Theorem 9.1.

It remains to show that (4) implies (3).

Now let C denote the set of all left weakly almost periodic forms in $\tilde{A}'$. C is clearly a linear subspace of $\tilde{A}'$ and $A \cdot C \subset C$. Now let $\phi \in C$, $H \in \mathcal{A}$. We have $H \cdot (H \cdot \phi)^{\infty} \subset (HH \cdot \phi)^{\infty} \subset \tilde{A}'$. Since this latter set is $\sigma(\tilde{A}', A'')$-compact, we have $(H \cdot \phi)^{\infty} \subset C$, and so $H \cdot \phi$ is relatively $\sigma(C, C')$-compact.

We use the notation $\mathcal{T}_{\mathcal{A}}$ also to denote $\mathcal{T}_{\mathcal{A}}|_C$. The natural homomorphism ℓ also defines a homomorphism

$$m: \quad A \to L(C[\mathcal{T}_{\mathcal{A}}])$$

since $A \cdot C \subset C$. If $H \in \mathcal{A}$, then m(H) is $\mathcal{T}_{\mathcal{A}}$-equicontinuous. Hence by 3.2.7, the closure of m(H) in $C[\mathcal{T}_{\mathcal{A}}]^C$ is also $\mathcal{T}_{\mathcal{A}}$-equicontinuous. Hence it is contained in $L(C[\mathcal{T}_{\mathcal{A}}])$. But, since m(H) is a convex subset of $C[\mathcal{T}_{\mathcal{A}}]^C$, its closure in that space coincides with its closure in $C[\sigma(C, C')]^C$. (See Köthe [1], 22.5.) But, since $H \cdot \phi$ is relatively $\sigma(C, C')$-compact for each $\phi \in C$, this latter closure is compact. We have just proved that m(H) is relatively compact in $L(C[\mathcal{T}_{\mathcal{A}}])$ with respect to the $\sigma(C, C')$-operator topology.

If $H \in \mathcal{A}$, $\phi \in C$, the fact that $(H \cdot \phi)^{\infty}$ is $\sigma(C, C')$-compact, forces $\sigma(C, C')|_{H \cdot \phi}$ to coincide with $\sigma(C, A)|_{H \cdot \phi}$. But the map

$$A \to \tilde{A}'$$
$$x \to x \cdot \phi$$

is $\sigma(A, \tilde{A}')$-$\sigma(\tilde{A}', A)$ continuous. Hence, since $\sigma(A, A')|_H = \sigma(A, \tilde{A}')|_H$, it follows that m is locally uniformly continuous on E with respect to $\sigma(A, A')$ and the $\sigma(C, C')$ operator topology.

The above facts, and the definition of an inductive compactly covered reflection force the existence of a homomorphism

$$n\colon \quad B \to \mathcal{L}(C[\mathcal{T}_A])$$

which is uniformly continuous with respect to $\sigma(B, B')$ and the $\sigma(C, C')$-operator topology and which satisfies the condition

$$m = n\psi \ .$$

Now let $\phi \in C$. We define $\theta \in B'$ by

$$\theta\colon \quad B \to K$$
$$x \to (n(x) \cdot \phi)\ (1)$$

Then, if $x \in A$, we have

$$\theta(\psi(x)) = (n\psi(x) \cdot \phi)\ (1)$$
$$= (x \cdot \phi)\ (1) = \phi(x)$$

That is, $\phi = {}^t\psi(\theta)$. So $C \subset {}^t\psi(B')$.

This completes the proof.

8. <u>Definition</u>: If $\phi \in \tilde{A}'$ is left weakly almost periodic, we say simply that <u>ϕ is weakly almost periodic</u>.

Let us notice two things. Since the space C of weakly almost periodic forms is isomorphic to B' via ${}^t\psi$, and B" is simply B, it follows that

(a) $E[\sigma(A, C)]$ is compactifiable with respect to w.

(b) C', with convolution as its multiplication is a compactification of $E[\sigma(A, C)]$ and an inductive compactly covered reflection of $E[\sigma(A, A')]$ with respect to w. It is an inductive compactly covered reflection also of $E[\mathcal{T}]$ with respect to w.

But this is not the only way of representing F. We noticed that the map

$$n: \quad B \to L(C[\mathcal{T}_A])$$

was continuous with respect to the $\sigma(C, C')$-operator topology. But, since $C = {}^t\psi(B')$, n can be viewed as simply being the map

$$n: \quad B \to L(B'[\mathcal{T}_A])$$

defined by

$$n(x): \quad \phi \to x \cdot \phi \ .$$

Since $B'' = B$, this map is a topological embedding with respect to $\sigma(B, B')$ and the $\sigma(B', B'')$-operator topology. That is, our original homomorphism n is an embedding with respect to $\sigma(B, B')$ and the $\sigma(C, C')$-operator topology.

Let us now sum up what we have just done.

9. Theorem: Let C be the space of all weakly almost periodic forms in $\tilde{A}'$.

(1) If $\mathcal{C}'$ is all $\mathcal{T}_A$-equicontinuous subsets of C' which are balanced and convex, then convolution in C' makes $(C', \mathcal{C}')$ into a covered algebra and if

$$e: \quad A \to C'$$

is the evaluation map,

$$(e, (C', \mathcal{C}')[\sigma(C', C)])$$

is an inductive compactly covered reflection of $E[\sigma(A, A')]$ and of $E[\mathcal{T}]$ with respect to w.

(2) $C[\mathcal{T}_A]$ is a complete locally convex space. The homomorphism

$$m: \quad A \to L(C[\mathcal{T}_A])$$

given by

$$m(x): \quad \phi \to x \cdot \phi$$

is a morphism from E to the covered algebra $L(C[T_A])$. (See 4.6.4.) If $\overline{m(E)}$ denotes the cover-closed envelope of m(E) in $L(C[T_A])$ with respect to the σ(C, C')-operator topology and S denotes this topology, then

$$(m, \overline{m(E)}[S])$$

is an inductive compactly covered reflection of E[σ(A, A')] and of E[T] with respect to w.

The usual definition of a locally convex algebra makes it a K-algebra with a locally convex topology and a separately continuous multiplication. If one assumes in addition that the bounded sets are stable under multiplication (as was the case in the bornological algebras defined in §7) then one can apply all the results of this section to E = (A, A) where A is such an algebra and A is the bounded sets. In this case, $T_A = \beta(A', A)$ and $\tilde{A}'$ is the completion of the strong dual. A" is the usual bidual of A.

The following definition should seem justified by Theorem 9.

10. Definition: Any inductive compactly covered reflection of E[T] with respect to w will be called a weakly almost periodic compactly covered reflection of E[T].

The resemblance between this section and Section 4.6 should by now be quite apparent. The following corollary to Theorem 9 establishes the precise relationship between almost periodic and weakly periodic linear forms.

11. Corollary: Let C denote the space of all almost periodic linear forms on E[T] and let (j, G[R]) denote a Bohr compactly covered reflection of E[T].

(1) Each form in C is a weakly almost periodic linear form on E[T]

(2) In fact, C is precisely the space of all weakly almost periodic linear forms on $E[j^{-1}(R)]$

(3) We can introduce a convolution multiplication in C' via the relation

$$\langle \alpha \times \beta, \phi \rangle = \langle \alpha, \beta \cdot \phi \rangle = \langle \beta, \phi \cdot \alpha \rangle$$

for $\alpha, \beta \in C'$, $\phi \in C$. With this multiplication and with $\mathcal{C}'$ denoting the balanced, convex equicontinuous sets in C', $(C', \mathcal{C}')[\sigma(C', C)]$ becomes a compactly covered weak locally convex algebra.

(4) There is a unique covered algebra morphism

$$k\colon \quad G \to (C', \mathcal{C}')$$

which is $\mathcal{R}$-$\sigma(C', C)$ continuous and which satisfies the condition

$$kj = e$$

(5) If $\mathcal{T}_A^o$ denotes the topology on C' of uniform convergence on the compact subsets of C, then the morphism

$$k\colon \quad G \to (C', \mathcal{C}')$$

is an isomorphism with respect to $\mathcal{R}$ and $\mathcal{T}_A^o$ and is an isomorphism with respect to the weak topology on spG and $\sigma(C', C)$.

(6) $(e, (C', \mathcal{C}')[\sigma(C', C)])$ is a weak Bohr compactly covered reflection of $E[\mathcal{T}]$.

Proof: (1) and (2) are quite clear (given a familiarity with this section and Section 4.6), as is (3).

It is not hard to deduce from the equivalence of (1) and (2) in Corollary 4.6.8 that, with $\mathcal{W}$ denoting the weak topology of $\mathcal{R}$, $(j, G[\mathcal{W}])$ is a weakly almost periodic c.c. reflection for $E[\sigma(A, C)]$. This implies (4).

It is also not hard to deduce from the results of Sections 4.5 and 4.6 that $\mathcal{R}$ must be the topology of uniform convergence on the compact sets of $spG'[\mathcal{T}_{c(G)}]$. But since $(e, (C', \mathcal{C}')[\sigma(C', C)])$ is also a weakly periodic compact hull of $E[\sigma(A, C)]$, this statement is equivalent to (5).

(6) follows from (5) and 2.8.8.

12. Corollary: Let C denote the space of all almost periodic linear forms on $E[\mathcal{T}]$, let $\mathcal{C}'$ denote the balanced, convex, equicontinuous sets in C', the dual of $C[\mathcal{T}_A]$, and equip C' with convolution multiplication.

(1) If $\mathcal{T}_A^o$ is the topology on C' of uniform convergence on the compact subsets of $C[\mathcal{T}_A]$, then $(e, (C', \mathcal{C}')[\mathcal{T}_A^o])$ is a Bohr compactly covered reflection of $E[\mathcal{T}]$.

(2) $(e, (C', \mathcal{C}')[\sigma(C', C)])$ is a weak Bohr compactly covered reflection of $E[\mathcal{T}]$.

The results of this section can be used to describe a construction of an inductive compactly covered reflection of $E[\mathcal{T}]$ with respect to the rule u. This can be done as follows:

Let $(k, G[\mathcal{W}])$ be an inductive compactly covered reflection of $E[\mathcal{T}]$ with respect to u, where $G = (C, \mathcal{C})$. Then, by 2.8.8, $(k, G[\sigma(C, C')])$ is an inductive compactly covered reflection of $E[\mathcal{T}]$ with respect to w. Also, since C' can be easily seen to be equal to $\tilde{C}'$ $((k, G[\sigma(C, \tilde{C}')])$ is a compactly covered local reflection of $E[\mathcal{T}])$, it follows that $C'[\mathcal{T}_{\mathcal{C}}]$ is complete. Finally, since each set of $\mathcal{C}$ is $\sigma(C, C')$-complete (in fact, compact) it follows by 3.4.3 that for any directed covering $\mathcal{C}'$ of C' by bounded sets, the locally convex topology $\mathcal{T}_{\mathcal{C}'}$ on C makes each set of $\mathcal{C}$ complete.

It is now a trivial matter to apply 3.5.5 (more properly, to apply Grothendieck's special case concerning locally convex spaces) and obtain the following result:

13. Lemma: (Notation as above.) Let $\mathcal{C}'$ denote the family of all $\mathcal{T}_{\mathcal{C}}$-compact subsets of C'.

$\mathcal{T}_{\mathcal{C}'}$ is the strongest locally convex topology on C with the following two properties:

(1) Each set of $\mathcal{C}$ is $\mathcal{T}_{\mathcal{C}'}$-compact.

(2) $C' = C[\mathcal{T}_{\mathcal{C}'}]'$.

Moreover, $\mathcal{T}_{C'}$ is locally equivalent to $\sigma(C, C')$ and we have

$$x \cdot D, \quad D \cdot x \in \mathcal{C}' \quad (x \in C, \ D \in C').$$

(Hence, $\mathcal{T}_{C'}$ makes the multiplication of C separately continuous.)

The above line of reasoning constitutes a proof of the following theorem:

14. Theorem: Let $(k, G[\mathcal{W}])$ be an inductive compactly covered reflection of $E[\mathcal{T}]$ with respect to u, where $G = (C, C)$.

(1) $(k, G[\sigma(C, C')])$ is a weakly almost periodic compactly covered reflection of $E[\mathcal{T}]$.

(2) $\mathcal{W}$ is precisely the topology on C of uniform convergence on the $\mathcal{T}_C$-compact sets of C'.

15. Corollary: Let P denote the space of all weakly almost periodic linear forms on $E[\mathcal{T}]$ and make $P' = P[\mathcal{T}_A]'$ into a K-algebra via convolution.

We denote by $\mathcal{P}'$ the balanced, convex, equicontinuous subsets of P'. We denote by $\mathcal{T}_A^o$ the topology on P' of compact convergence. We denote by

$$e: \quad A \to P'$$

the evaluation map.

$(e, (P', \mathcal{P}')[\mathcal{T}_A^o])$ is an inductive compactly covered reflection of $E[\mathcal{T}]$ with respect to u.

Chapter 6. LINEAR EXTENSION OF UNIFORM DUALITIES

§1. Synopsis

This chapter is very similar to Chapter 5. The basic object of inquiry, a duality of covered sets over a covered locally convex space, is less general than those of Chapter 5, but the kind of extension that is desired is more difficult.

As in Chapter 5, the problem of extension is first approached internally, within the duality itself. The concept of a linear extension context is introduced in Section 2 and these contexts are reduced, by a canonical process, to extension contexts in the category of covered vector spaces. Therefore, as in Chapter 5, the extension process will break into two steps.

In Section 3, the principal tool that is needed in the extension process is introduced, the notion of the convex double sequence property. Here it is noticed that if, when we reduce our extension context to an extension context of covered vector spaces, we can still assert the convex double sequence property in the new context, then we can proceed as in Chapter 5.

The transition mentioned in the above paragraph is however very non-trivial. In Section 4 we state the crucial lemma we need to do so, based on a combinatorial lemma of Pták. In Section 5, we draw the immediate consequences and prove that, if we are given the first step in the extension process and given the convex double sequence property, then the second step is forced.

In Section 6, the first step in the extension process is handled by means of the convex double sequence property. As in Section 5.8, the crucial theorem turns out to generalize a weak compactness theorem about locally convex spaces, but this time the Pták lemma allows us to generalize the Krein Theorem as well as the Eberlein-Grothendieck Theorem. In order to make this clear, Krein's theorem is proved as a corollary.

In Section 7, the two steps are put together and our linear extension theorems are stated and proved.

In Section 8, the application of Section 5.10 is combined with Krein's Theorem and applied to the theory of weakly almost periodic functions on a covered uniform monoid.

In Section 9, the theory developed in Section 8 is applied to obtain generalizations of some results by DeLeeuw and Glicksberg.

§2. Linear Extension Contexts

1. Definition: By a duality <A, B> of covered sets over a covered vector space E, we mean

(1) Covered sets A and B

(2) A covered vector space E

(3) A duality <A, B> over csp(E) in the category of covered sets.

We mentioned in §2.3 that covered sets have reflections in the category of covered vector spaces. In fact, if $(X, \mathcal{A})$ is a covered set, we can easily construct a (quite familiar) reflection for $(X, \mathcal{A})$. We take F to be the K-vector space with formal basis X and define

$$i: X \to F$$

to be the map which takes $x \in X$ to the corresponding basis element. For each $A \in \mathcal{A}$, let $\nu(A)$ be the balanced, convex hull of $i(A)$ in F. The family $\{\nu(A): A \in \mathcal{A}\}$ is directed. If we let $\mathcal{S}$ be the smallest family which contains this family and is stable under multiplication by scalars, then $(i, (F, \mathcal{S}))$ is a reflection for $(X, \mathcal{A})$.

Now let $(E, \mathcal{T})$ be any covered vector space. We have a function

$$\phi_X: \mathcal{L}(F, E) \to E^X$$
$$k \to k \circ i$$

where $\mathcal{L}(F, E)$ will denote the linear maps from F to E. By the definition of a reflection, ϕ_X is a bijection and ϕ_X maps $\mathrm{Mor}((F, \mathcal{S}), (E, \mathcal{T}))$ onto $\mathrm{Mor}((X, \mathcal{A}), (E, \mathcal{T}))$. With respect to the usual linear structures, ϕ_X *is easily seen to be a linear isomorphism*. Finally, *the map*

$$\phi_X\colon \ \mathrm{Mor}((F, \mathcal{S}), (E, \mathcal{T})) \to \mathrm{Mor}((X, \mathcal{A}), (E, \mathcal{T}))$$

is actually a covered vector space isomorphism

$$\phi_X\colon \ \mathcal{D}((F, \mathcal{S}), (E, \mathcal{T})) \to \mathcal{D}((X, \mathcal{A}), (E, \mathcal{T}))$$

where the linear structures are the obvious ones and the covering families are all balanced, convex, bounded sets of morphisms.

Now suppose that $(Y, \mathcal{B})$ is a covered set and that we are given a duality $\langle (X, \mathcal{A}), (Y, \mathcal{B})\rangle$ over $(E, \mathcal{T})$. ($(E, \mathcal{T})$ is still assumed to be a covered vector space.) Let $(j, (G, \mathcal{V}))$ be a (covered vector space) reflection for $(Y, \mathcal{B})$. Let M be a *linear subspace* of $\mathrm{Mor}((Y, \mathcal{B}), (E, \mathcal{T}))$ which contains $r_X(X)$ and let N be a *linear subspace* of $\mathrm{Mor}((X, \mathcal{A}), (E, \mathcal{T}))$ which contains $r_Y(Y)$. (We abbreviate $r_X = r_{(X,\mathcal{A})}$, $r_Y = r_{(Y,\mathcal{B})}$.)

By the definition of a reflection, we have morphisms

$$\rho_X\colon \ (F, \mathcal{S}) \to (E, \mathcal{T})^Y$$

$$\rho_Y\colon \ (G, \mathcal{V}) \to (E, \mathcal{T})^X$$

such that $r_X = \rho_X \circ i$, $r_Y = \rho_Y \circ j$.

It is reasonably easy to check that we have commutative diagrams:

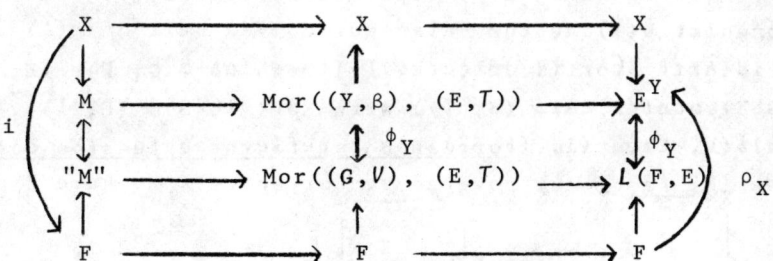

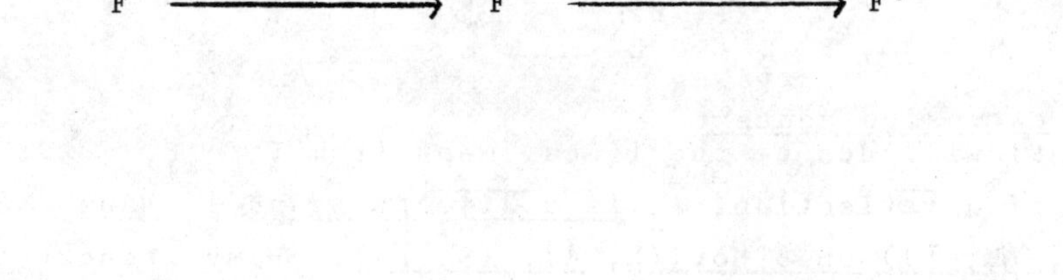

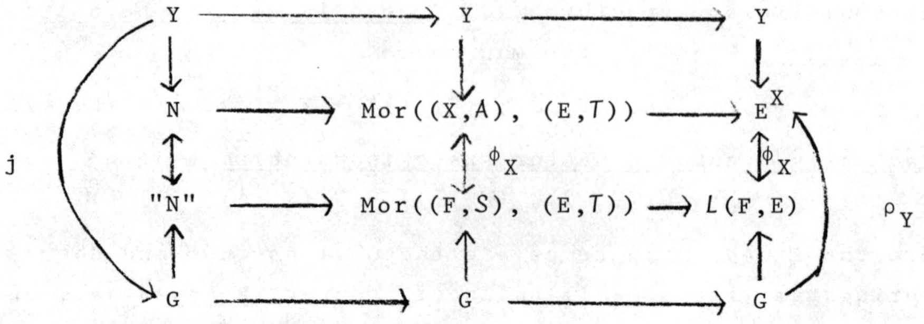

Moreover, if $\alpha = \Sigma_{x \in X} \, \underline{\alpha(x) \cdot x \in F}$ and $\beta = \Sigma_{y \in Y} \, \underline{\beta(y) \cdot y \in G}$, then we have

$$\phi_Y \rho_X \alpha(\beta) = \underset{x \in X}{\Sigma} \, \underset{y \in Y}{\Sigma} \, \alpha(x)\beta(y) \, <x,y>$$

$$= \phi_X \rho_Y \, \beta(\alpha) .$$

Therefore, we can define a bilinear map

$$<, \, >: \quad F \times G \to E$$

$$(\alpha, \, \beta) \to \underset{x}{\Sigma} \, \underset{y}{\Sigma} \, \alpha(x) \, \beta(y) \, <x, \, y>$$

and obtain a duality $<(F, \, S), \, (G, \, \mathcal{B})>$ over $(E, \, T)$ in the category of covered vector spaces. If the duality $<(X, \, A), \, (Y, \, \mathcal{B})>$ is bounded, then so is $<(F, \, S), \, (G, \, V)>$. (This particular statement does not warrant all the trouble we have gone to. But the following ones might:)

If we identify $Mor((Y, \, \mathcal{B}), \, (E, \, T))$ with $Mor((G, \, V), \, (E, \, T))$, E^Y with $L(G,E)$ $Mor((X, \, A), \, (E, \, T))$ with $Mor((F, \, S), \, (E, \, T))$, and and E^X with $L(F, \, E)$, then, corresponding to the extension context

$$
\begin{array}{ccc}
X & \longrightarrow & X \\
\downarrow & & \downarrow \\
M & \longrightarrow & E^Y
\end{array}
\qquad
\begin{array}{ccc}
Y & \longleftarrow & Y \\
\downarrow & & \downarrow \\
E^X & \longleftarrow & N
\end{array}
$$

we have an extension context

$$
\begin{array}{ccc}
F & \longrightarrow & F \\
\downarrow & & \downarrow \\
M & \longrightarrow L(G,E)
\end{array}
\qquad
\begin{array}{ccc}
F & \longleftarrow & G \\
\downarrow & & \downarrow \\
L(F,E) & \longleftarrow & N
\end{array}
$$

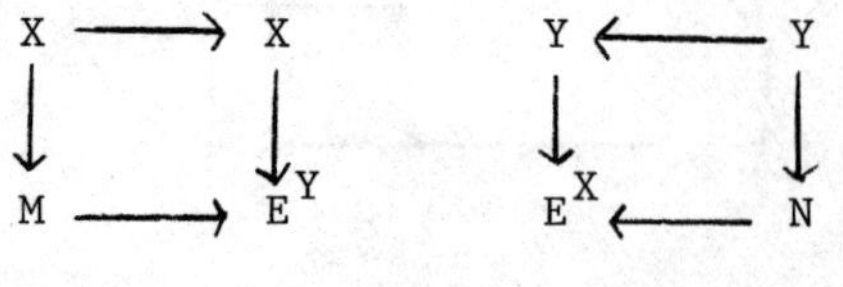

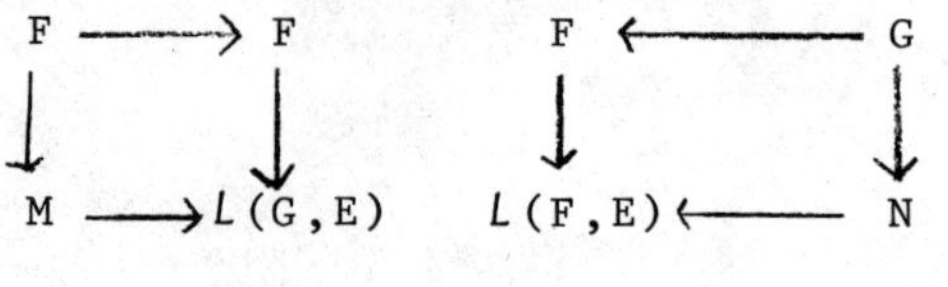

Things get even more interesting if we consider the expanded diagram:

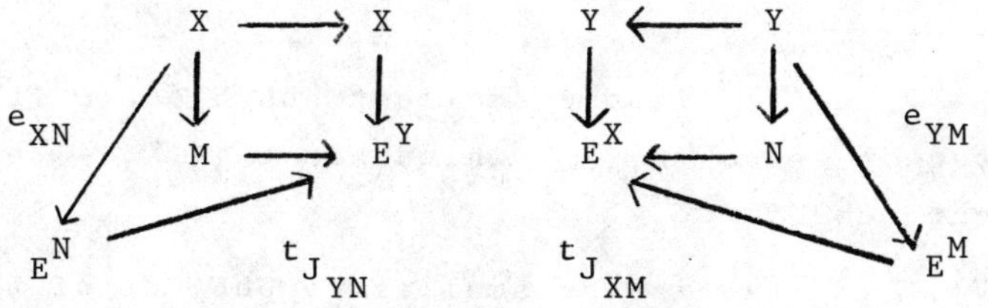

there are (unique) linear maps (in fact covered vector space morphisms).

$$e_{FN}: \quad F \to E^N$$

$$e_{GM}: \quad G \to E^M$$

such that $e_{XN} = e_{FN} \circ i$, $e_{YM} = e_{GM} \circ j$.

Corresponding to this expanded diagram, we then obtain a commutative diagram, by noting that, with our identifications,

$$e_{FN}(F) \subset L(N,E) \quad \text{and}$$

$$e_{GM}(G) \subset L(M,E) \quad .$$

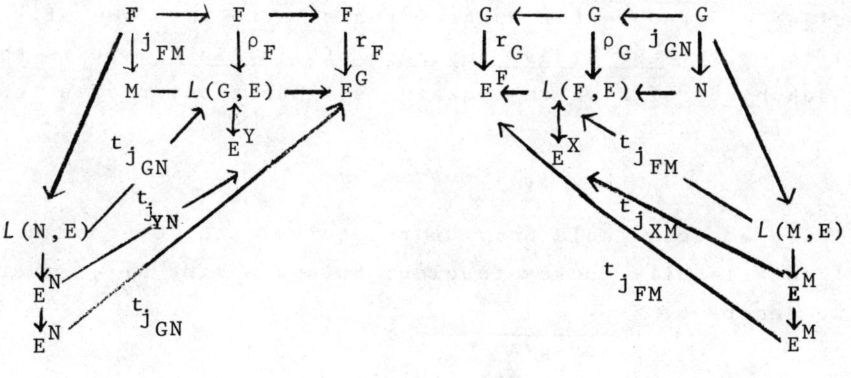

Moreover, we have

(1) $\rho_F((F, S)) \subset (E, T)^Y$ is the smallest subobject of the covered vector space $(E, T)^Y$ which has $r_X((X, A))$ as a covered set subobject.

(2) $\rho_G((G, \mathcal{V})) \subset (E, \mathcal{T})^X$ is the smallest subobject of the covered vector space $(E, \mathcal{T})^X$ which has $r_Y((Y, \mathcal{B}))$ as a covered set subobject.

(3) $e_{FN}((F, \mathcal{S})) \subset (E, \mathcal{T})^N$ is the smallest subobject of the covered vector space $(E, \mathcal{T})^N$ which has $e_{XN}((X, \mathcal{A})$ as a covered set subobject.

(4) $e_{GM}((G, \mathcal{V})) \subset (E, \mathcal{T})^M$ is the smallest subobject of the covered vector space $(E, \mathcal{T})^M$ which has $e_{YM}((Y, \mathcal{B}))$ as a covered set subobject.

This prompts the following definition.

2. <u>Definition</u>: Let A be a covered set, (i, F) a reflection for A in the category of covered vector spaces, let E be a covered vector space, and let

$$\phi: \quad A \to E$$

be a covered set morphism.

Let

$$\psi: \quad F \to E$$

be the unique covered vector space morphism such that $\phi = \psi i$.

$\psi(F)$ is called <u>the linear envelope of $\phi(A)$ in E</u>. It is the smallest subobject of E which contains $\phi(A)$ as a covered set subobject. It is denoted by

$$\text{env } \phi(A)$$

(All definite articles hold only up to equivalence, of course.)

If $\mathcal{T}$ is a locally convex topology on spE making $E[\mathcal{T}]$ cover-closed, we denote by

$$\overline{\text{env } \phi(A)}$$

the cover-closed envelope of env $\phi(A)$ in $E[\mathcal{T}]$. It is called <u>the cover-closed linear envelope of $\phi(A)$ in $E[\mathcal{T}]$</u>. It is the smallest cover-closed subobject of E which contains $\phi(A)$ as a covered set subobject.

3. Definition: By *a duality $\langle A, B\rangle$ of covered sets over a covered locally convex space $E[\mathcal{T}]$*, we mean a duality $\langle A, B\rangle$ of covered sets over the covered vector space E, together with a locally convex topology $\mathcal{T}$ on spE.

4. Definition: Let $\langle A, B\rangle$ be a *bounded* duality of covered sets over a *cover-closed* locally convex space $E[\mathcal{T}]$.

An extension context

$$\begin{array}{ccccccc} C & \longrightarrow & A & \qquad & B & \longleftarrow & D \\ \downarrow & & \downarrow & & \downarrow & & \downarrow \\ M & \longrightarrow & E^D & & E^C & \longleftarrow & N \end{array}$$

will be called *a linear extension context* if M is a linear subspace of E^D and N is a linear subspace of E^C.

C and D will be said to be *linearly compatible* in this context if env $e_{CN}(C)$ and env $e_{DM}(D)$ are compatible in this context.

C and D will be said to have *the linear extension property* in this context if the env $e_{CN}(C)$-env $e_{DM}(D)$ extension problem has an affirmative solution.

If C and D have the linear extension property in this context, then the extended duality $\langle \text{env } e_{CN}(C), \text{env } e_{DM}(D)\rangle$ over $E[\mathcal{T}]$, where env $e_{CN}(C)$ and env $e_{DM}(D)$ are given the product uniform structures will be called *the extended duality of covered locally convex spaces over $E[\mathcal{T}]$ obtained from this context*. (The linearity of transpose maps and the previous discussion should make it clear that this is indeed a duality in the category of covered locally convex spaces.)

The discussion which initiated this section should make the following proposition clear:

5. Proposition: *Let $\langle A, B\rangle$ be a bounded duality of covered sets over a cover-closed locally convex space $E[\mathcal{T}]$.*

Let (i, F), resp. (j, G), be a reflection for A, resp. B, in the category of covered vector spaces.

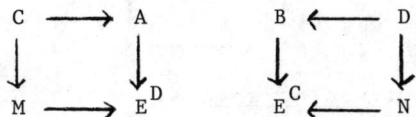

Suppose we are given a linear extension context

$$\begin{array}{ccc} C & \longrightarrow & A \\ \downarrow & & \downarrow \\ M & \longrightarrow & E^D \end{array} \qquad \begin{array}{ccc} B & \longleftarrow & D \\ \downarrow & & \downarrow \\ E^C & \longleftarrow & N \end{array}$$

Then we (canonically) obtain an extension context

$$\begin{array}{ccc} H = \mathrm{env}\ i(C) & \longrightarrow & F \\ \downarrow & & \downarrow \\ M & \longrightarrow & E^K \end{array} \qquad \begin{array}{ccc} G & \longleftarrow & \mathrm{env}\ j(D) = K \\ \downarrow & & \downarrow \\ E^H & \longleftarrow & N \end{array}$$

in the category of covered vector spaces.

(1) *C and D are linearly compatible in the first context if and only if H and K are compatible in the second context*.

(2) *C and D have the linear extension property in the first context if and only if H and K have the extension property in the second context*.

As a corollary to the above result, with the help of Proposition 5.4.8, we obtain the following result:

6. *Corollary*: *Let <A, B> be a bounded duality of covered sets over a covered locally convex space* $E[\mathcal{T}]$ *which is cover-closed*.

Suppose we are given a linear extension context

$$\begin{array}{ccc} C & \longrightarrow & A \\ \downarrow & & \downarrow \\ M & \longrightarrow & E^D \end{array} \qquad \begin{array}{ccc} B & \longleftarrow & D \\ \downarrow & & \downarrow \\ E^C & \longleftarrow & N \end{array}$$

A sufficient condition that C and D be linearly compatible in this context is that

$$\mathrm{sp}(\overline{\mathrm{env}\ r_{AD}(C)}) \subset M$$
$$\mathrm{sp}(\overline{\mathrm{env}\ r_{BC}(D)}) \subset N$$

If $E[\mathcal{T}]$ *is compactly covered, this condition is necessary*.

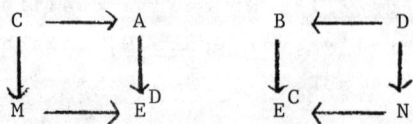

§3. The Convex Double Sequence Property

1. Definition: Let $E[\mathcal{T}]$ be a locally convex space and let $\{a_{ij}\}$ be a double sequence in E.

We say the convex double sequence property holds for $\{a_{ij}\}$ in $E[\mathcal{T}]$ if for every neighborhood U of o in E, every pair C, D of convex subsets of E such that $(C + U) \cap D = \emptyset$, and every subsequence $\{a_{m_i n_j}\}$ of $\{a_{ij}\}$, one of the following statements is false:

(a) For each $i \geq 1$, the sequence $\{a_{m_i n_j}\}_j$ is eventually in C.

(b) For each $j \geq 1$, the sequence $\{a_{m_i n_j}\}_i$ is eventually in D.

(See the comments after Theorem 5.7.14.)

2. Definition: Let $E[\mathcal{T}]$ be a covered locally convex space where $E = (F, \mathcal{S})$. Let $\{a_{ij}\}$ be a double sequence in F.

We say the convex double sequence property holds for $\{a_{ij}\}$ in $E[\mathcal{T}]$ if there is a set $S \in \mathcal{S}$ which contains every term of $\{a_{ij}\}$ and if the convex double sequence property holds for $\{a_{ij}\}$ in $F[\mathcal{T}]$.

3. Proposition: Let $E[\mathcal{T}]$ and $F[\mathcal{S}]$ be covered locally convex spaces, and let

$$\psi: \quad E \to F$$

be a locally $\mathcal{T}$-$\mathcal{S}$ continuous morphism. For notational convenience, let $E = (A, \mathcal{A})$, $F = (B, \mathcal{B})$.

Let $\{a_{ij}\}$ be a double sequence in some set of $\mathcal{A}$.

The following statements are equivalent:

(I) The convex double sequence property holds for $\{a_{ij}\}$ in $E[\mathcal{T}]$

(II) The convex double sequence property holds for $\{a_{ij}\}$ in $E[\sigma(A, A')]$

(III) For every form $\phi \in A'$, the double limit property holds for $\{\phi(a_{ij})\}$ in K.

(IV) For every form $\phi \in \tilde{A}'$ (i.e., every form in A* which is $\sigma(A,A')$-continuous on each set of A) the double limit property holds for $\{\phi(a_{ij})\}$ in K.

<u>Any of these statements implies the following statement</u>:

(V) The convex double sequence property holds for

$$\{\psi(a_{ij})\} \text{ in } F[S].$$

<u>In case $\psi^{-1}(S)|_H = T|_H$ for each $H \in A$, then (V) implies (I) through (IV)</u>.

<u>If (I) is true, then so is the following statement. If some countably compact set of A contains each terms of</u> $\{a_{ij}\}$, <u>then the converse also holds</u>:

(VI) If p is any continuous semi-norm on A, then the convex double sequence property holds for $\{a_{ij}\}$ in E[p].

<u>This statement in turn implies the following statement</u>:

(VII) The double limit property holds for $\{a_{ij}\}$ in $E[T]$.

<u>In case some sequentially compact set of A contains each term of</u> $\{a_{ij}\}$, <u>then statement (VII) implies statement (I)</u>.

<u>Proof</u>: The equivalence of (I), (II) and (III) follows from the Hahn-Banach Theorem. Clearly, (IV) $\rightarrow$ (III). If (IV) fails, then the convex double sequence property does not hold for $\{a_{ij}\}$ in $E[U]$, where U is the strongest locally convex topology on A which coincides with $\sigma(A,A')$ on each set of A. But then there is a set $H \in A$, and convex sets, C, $D \subset H$, and a U-neighborhood of o, U, such that $(C + U) \cap D = \emptyset$ and both of statements (a) and (b) of Definition (1) hold for some subsequence $\{a_{m_i n_j}\}$. But there is a T-neighborhood of o, V, such that x, $y \in H$ and $x-y \in V \rightarrow x-y \in U$. Therefore $(C + V) \cap D = \emptyset$ and (I) fails.

The remainder of the proof is quite analogous to that of 5.3.3, except for (I) $\rightarrow$ (V). This follows from the equivalence of (I) and (IV).

4. *Definition*: Let <A, B> be a bounded duality of covered vector spaces over a covered locally convex space $E[\mathcal{T}]$.

Let C be a subobject of A and let D be a subobject of B.

We say that *C and D have the convex double sequence property (with respect to this duality)* if for every set $F \in c(C)$, every sequence $\{x_i\}$ in F, every set $G \in c(D)$, and every sequence $\{y_j\}$ in G, the convex double sequence property holds for $\{\langle x_i, y_j \rangle\}$ in $E[\mathcal{T}]$. We often abbreviate this by saying that *C and D have the CDSP*.

5. *Proposition*: *Let <A, B> be a bounded duality of covered vector spaces over a cover-closed, separated covered locally convex space $E[\mathcal{T}]$.*

Suppose we are given an extension context

$$\begin{array}{ccc} C & \longrightarrow & A \\ \downarrow & & \downarrow \\ M & \longrightarrow & E^D \end{array} \qquad \begin{array}{ccc} B & \longleftarrow & D \\ \downarrow & & \downarrow \\ E^C & \longleftarrow & N \end{array}$$

in which C and D are compatible.

A sufficient condition for C and D to have the extension property in this context is that C and D have CDSP.

If $E[\mathcal{T}]$ is compactly covered, the condition is also necessary.

Proof: Simply notice that in the proof of 5.6.6, we may assume the pseudo-metric g to be of the form

$$g(x,y) = p(x-y) \quad (x,y \in spE)$$

for some $\mathcal{T}$-continuous semi-norm p. Then apply Proposition 3 in place of 5.5.3.

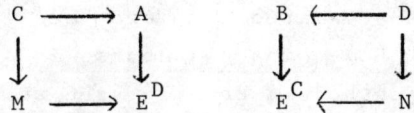

The above proposition was introduced at this time in order to make clear how all the pieces of our situation fit together except for one difficulty: In Section 2, we reduced a linear extension context in a canonical way to an extension context in the category of covered vector spaces and showed that our extension problems can be viewed as problems in the new context. In this section we introduced the tool we wish to use in handling extension problems and we showed that we can get results with this tool if we can assume the CDSP holds in the new context. The piece that remains to be fitted in is how to move from the CDSP in the first context (we will make the definition in §5) to the CDSP in the second context. This is entirely non-trivial. The next section is devoted to a lemma which will allow the transition.

§4. Pták's Combinatorial Lemma and the Double Limit Property

Our intention is to state a result like our generalized Eberlein-Grothendieck theorem which will be called a generalized Eberlein-Grothendieck-Krein Theorem. As the name suggests, we will be able to state, as a corollary of this theorem, the theorem of Krein in the theory of locally convex spaces which states that if $E[\mathcal{T}]$ is a separated complete locally convex space and if a set $A \subset E$ is $\sigma(E, E')$-compact, then so is A^{oo}. Broadly speaking, there are two methods generally used to prove this theorem, the measure theoretic and the combinatorial. One kind of measure theoretic proof is got by using a lemma of Grothendieck's (See Köthe [1], p. 328.) which states that if X is a compact space and C(X) is the space of continuous K-valued functions on X with the uniform norm, then a set $F \subset C(X)$ is $\sigma(C(X), C(X)')$-compact if and only if it is bounded in the norm and is compact in the topology of simple convergence on X. This lemma is usually proved with the help of Lebesgue's dominated convergence theorem. However, in using the Lebesgue theorem, it turns out that the only sequences of functions that one uses it on are sequences of continuous functions. This has caught the attention of more than one person if for no other reason--I suppose--than because of the seeming lack of economy on using such a powerful tool on such an elementary situation. Accordingly, there have been several successful attempts to prove Krein's theorem without using measure theory, using combinatorial methods instead. One way to do this would be to prove Lebesgue's Theorem in the special case of continuous functions without measure theoretic arguments. One such proof is Simon's "Front-Ended Proof of Lebesgue's Theorem" in which a combinatorial theorem is used to reduce matters to a point where Dini's Theorem can be applied (Simons [1]).

One can also approach Krein's Theorem directly by combinatorial methods. Perhaps the two most notable attempts of this kind are those of Namioka (Namioka [1]; Kelley and Namioka [1], pp. 157-160) and of Pták (Köthe [1], §24.6; Pták [1]). A paper which gives proofs of the combinatorial lemmas of both these men is that of Simons (Simons [1]).

The treatment outlined here will be combinatorial and will be based on Pták's combinatorial lemma, which we will state without proof. (For a proof, see the references above.) Since it seems satisfying to me to be able to do so, after I prove my generalized Eberlein-Grothendieck-Krein Theorem in §6, I will use it to give a proof of Grothendieck's lemma and then use Grothendieck's lemma to prove Lebesgue's Theorem in the special case of continuous functions.

1. <u>Pták's Combinatorial Lemma</u>

Let K be an infinite set and let X be a non-empty family of subsets of K. Let P(K) denote the collection of all positive, real valued functions λ on K such that $\{k \in K: \lambda(k) > 0\}$ is finite and $\Sigma_{k \in K} \lambda(k) = 1$. For $x \in X$, we write $\lambda(x) = \Sigma_{k \in x} \lambda(k)$. If

$$\inf_{\lambda \in P(K)} \sup_{x \in X} \lambda(x) > 0$$

then there are infinite sequences $\{x_i\}$ in X and $\{k_i\}$ in K such that the terms of $\{k_i\}$ are distinct and such that

$$\{k_1, \ldots, k_n\} \subset x_n \quad (n \geq 1).$$

Our use of Pták's lemma will be to prove the following result:

2. <u>Lemma</u>: Let S be a non-empty set and let $B(S)$ denote the space of all bounded functions from S to K, with the uniform norm.

A bounded subset $F \subset B(S)$ is said to have the double limit property if for every sequence $\{s_j\}$ in S and every sequence $\{f_i\}$ in F, the double limit property holds for $\{f_i(s_j)\}$ in K.

If a bounded set $F \subset B(S)$ has the double limit property, so does its balanced convex hull in B(S).

<u>Proof</u>: First, it is quite easy to see that we may assume F is balanced. (One has only to use the fact that $\{\lambda \in K: \ |\lambda| \leq 1\}$ is sequentially compact.) Having made this reduction, all that is necessary is to prove that if F has the DLP, so does its convex hull. Also, we may assume K = R.

So our problem is to show that if there is a sequence $\{f_i\}$ in the convex hull of F and a sequence $\{s_j\}$ in S such that

$$\lim_i \lim_j f_i(s_j) \neq \lim_j \lim_i f_i(s_j)$$

then F does not have the DLP. But if e: $S \to B(S)'$ is evaluation, we have

$$\lim_i \lim_j e(s_j)(f_i) \neq \lim_j \lim_i e(s_j)(f_i)$$

and e(S) is relatively $\sigma(B(S)', B(S))$-compact. The rest of the proof can therefore be carried out (using Pták's Lemma) exactly as in the corresponding theorem in §24.6 of Köthe [1].

§5. <u>The Convex Double Sequence Property and Linear Extension Contents</u>

1. <u>Definition</u>: Let <A, B> be a <u>bounded</u> duality of covered sets over a covered locally convex space $E[\mathcal{T}]$.

Let C be a subobject of A, D a subobject of B.

We say that <u>C and D have the convex double sequence property (in this duality)</u> if for every set $F \in c(C)$, every sequence $\{x_i\}$ in F, every set $G \in c(D)$ and every sequence $\{y_j\}$ in G, the convex double sequence property holds for $\{\langle x_i, y_j \rangle\}$ in $E[\mathcal{T}]$. We often abbreviate this by saying that <u>C and D have the CDSP</u>.

It is quite clear that if C and D have the DSP, then they have the CDSP.

2. *Theorem*: *Let $\langle A, B\rangle$ be a bounded duality of covered sets over a covered locally convex space $E[\mathcal{T}]$.*

Let (i, F), resp. (j, G), be a reflection for A, resp. B, in the category of covered vector spaces.

A necessary and sufficient condition that A and B have the CDSP in this duality is that F and G have the CDSP in the covered vector space duality $\langle F, G\rangle$ over $E[\mathcal{T}]$ given by

$$\langle \sum_x \alpha(x)i(x), \sum_y \beta(y)j(y)\rangle = \sum_x \sum_y \alpha(x)\beta(y)\langle x,y\rangle$$

Proof: By Proposition 2.3, we can reduce the matter to the case where E = K. But then we need only apply Lemma 4.2 (twice) in the obvious way.

3. *Theorem*: *Let $\langle A, B\rangle$ be a bounded duality of covered sets over a separated covered locally convex space $E[\mathcal{T}]$ which is cover-closed.*

Suppose we are given a linear extension context

$$\begin{array}{ccc} C & \longrightarrow & A \\ \downarrow & & \downarrow \\ M & \longrightarrow & E^D \end{array} \qquad \begin{array}{ccc} B & \longleftarrow & D \\ \downarrow & & \downarrow \\ E^C & \longleftarrow & N \end{array}$$

and that C and D are linearly compatible in this context.

A sufficient condition for C and D to have the linear extension property in this context is that C and D have the CDSP.

If $E[\mathcal{T}]$ is compactly covered the condition is also necessary.

Proof: This is just a matter of putting together Proposition 2.5, Proposition 3.5 and Theorem 2.

§6. *A Generalized Eberlein-Grothendieck-Krein Theorem*

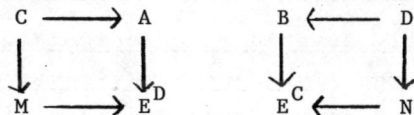

It is possible to prove Krein's theorem in the theory of locally convex spaces in such a way that one obtains the Eberlein-Grothendieck theorem at the same time. (See, for instance, Pták [1], Theorem (3.3).) The result, of course, has to be called the Eberlein-Grothendeick-Krein Theorem if one wants to acknowledge at least the most important pioneers. The following theorem generalizes this result and so will be called a Generalized Eberlein-Grothendieck-Krein Theorem. In order to make the fact of generalization clear, we will state and prove the original theorem as a corollary of the general theorem.

1. *Definition*: *By a local duality* $\langle A[\mathcal{V}], B[\mathcal{W}]\rangle$ *of covered uniform spaces over a covered locally convex space* $E[\mathcal{T}]$, we mean a locally uniform duality $\langle A[\mathcal{V}], B[\mathcal{W}]\rangle$ over $csp(E)[\mathcal{T}]$.

2. *Theorem*: *Let* $\langle A[\mathcal{V}], B[\mathcal{W}]\rangle$ *be a bounded local duality of covered uniform spaces over a compactly covered locally convex space* $E[\mathcal{T}]$.

Suppose A and B have the CDSP in this duality.

The following statements are true:

(1) $\overline{\mathrm{env}\ r_A(A)}$ *is a compactly covered subobject of* $\mathcal{LD}(B[\mathcal{W}], E[\mathcal{T}])$ *where the latter is given its (canonical) covered vector space structure and the product topology from* $E[\mathcal{T}]^B$.

(2) $\overline{\mathrm{env}\ r_B(B)}$ *is a compactly covered subobject of* $\mathcal{LD}(A[\mathcal{V}], E[\mathcal{T}])$ *where the latter is given its (canonical) covered vector space structure and the product topology from* $E[\mathcal{T}]^A$.

Now let (i,F), *resp.* (j,G), *be a reflection for A, resp. B*, *in the category of covered vector spaces and let* $\langle F, G\rangle$ *be the canonical covered vector space duality over E defined by* $\langle A, B\rangle$.

We make the canonical identification of E^B *with* $L(G, E)$ *and of* E^A *with* $L(F, E)$. *(*$L(G, E)$*, resp.* $L(F, E)$*, is all linear maps from spG to spE, resp. spF to spE*).

The following statements are also true:

(3) $\overline{\mathrm{env}\ r_A(A)}$ *is a compactly covered subobject of* $\mathcal{LD}(G[\sigma(F,\mathcal{T})]$, $E[\mathcal{T}])$.

(4) $\overline{\mathrm{env}\ r_B(B)}$ *is a compactly covered subobject of* $\mathcal{LD}(F[\sigma(G,\mathcal{T})]$, $E[\mathcal{T}])$.

Proof: As for the various canonical identifications involved, we simply must refer the reader back to (a good part of) §2. Given these, however, it suffices to prove that (3) and (4) are true and, in order to do this, Theorem 5.2 implies that it suffices to prove Theorem 5.8.3 in the special case of $\langle F[\sigma(G,\mathcal{T})], G[\sigma(F,\mathcal{T})]\rangle$ over $E[\mathcal{T}]$ in the category of covered locally convex spaces, but with the hypothesis altered from DSP to CDSP. In order to do this, one has only to prove Lemma 5.8.1 in the special case where $E[\mathcal{U}]$ is a compact, convex subset of a locally convex space and X and Y have the CDSP (obvious meaning). In order to do this, one has only to notice that that pseudo-meteric g in the proof of Lemma 5.8.1 can be taken to be of the form

$$g(x,y) = p(x-y)$$

where p is a continuous semi-norm on the locally convex space involved and then apply Proposition 3.3 in place of 5.5.3.

3. Corollary: (The Eberlein-Grothendieck-Krein Theorem) *Let $E[\mathcal{T}]$ be a separated, complete locally convex space. Let $\mathcal{B}$ denote the family of all equicontinuous subsets of E'. Let $\mathcal{A}$ be a directed covering of E by bounded sets.*

The following statements are equivalent:

(1) *Each set of $\mathcal{A}$ is relatively $\sigma(E, E')$-countably compact*.

(2) *In the canonical duality $\langle E, E'\rangle$ over K, $(E, \mathcal{A})$ and $(E', \mathcal{B})$ have the DLP*.

(3) *For each $A \in \mathcal{A}$, A^{oo} is $\sigma(E, E')$-compact*.

Proof: This follows from the above theorem in the same way that 5.8.4 followed from 5.8.3. Namely, we use 3.4.6, 5.6.3, and the fact that $E'^{*}[\sigma(E'^{*}, E')]$ is complete.

We said in Section 4 that we would use the results we obtained from our essentially combinatorial approach to prove the key lemma of the measure theoretic approach to Krein's Theorem; Grothendieck's Theorem on weak compactness in C(X), where X is a compact space (Köthe [1], p. 328). This theorem is a special case of the next corollary.

4. _Corollary_: _Let $(X, \mathcal{A})[\mathcal{U}]$ be a compactly covered uniform space and let E denote the space of all K-valued functions on X which are continuous on each set of $\mathcal{A}$._

Let $\mathcal{T}_{\mathcal{A}}$ denote the locally convex topology on E of uniform convergence on sets of $\mathcal{A}$. Let E' denote the dual space of $E[\mathcal{T}_{\mathcal{A}}]$.

Let $F \subset E$ be $\sigma(E, E')$-closed. The following statements about F are equivalent:

(1) _F is $\sigma(E, E')$-compact._

(2) _F is uniformly bounded on each set of $\mathcal{A}$ and is compact in the topology of simple convergence on X._

(3) _F^{oo} is $\sigma(E, E')$-compact._

In case these statements hold, then the topology of simple convergence on X and $\sigma(E, E')$ coincide on F^{oo}.

Proof: The equivalence of (1) and (3) follows from the fact that $E[\mathcal{T}_{\mathcal{A}}]$ is complete and from Krein's Theorem.

If (3) holds, then, since $\sigma(E, E')$ is stronger than the topology of simple convergence on X, which in turn is a separated topology, the two must coincide on F^{oo}.

The statement that F is uniformly bounded on each set of $\mathcal{A}$ is simply the statement that F is $\mathcal{T}_{\mathcal{A}}$-bounded, which is equivalent to being $\sigma(E, E')$-bounded. So, clearly, (1) $\rightarrow$ (2).

Now let $\mathcal{F}$ be the set of all subsets of E which satisfy (2). Then $(E, \mathcal{F})[\sigma(X)]$ is a compactly covered uniform space and we have a bounded local duality

$$<(E, \mathcal{F})[\sigma(X)], (X, \mathcal{A})[\mathcal{U}]>$$

of covered uniform spaces over the locally convex space K given by

$$<,>: \; E \times X \rightarrow K$$
$$(f,x) \rightarrow f(x)$$

By compactness and Proposition 5.6.3, the DLP holds for $(E, \mathcal{F})$ and $(X, \mathcal{A})$ in this duality.

By Theorem 2, every function in the cover-closed linear envelope of $r_X(X,\mathcal{A})$ in the covered vector space K^E (i.e., in $\overline{\text{env } r_X(X,\mathcal{A})}$) is continuous on each set of $\mathcal{F}$ with respect to the topology of simple convergence on X. But this cover-closed envelope is simply E'. Hence, we have $\sigma(E, E')|_F = \sigma(X)|_F$ for each $F \in \mathcal{F}$. So each $F \in \mathcal{F}$ is $\sigma(E, E')$-compact.

We have proved that (2) → (1).

We mentioned in §4 that the particular measure-theoretic tool used in proving Grothendieck's theorem on weak compactness in C(X) was the Lebesgue dominated convergence theorem. Since, in that application, Lebesgue's Theorem has only to be used on continuous functions, the following proof seems rather satisfying.

5. Corollary: Let $(X, \mathcal{A})[\mathcal{U}]$ be a compactly covered uniform space and let E denote the space of all K-valued functions on X which are continuous on each set of $\mathcal{A}$.

Suppose a sequence $\{f_n\}$ in E is uniformly bounded on each set of $\mathcal{A}$ and converges pointwise on X to a function $f \in E$.

Let E' denote the dual space of $E[\mathcal{T}_{\mathcal{A}}]$ where $\mathcal{T}_{\mathcal{A}}$ is uniform convergence on sets of $\mathcal{A}$.

Then $\{f_n\}$ converges to f with respect to $\sigma(E, E')$.

Proof: Since $\{f_n\}$ converges to f in the topology of simple convergence on X, the set

$$F = \{f, f_1, f_2, \ldots\}$$

is compact in that topology. (The fact that $\{f_n\}$ is a sequence is being used here.) By Corollary 4, $\sigma(E, E')$ and the topology of simple convergence on X coincide on F. So f_n converges to f with respect to $\sigma(E, E')$.

§7. Linear Extension Theorems

If we apply Theorem 5.9.1, Corollary 2.6, Theorem 5.3 and Theorem 6.2, the following theorem is immediate.

1. Theorem: Let $\langle A[\mathcal{V}], B[\mathcal{W}]\rangle$ be a bounded local duality of covered uniform spaces over a compactly covered locally

convex space $E[\mathcal{T}]$.

The following statements are equivalent:

(1) *A and B have the CDSP in this duality*.

(2) *In the extension context*

$$\begin{array}{ccc} A & \longrightarrow & A \\ \downarrow & & \downarrow \\ M & \longrightarrow & E^B \end{array} \qquad \begin{array}{ccc} B & \longleftarrow & B \\ \downarrow & & \downarrow \\ E^A & \longleftarrow & N \end{array}$$

where M is all locally $\mathcal{W}$-$\mathcal{T}$ *uniformly continuous morphisms in Mor(B, csp(E)) and N is all locally* $\mathcal{V}$-$\mathcal{T}$ *uniformly continuous morphisms in Mor(A, csp(E)), A and B have the linear extension property*.

(3) *In the extension context given in (2), if* $F \in c(A)$ *then* $r_A(F)$ *is relatively* $\sigma(\overline{e_{BM}(B)}, \mathcal{U})$-*compact in M*.

(4) *In the extension context given in (2), if* $F \in c(A)$ *then the balanced, convex hull of* $r_A(F)$ *is relatively* $\sigma(\overline{\text{env } e_{BM}(B)}, \mathcal{U})$-*compact in M*.

(5) *In the extension context given in (2), if* $G \in c(B)$ *then* $r_B(G)$ *is relatively* $\sigma(\overline{e_{AN}(A)}, \mathcal{U})$-*compact in N.*

(6) *In the extension context given in (2), if* $G \in c(B)$ *then the balanced, convex hull of* $r_B(G)$ *is relatively* $\sigma(\overline{\text{env } e_{AN}(A)}, \mathcal{U})$-*compact in N*.

2. *Definition*: By *a locally convex uniformizing rule for the category* of covered vector spaces, we mean a uniformizing rule u which assigns to each covered vector space $(E, \mathcal{S})$ a set of locally convex topologies on E.

If u is such a rule, then by *a local duality* $\langle A[\mathcal{V}], B[\mathcal{W}]\rangle$ *of covered uniform spaces over an object* $E[\mathcal{T}]$ *in* $\mathcal{C}_u$ (where $\mathcal{C}$ is the category of covered vector spaces) we mean a locally uniform duality $\langle A[\mathcal{V}], B[\mathcal{W}]\rangle$ over $csp(E)[\mathcal{T}]$, where $\mathcal{T} \in u(E)$.

3. *Corollary*: *Let u be a locally convex uniformizing rule for the category* $\mathcal{C}$ *of covered vector spaces*.

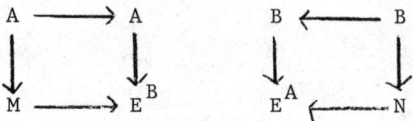

Let $\langle A[\mathcal{V}], B[\mathcal{W}]\rangle$ be a bounded local duality of covered uniform spaces over an object $E[\mathcal{T}]$ in $\mathcal{C}_u$.

Let $(i, \tilde{A}[\tilde{\mathcal{V}}])$, resp. $(j, \tilde{B}[\tilde{\mathcal{W}}])$, be a compactly covered local reflection for $A[\mathcal{V}]$, resp. $B[\mathcal{W}]$, in $\mathcal{C}$. w.r.t. u.

Let $(k, \tilde{E}[\tilde{\mathcal{T}}])$ be a compactly covered local reflection of $E[\mathcal{T}]$ with respect to u.

If A and B have the CDSP in this duality, then there is a bounded local duality $\langle \tilde{A}[\tilde{\mathcal{V}}], \tilde{B}[\tilde{\mathcal{W}}]\rangle$ in $\mathcal{C}_u$ over $\tilde{E}[\tilde{\mathcal{T}}]$ such that for $x \in spA$, $y \in spB$, we have

$$k(\langle x, y\rangle) = \langle i(x), j(y)\rangle$$

If $\tilde{E}[\tilde{\mathcal{T}}]$ is a local compactification of $E[\mathcal{T}]$, then the converse is also true.

The proof of the above corollary is entirely analogous to the proof of 5.9.2. Just as 5.9.3 was an obvious variant of 5.9.2, so the following corollary is an obvious variant of Corollary 3.

4. Corollary: Let u be a locally convex uniformizing rule for the category $\mathcal{C}$ of covered vector spaces.

Let $\langle A[\mathcal{V}], B[\mathcal{W}]\rangle$ be a bounded local duality of covered uniform spaces over an object $E[\mathcal{T}]$ in $\mathcal{C}_u$.

Let $(i, \tilde{A}[\tilde{\mathcal{V}}])$, resp. $(j, \tilde{B}[\tilde{\mathcal{W}}])$, be a compactly covered reflection for $A[\mathcal{V}]$, resp. $B[\mathcal{W}]$, in $\mathcal{C}$ w.r.t. u.

Let $(k, \tilde{E}[\tilde{\mathcal{T}}])$ be a compactly covered reflection of $E[\mathcal{T}]$ with respect to u.

We suppose that each locally $\mathcal{W}$-$\mathcal{U}$ uniformly continuous morphism in Mor(B, csp(E)) and each locally $\mathcal{W}$-$\mathcal{U}$ uniformly continuous morphism in Mor(A, csp(E)) is uniformly continuous.

If A and B have the CDSP in this duality, then there is a bounded duality $\langle \tilde{A}[\tilde{\mathcal{V}}], \tilde{B}[\tilde{\mathcal{W}}]\rangle$ in $\mathcal{C}_u$ over $\tilde{E}[\tilde{\mathcal{T}}]$ such that for all $x \in spA$, $y \in spB$, we have

$$k(\langle x,y\rangle) = \langle i(x), j(y)\rangle$$

As in §5.9, the rest of this section will be devoted to briefly treated examples and the following section will be devoted to one example which will be treated in more detail.

Our first example will be the remainder of Pták's result (Pták, V. [2]) part of which was stated in 5.9.4.

Because of the obvious way in which Corollary 3 generalizes Pták's result, we will call it the Generalized Pták Linear Extension Theorem.

5. Example: (The Pták Extension Theorem.) Let $X[\mathcal{T}]$ and $Y[\mathcal{S}]$ be topological spaces. Let C(X), resp. C(Y), denote the space of all bounded, continuous K-valued functions on X, resp. Y.

Let

$$e_X:\quad X \to C(X)'$$

$$e_Y:\quad Y \to C(Y)'$$

be the evaluation maps.

Let

$$\langle\, ,\, \rangle:\quad X \times Y \to K$$

be a separately continuous map from $X \times Y$ to a bounded subset of K.

The following statements are equivalent:

(1) X and Y have the DLP in this duality

(2) There is a bilinear uniform duality

$$\langle C(X)'[\sigma(C(X)', C(X))],\ C(Y)'[\sigma(C(Y)', C(Y))]\rangle$$

over K such that

$$\langle x, y\rangle = \langle e_X(x), e_Y(y)\rangle \quad (x \in X,\ y \in Y)$$

Proof: $(e_X, C(X)'[\sigma(C(X)', C(X)])$ is a compactly covered reflection of $X[\mathcal{T}]$ in the category of weak locally convex spaces.

As Simons noted (See Simons [2], §3) Pták's Theorem is really a kind of Fubini Theorem. To see this, it is better to use Theorem 1, rather than Corollary 3. First, however, we introduce some terminology:

If $A = (X, \mathcal{A})$ and $B = (Y, \mathcal{B})$ are covered sets, then a map

$$\phi:\quad X \times X \to K$$

will be called <u>bounded</u> if it defines a morphism from the product covered set $A \times B$ to the covered vector space K, i.e., if it defines a bounded duality of A and B over K.

A bounded function

$$\phi: \quad X \times Y \to K$$

will be called <u>a double limit function</u> if, in the bounded duality it defines, A and B have the DLP.

We now fix uniform structures $\mathcal{V}$ on X and $\mathcal{W}$ on Y. We denote by E, resp. F, the space of all K-valued, locally uniformly continuous functions on X, resp. Y, which are bounded on each set of $\mathcal{A}$, resp. $\mathcal{B}$. We denote by $\mathcal{T}_{\mathcal{A}}$, resp. $\mathcal{T}_{\mathcal{B}}$, the topology on E, resp. F, of uniform convergence on sets of $\mathcal{A}$, resp. $\mathcal{B}$. We denote by E', resp. F', the dual of the locally convex space $E[\mathcal{T}_{\mathcal{A}}]$, resp. $F[\mathcal{T}_{\mathcal{B}}]$. For heuristic reasons, we will write the elements of E', resp. F', as integrals. That is, if $\alpha \in E'$, $\beta \in F'$, $\theta \in E$, $\psi \in F$, we write

$$<\alpha, \theta> = \int \theta(x) \, d \, \alpha(x)$$

$$<\beta, \psi> = \int \psi(x) \, d \, \beta(x)$$

Now let

$$\phi: \quad X \times Y \to K$$

be a bounded function. We say that ϕ is <u>separately locally uniformly continuous</u> if the bounded duality it defines is a locally uniform duality. If, in addition, it happens that for each $\alpha \in E'$, and each $\beta \in F'$, the function

$$y \to \int \phi(x, y) \, d \, \alpha(x)$$

on Y is in F and the function

$$x \to \int \phi(x, y) \, d \, \beta(y)$$

on X is in E, and we have

$$\iint \phi(xy) \, d \, \beta(y) \, d \, \alpha(x) = \iint \phi(xy) \, d \, \alpha(x) \, d \, \beta(y)$$

then ϕ will be called <u>a Fubini Function</u>.

6. Example: Let $(X, \mathcal{A})[\mathcal{U}]$ and $(Y, \mathcal{B})[\mathcal{V}]$ be covered uniform spaces and let

$$\phi: \quad X \times Y \to K$$

be a bounded, separately locally uniformly continuous function.

ϕ is a Fubini function if and only if ϕ is a double limit function.

Proof: This is an immediate (after sorting out notation) corollary of Theorem 1.

We conclude this section with a special case of the above example.

7. Example: Let X and Y be locally compact topological spaces.

Let α be a Radon measure with compact support on X.

Let β be a Radon measure with compact support on Y.

Let

$$\phi: \quad X \times Y \to K$$

be continuous.

The two functions

$$Y \to K$$
$$y \to \int \phi(x, y) \; d\, \alpha(x)$$
$$X \to K$$
$$x \to \int \phi(x, y) \; d\, \beta(y)$$

are continuous and we have

$$\iint \phi(xy) \; d\, \beta(y) \; d\, \alpha(x) = \iint \phi(xy) \; d\, \alpha(x) \; d\, \beta(y)$$

Proof: If the terminology is unfamiliar, a Radon measure on X with compact support is simply a continuous linear form on the space of continuous functions on X, equipped with the topology of uniform convergence on compact sets.

§8. An Application: Weakly Almost Periodic Functions on a Covered Uniform Monoid

1. Convention: For the rest of this section, w will denote the uniformizing rule for the category of covered algebras over K which assigns to each covered algebra E = (A, $\mathcal{A}$) the set w(E) of all structures $\mathcal{T}$ on E making E[$\mathcal{T}$] a covered weak locally convex algebra. (See 2.5.8.) u will denote the uniformizing rule for the category of covered monoids which assigns to each covered monoid S = (M, $\mathcal{M}$) the set u(S) of all uniform structures on M which make the multiplication separately uniformly continuous.

2. Convention: For the rest of this section, S = (M, $\mathcal{M}$) will denote a fixed covered monoid and $\mathcal{U}$ a fixed structure in u(S).

As an immediate consequence of Proposition 2.8.6, of Corollary 5.9.2, of Example 7.6 and of Proposition 5.5.3, we get the following result.

3. Proposition: Suppose S[$\mathcal{U}$] is precompactly covered. Then the following statements are equivalent:

(1) S[$\mathcal{U}$] is locally compactifiable with respect to u.

(2) With respect to the duality <S, S> over S[$\mathcal{U}$] given by

$$M \times M \to M$$
$$(x,y) \to xy$$

the DSP holds.

(3) If ϕ is any locally uniformly continuous K-valued function on M, then the function

$$M \times M \to K$$
$$(x,y) \to \phi(xy)$$

is a double limit function.

(4) If ϕ is any locally uniformly continuous K-valued function on M, then the function

$$M \times M \to K$$
$$(x,y) \to \phi(xy)$$

is a Fubini function.

There is, of course, a suspicious resemblance between this proposition and Theorem 5.10.2. This resemblance is more than just superficial. Accordingly, our plan for the rest of this section will be pretty much that of §5.10. We will attempt to describe, in the case where $S[\mathcal{U}]$ may not be locally compactifiable, one distinguished compactly covered local reflection of $S[\mathcal{U}]$. Fortunately, we will be able to do this by reducing our problem here to a special case of the problem of §5.10. The reason that we had to wait until now, rather than attempting it in §5.10, was that we need Krein's Theorem to make the reduction.

The device we will use to make the reduction to the case of §5.10 is the same one we used at the end of §4.6.

4. Convention: We adopt the notation and terminology of Definition 4.5.5.

5. Convention: For the rest of this section, $(j, E[\mathcal{T}])$ will denote an inductive reflection for $S[\mathcal{U}]$ in the category of covered locally convex algebras and we will denote $E = (A, \mathcal{A})$. We recall that $A' = \mathcal{A}'$ and

$$^{t}j: \ A' \to C(S[\mathcal{U}])$$

is a topological and linear isomorphism with respect to $\mathcal{T}_{\mathcal{A}}$ and $\mathcal{T}_{\mathcal{M}}$ (see 4.6.12).

6. Convention: In order to facilitate reference to §5.10, if $T[\mathcal{V}]$ is a covered uniform monoid and if $(i, (B, \mathcal{B})[\mathcal{S}])$ is an inductive reflection for $T[\mathcal{V}]$ in the category of covered locally convex algebras, we will agree to identify $C(T[\mathcal{V}])$ with B' and $\mathcal{T}_{\mathcal{N}}$ with $\mathcal{T}_{\mathcal{B}}$ (where $T = (N, \mathcal{N})$).

The following theorem is fundamental and represents our use of Krein's Theorem (and the related results) in this section. It should be noted that the proof of the equivalence of (1), (5) and (6) in the following theorem was originally given, in the special case where $\mathcal{M} = \{M\}$, by Grothendieck. (See

Grothendieck [1], Proposition 7.)

7. Theorem: Let $\phi \in C(S[\mathcal{U}])$. The following statements are equivalent:

(1) The function

$$M \times M \to K$$

$$(x,y) \to \phi(xy)$$

is a double limit function.

(2) The function

$$M \times M \to K$$

$$(x,y) \to \phi(xy)$$

is a Fubini function.

(3) As a form in A', ϕ admits convolutions.

(4) As a form in A', ϕ is weakly almost periodic.

(5) If $X \in \mathcal{M}$, then $X \cdot \phi$ is relatively $\sigma(A', A'')$-compact.

(6) If $X \in \mathcal{M}$, then $\phi \cdot X$ is relative $\sigma(A', A'')$-compact.

Proof: There is very little to say except to notice that statements (2) and (3) are really the same statement and to notice that either (5) or (6) implies (4) by Krein's Theorem.

The following definition is a natural generalization of a concept originally due to Eberlein (Eberlein, W. F. [1]):

8. Definition: A function $\phi \in C(S[\mathcal{U}])$ which satisfies any of the statements of Theorem 7 will be called a weakly almost periodic function on $S[\mathcal{U}]$.

9. Corollary: If $S[\mathcal{U}]$ is compactly covered, every function in $C(S[\mathcal{U}])$ is weakly almost periodic.

Proof: Each function $C(S[\mathcal{U}])$ is a double limit function by Proposition 3.

10. Corollary: If $T[\mathcal{V}]$ is a covered uniform monoid, if

$$\rho: \quad S[\mathcal{U}] \to T[\mathcal{V}]$$

is a locally uniformly continuous covered monoid morphism, and if $\phi \in C(T[V])$ is weakly almost periodic, then ${}^t\rho(\phi) \in C(S[U])$ is weakly almost periodic.

Proof: Clearly, ${}^t\rho(\phi)$ is a double limit function.

11. Corollary: Let P denote the space of all weakly almost periodic functions in $C(S[U])$.

(1) P is T_M-complete

Let P' denote the dual space of $P[T_M]$ and let P' denote the family of all balanced, convex and T_M-equicontinuous subsets of P'. Let

$$e: \quad M \to P'$$

be the evaluation map.

(2) We can define a convolution multiplication in P' via the the relation

$$\begin{aligned} \langle \alpha \times \beta, \phi \rangle &= \iint \phi(xy)\ d\beta(y)\ d\alpha(x) \\ &= \iint \phi(xy)\ d\alpha(x)\ d\beta(y) \end{aligned}$$

for $\alpha, \beta \in P'$, $\phi \in P$.

With this multiplication, $(P', P')[\sigma(P', P)]$ is a compactly covered weak locally convex algebra and

$$e: \quad S[U] \to (P', P')[\sigma(P', P)]$$

is a locally uniformly continuous multiplicative covered monoid morphism.

Proof: This is an immediate consequence of the results of §5.10 (see 5.10.9 in particular) and of Theorem 7.

12. Corollary: Let P denote the space of all weakly almost periodic functions in $C[S[U])$, let P' be the dual of $P[T_M]$, let P' be the balanced, convex equicontinuous subsets of P', let

$$e: \quad M \to P'$$

be the evaluation map and make $(P', \mathcal{P}')[\sigma(P', P)]$ into a covered weak locally convex algebra as in Corollary 11.

(1) $e^{-1}(\sigma(P', P))$ is locally equivalent to $\mathcal{U}$ if and only if $\mathcal{U}$ is locally compactifiable with respect to u.

(2) e is a local uniform embedding if and only if $\mathcal{U}$ is locally compactifiable and separated.

Proof: This is an easy consequence of Proposition 3 and Corollary 11.

We recall that in §5.10, the dual space of the weakly almost periodic forms was an inductive compactly covered reflection of $A[\sigma(A, A')]$ with respect to w. Very nearly the same kind of result holds with respect to u.

13. Theorem: Let P denote the space of all weakly almost periodic functions in $C(S[\mathcal{U}])$, let P' be the dual of $P[\mathcal{T}_M]$, let $\mathcal{P}'$ be the balanced, convex, equicontinuous subsets of P', let

$$e: M \to P'$$

be the evaluation map, and make $(P', \mathcal{P}')[\sigma(P', P)]$ into a compactly covered weak locally convex algebra via convolution.

(1) $(e(P', \mathcal{P})[\sigma(P', P)])$ is an inductive compactly covered reflection for $S[\mathcal{U}]$ in the category of covered weak locally convex algebras.

Now let $\overline{e(S)}$ denote the cover-closed envelope of e(S) in $(P', \mathcal{P}')[\sigma(P', P)]$. $\overline{e(S)}[\sigma(P', P)]$ is compactly covered.

(2) Let $T[\mathcal{V}]$ be a compactly covered uniform monoid, let $T = (N, \mathcal{N})$, let

$$d: N \to C(T[\mathcal{V}])'$$

be the evaluation map and suppose we are given a locally uniformly continuous monoid pair morphism

$$i: S[\mathcal{U}] \to T[\mathcal{V}].$$

Then ${}^{t}i$ as a $\mathcal{T}_N$-$\mathcal{T}_M$ continuous linear map and, regarding $C(T[\mathcal{V}])'$ and its family of equicontinuous subsets as a compactly covered weak locally convex algebra with convolution as the multiplication, ${}^{tt}i$ is a $\sigma(P', P)$-$\sigma(C(T[V])', C(T[V]))$ continuous covered algebra morphism. (In fact, it is the unique such morphism with the property that ${}^{tt}i\ e = di$. (See part (1).)

(3) Notation as in Part (2). d is a local embedding of $T[V]$ onto $\overline{d(T)}$ with respect to $\sigma(C(T[V])', C(T[V]))$. If d^{-1}: $\overline{d(T)} \to T$ is the inverse map, then

$$d^{-1} \circ {}^{tt}i\Big|_{\overline{e(S)}}: \overline{e(S)} \to T$$

is the unique locally $\sigma(P', P)$-V uniformly continuous covered monoid morphism k such that ke = i.

Hence, $\sigma(e, \overline{e(S)}[\sigma(P', P)])$ is a compactly covered local reflection of $S[U]$, with respect to u.

(4) Notation as in Part (2). ${}^{t}i$ is a topological isomorphism if and only if $(i, T[V])$ is a compactly covered local reflection of $S[U]$ with respect to u.

Proof: (1) follows immediately from Theorem 5.10.9.

(2) The only thing that needs to be said is that the T_N-T_M continuity of ${}^{t}i$ follows from the fact that $i(M)$ refines N, and from Lemma 3.3.2.

(3) The fact that d is a local embedding follows from Part (2) of Corollary 12. The remainder of Part (3) follows immediately from this and from the $\sigma(P', P)$-$\sigma(C(T[V])', C(T[V]))$ continuity of ${}^{tt}i$.

(4) If ${}^{t}i$ is a topological isomorphism, then so is ${}^{tt}i$ with respect to the weak topologies. But then, since d is a local embedding, $d^{-1} \circ {}^{tt}i\Big|_{\overline{e(S)}}$ is a local embedding of $\overline{e(S)}$ into T. We will have proved that $(i, T[V])$ is a compactly covered local reflection of $S[U]$ with respect to u if we can show that each set of N is contained in the closure of some set in $i(M)$.

Suppose this is not the case. Then there is a compact set $F \in N$ such that, for each $G \in M$, $F \setminus \overline{i(G)} \neq \emptyset$. Therefore, for each $G \in M$, we may choose a V-uniformly continuous function

$$\phi_G: \; N \to K$$

such that $\phi_G|_{i(G)} = 0$ and such that $\sup\{|\phi_G(x)|: \; x \in F\} = 1$.

But now, for each $G \in M$, we define a semi-norm on $C(T[V])$

$$P_G: \; \phi \to \sup\{|\phi(x)|: \; x \in i(G)\}$$

We also define

$$P_F: \; \phi \to \sup\{|\phi(x)|: \; x \in F\}$$

Then each P_G, and P_F also, is a continuous semi-norm on $C(T[V])$. Moreover, the fact that ${}^t i$ is a topological isomorphism and that M is directed forces $C(T[V])$ to have a neighborhood base at 0 of the form

$$\{\phi: \; P_G(\phi) < \epsilon\}_{G \in M, \; \epsilon > 0}$$

But then, if U is any neighborhood of 0 in $C(T[V])$ there is some $G \in M$ and some $\epsilon > 0$ such that $P_G(\phi) < \epsilon$ implies $\phi \in U$. In particular, since $P_G(\phi_G) = 0$, $\phi_G \in U$. But $P_F(\phi_G) = 1$. This contradiction proves that T is the cover-closed envelope of $i(S)$ in $T[V]$ and so that $(i, T[V])$ is a compactly covered local reflection of $S[U]$ with respect to u.

Conversely, suppose that $(i, T[V])$ is a compactly covered local reflection of $S[U]$ with respect to u. The fact that T is the cover-closed envelope of $i(S)$ in $T[V]$ clearly forces ${}^t i$ to be a T_N-T_M embedding of $C(T[V])$ into P. But there is a unique locally uniformly continuous covered monoid morphism

$$\ell: \; T \to \overline{e(S)}$$

such that $e = \ell i$. Therefore, if $\phi \in P$, the function

$$\psi: \; x \to \langle \ell(x), \phi \rangle$$

is in $C(T[V])$. But, if $x \in M$, we have

$$\begin{aligned} {}^t i\psi(x) &= \psi(i(x)) = \langle \ell i(x), \phi \rangle \\ &= \langle e(x), \phi \rangle = \phi(x) \; . \end{aligned}$$

Hence, we have $\phi = {}^t i(\psi)$.
So ${}^t i$ is a surjection.

14. Corollary: Let $(i, T[\mathcal{V}])$ be any compactly covered local reflection of $S[\mathcal{U}]$ with respect to u. A function $\phi \in C(S[\mathcal{U}])$ is weakly almost periodic if and only if ϕ is locally uniformly continuous with respect to $i^{-1}(\mathcal{V})$.

15. Definition: A compactly covered reflection for $S[\mathcal{U}]$ in the category of covered weak locally convex algebras will be called a weakly almost periodic compactly covered algebra reflection for $S[\mathcal{U}]$.

If $(i, F[\sigma(B, B')])$ is such a reflection and if $(m, T[\mathcal{V}])$ is a compactly covered local reflection of $S[\mathcal{U}]$ with respect to u such that the unique locally uniformly continuous covered monoid morphism

$$n: \ T[\mathcal{V}] \to F[\sigma(B, B')]$$

such that $i = nm$ has the added property of being a uniform embedding, then $(m, T[\mathcal{V}])$ will be called a weakly almost periodic compactly covered reflection of $S[\mathcal{U}]$.

It is quite clear that a weakly almost periodic compactly covered reflection $(m, T[\mathcal{V}])$ of $S[\mathcal{U}]$ is characterized by the property that

(1) If $G[\sigma(C, C')]$ is a compactly covered weak locally convex algebra and if

$$j: \ S[\mathcal{U}] \to G[\sigma(C, C')]$$

is a locally uniformly continuous covered monoid morphism, then there is a unique uniformly continuous covered monoid morphism

$$k: \ T[\mathcal{V}] \to G[\sigma(C, C')]$$

such that $km = j$.

(2) For one such pair $(j, G[\sigma(C, C')])$ the map

$$k: \ T[\mathcal{V}] \to G[\sigma(C, C')]$$

is a uniform embedding.

16. Corollary: Let P denote the space of all weakly almost periodic functions in $C(S[\mathcal{U}])$. Let

$$\ell: \quad M \to \mathcal{L}(P[\mathcal{T}_M])$$

be the monoid homomorphism defined by the relation

$$\ell(x): \quad \phi \to x \cdot \phi \quad (x \in M).$$

Then ℓ is a locally uniformly continuous covered monoid morphism of S into $\mathcal{L}(P[\mathcal{T}_M])$ with respect to the $\sigma(P, P')$-operator topology.

If $\overline{\ell(S)}$ is the cover-closed envelope of $\ell(S)$ in $\mathcal{L}(P[\mathcal{T}_A])$ with respect to the $\sigma(P, P')$-operator topology, then $(\ell, \overline{\ell(S)})$ is a weakly almost periodic compactly covered reflection of $S[\mathcal{U}]$.

Proof: Use 5.10.9.

All of the above results apply, of course, to a uniform monoid $M[\mathcal{U}]$, i.e., to the case where $\mathcal{M} = \{M\}$. In this case, the word "local" can be left out everywhere. In particular, any compact reflection of $M[\mathcal{U}]$ will be a weakly almost periodic compact reflection, and vice-versa. The case for a "semi-topological" monoid $M[\mathcal{T}]$, i.e., a monoid M together with a topology $\mathcal{T}$ making the multiplication separately continuous is handled by replacing $\mathcal{T}$ with the strongest uniform structure $\mathcal{U}$ on M such that $t(\mathcal{U}) \subset \mathcal{T}$. Then $M[\mathcal{U}]$ is a uniform monoid and the results obtained for it can be readily translated into results about $M[\mathcal{T}]$.

Just as in Section 5.10, the resemblance between this section and Sections 4.5 and 4.6 should be evident. The following corollary is a close analogue of Corollary 5.10.11 and its proof will be omitted.

17. Corollary: Let C denote the space of all almost periodic functions on $S[\mathcal{U}]$ and let $(i, T[\mathcal{V}])$ be a Bohr compactly covered reflection of $S[\mathcal{U}]$.

(1) Each function in C is a weakly almost periodic function on $S[\mathcal{U}]$.

(2) In fact, C is precisely the space of all weakly almost periodic functions on $S[i^{-1}(\mathcal{V})]$.

(3) We can introduce a convolution multiplication in C' via the relation

$$\langle \alpha \times \beta, \phi \rangle = \langle \alpha, \beta \cdot \phi \rangle = \langle \beta, \phi \cdot \alpha \rangle$$

for α, $\beta \in C'$, $\phi \in C$. With this multiplication and with $\mathcal{C}'$ denoting the balanced, convex, equicontinuous sets in C', $(C', \mathcal{C}')[\sigma(C'C')]$ becomes a compactly covered weak locally convex algebra.

Now let $\mathcal{T}_M^o$ denote the topology on C' of uniform convergence on the compact sets of $C[\mathcal{T}_M]$ and let $(k, F[\mathcal{S}])$ be a Bohr compactly covered reflection of $E[\mathcal{T}]$, where $F = (B, \mathcal{B})$.

(4) There is a unique uniformly continuous covered monoid morphism

$$h: \quad T[\mathcal{V}] \to F[\mathcal{S}]$$

such that $hi = kj$, and a unique continuous covered algebra morphism

$$\ell: \quad F[\mathcal{S}] \to (C', \mathcal{C}')[\sigma(C', C)]$$

such that $\ell k = e$, where

$$e: \quad A \to C'$$

is evaluation (identifying C' with A").

(5) h is a uniform embedding and ℓ is a topological isomorphism with respect to $\mathcal{S}$ and $\mathcal{T}_M^o$. ℓ is also a topological isomorphism with respect to $\sigma(B, B')$ and $\sigma(C', C)$.

Now let $H = (D, \mathcal{D})$ be any covered algebra, let $\mathcal{W}$ be a locally convex topology on D making $H[\mathcal{W}]$ a compactly covered locally convex algebra and making each map

$$P \times P \to D$$

$$(a,b) \to ab$$

where $P \in \mathcal{D}$, jointly uniformly continuous. Suppose we are given a locally uniformly continuous covered monoid morphism

$$m: \quad S[\mathcal{U}] \to H[\mathcal{W}]$$

(6) *There is a unique continuous covered algebra morphism*

$$n: \quad (C', \mathcal{C}')[\mathcal{T}^{o}_{\mathcal{M}}] \to H[\mathcal{W}]$$

such that $ne = m$. That is, $(e, (C', \mathcal{C}')[\mathcal{T}^{o}_{\mathcal{M}}])$ is a Bohr compactly covered algebra reflection for $S[\mathcal{U}]$.

(7) *If $\mathcal{W} = \sigma(D, D')$, then n is $\sigma(C', C)$-$\mathcal{W}$ continuous. That is, $(e, (C', \mathcal{C}')[\sigma(C', C)])$ is a weak Bohr compactly covered algebra reflection for $S[\mathcal{U}]$.*

18. *Corollary*: *Let $(k, F[\mathcal{S}])$ be a Bohr compactly covered algebra reflection of $S[\mathcal{U}]$ where $F = (B, \mathcal{B})$, let $(i, T[\mathcal{V}])$ be a Bohr compactly covered reflection of $S[\mathcal{U}]$ and let*

$$\ell: \quad T[\mathcal{V}] \to F[\mathcal{S}]$$

be the unique uniformly continuous covered monoid morphism such that $k = \ell i$.

(1) *ℓ is a uniform embedding.*

(2) *$T[\ell^{-1}(\sigma(B, B'))]$ is a covered uniform monoid and $\ell^{-1}(\sigma(B, B'))$ is a locally equivalent to $\mathcal{V}$.*

Now suppose that $H[\mathcal{W}]$ is a compactly covered weak locally convex algebra and that for each set P in the covering family of H the map

$$(a, b) \to ab$$

is uniformly continuous on $P \times P$. Suppose we are given a locally uniformly continuous covered monoid morphism

$$m: \quad S[\mathcal{U}] \to H[\mathcal{W}]$$

(3) *There is a unique uniformly continuous covered monoid morphism*

$$n: \quad T[\ell^{-1}(\sigma(B, B'))] \to H[\mathcal{W}]$$

such that $ni = m$.

19. Definition: If (i, T[$\mathcal{V}$]) is a Bohr compactly covered reflection of S[$\mathcal{U}$], if (k, F[$\mathcal{S}$]) is a Bohr compactly covered algebra reflection for S[$\mathcal{U}$], (we write F = (B, $\mathcal{B}$)) and if

$$\ell: \; T[\mathcal{V}] \to F[\mathcal{S}]$$

is the unique uniformly continuous covered monoid morphism such that $\ell i = k$, then (i, T[ℓ^{-1}[σ(B, B'))]) will be called a weak Bohr compactly covered reflection of S[$\mathcal{U}$].

20. Corollary: If (i, T[$\mathcal{V}$]) is a Bohr compactly covered reflection of S[$\mathcal{U}$], any weakly almost periodic compactly covered reflection of S[i^{-1}($\mathcal{V}$)] is a weak Bohr compactly covered reflection of S[$\mathcal{U}$].

§9. Compact Hulls of Uniform Monoids; Extensions of Some Results of DeLeeuw and Glicksberg

1. Definition: Let S[$\mathcal{U}$] be a covered uniform monoid (resp. a covered locally convex algebra) where S = (M, $\mathcal{M}$). By a left locally convex S[$\mathcal{U}$]-module, we will mean

(1) a locally convex space G[$\mathcal{S}$]

(2) an action (resp. a bilinear action) of S (i.e., of M) on the left of G[$\mathcal{S}$] such that

(a) For each P∈$\mathcal{M}$, the set of maps

$$G \to G$$
$$x \to a \cdot x \;(a \in P)$$

is a $\mathcal{S}$-equicontinuous set of linear operators on G.

(b) For each x∈G, the map

$$M \to G$$
$$a \to a \cdot x$$

is $\mathcal{U}$-σ(G, G') locally uniformly continuous.

We denote G[$\mathcal{S}$], together with this left S[$\mathcal{U}$]-module structure, by

$$S[\mathcal{U}]^{G[\mathcal{S}]}$$

We call this module separated if $G[\mathcal{S}]$ is.

To say that we are given a left locally convex $S[\mathcal{U}]$-module structure on a locally convex space $G[\mathcal{S}]$ is equivalent to giving a covered monoid (resp. covered algebra) morphism of S into the covered algebra $L(G[\mathcal{S}])$ (see 4.6.4.) which is locally uniformly continuous with respect to $\mathcal{U}$ and the weak operator topology. Therefore, if $S[\mathcal{U}]$ is a covered uniform monoid and $(j, E[\mathcal{T}])$ is an inductive reflection for $S[\mathcal{U}]$ in the category of locally convex algebras, every left locally convex $S[\mathcal{U}]$-module structure on $G[\mathcal{V}]$ induces a (unique) left locally convex $E[\mathcal{T}]$-module structure on $G[\mathcal{V}]$ such that $a \cdot x = j(a) \cdot x$ for all $a \in M$, $x \in G$. Moreover, if $x \in G$, the map $a \to a \cdot x$ on sp(E) is continuous w.r.t. $\sigma(G, G')$.

If we are given a barreled locally convex space $G[\mathcal{S}]$ and an action of S on the left of G such that condition (b) of the above definition along with the following condition

(a') For each $a \in M$ the map

$$G \to G$$

$$x \to a \cdot x$$

is $\mathcal{S}$-continuous and for each $x \in G$, $P \in M$, the set $P \cdot x$ is $\mathcal{S}$-bounded

both hold, then we obtain a left locally convex $S[\mathcal{U}]$-module. In particular, this is the case if $G[\mathcal{S}]$ is a Banach Space.

2. <u>Theorem</u>: <u>Let $S[\mathcal{U}]$ be a covered uniform monoid (resp. covered locally convex algebra) and let</u> ${}_{S[\mathcal{U}]}G[\mathcal{S}]$ <u>be a separated left locally convex $S[\mathcal{U}]$-module. The following two statements are equivalent</u>:

(1) <u>For each $P \in M$ and each $x \in G$, $(P \cdot x)^{\infty}$ is $\sigma(G, G')$-compact in G</u>.

(2) <u>There is a covered algebra subobject of $L(G[\mathcal{S}])$ which is compactly covered with respect to the weak operator topology and contains $\phi(S)$, where</u>

$$\phi: \quad S \to L(G[S])$$

is the natural covered monoid (resp. covered algebra) morphism.

Proof: Since the covering family of any covered algebra subobject is comprised of balanced, convex sets, it is clear that (2) → (1).

Suppose (1) holds. It suffices to show that if $P \in M$, then the set $\phi(P)^{\infty}$ in $L(G[S])$ is compact with respect to the weak operator topology. Let F denote the balanced, convex hull of $\phi(P)$ in $L(G[S])$. Then F is S-equicontinuous. Therefore, by 3.2.7, the closure of F in the product space $G[S]^G$ is an S-equicontinuous subset of $L(G[S])$. But the weak topology of $G[S]^G$ is the topology of $G[\sigma(G, G')]^G$ and so, since F is convex, the closure of F in $G[\sigma(G, G')]^G$ is an S-equicontinuous subset of $L(G[S])$. But, by (1), the closure of F in $G[\sigma(G, G')]^G$ is compact. So the closure of F with respect to the weak operator topology on $L(G[S])$ is compact. That is, $\phi(P)^{\infty}$ is compact.

3. Definition: Let $S[U]$ be a covered uniform monoid (resp. a covered locally convex algebra). A separated left locally convex $S[U]$-module ${}_{S[U]}G[S]$ which satisfies either of the statements of Theorem 2 will be called a weakly almost periodic left $S[U]$-module.

4. Corollary: Let $S[U]$ be a covered uniform monoid (resp. a covered locally convex algebra) and let $(j, E[T])$ be a weakly almost periodic compactly covered algebra reflection for $S[U]$. (Note that $E[T]$ is a covered algebra in either case.)

Let ${}_{S[U]}G[U]$ be a separated left locally convex $S[U]$-module. The following statements are equivalent:

(1) ${}_{S[U]}G[U]$ is a weakly almost periodic left $S[U]$-module.

(2) There is a (unique) left locally convex $E[T]$-module structure on $G[V]$ such that

$$a \cdot x = j(a) \cdot x$$

for all $a \in M$, $x \in G$.

<u>If these statements hold, then the map</u>

$$a \to a \cdot x$$

<u>of spE into G is σ(G, G')-continuous for each x∈G</u>.

<u>Proof</u>: This follows directly from the theorem and the definition of a weakly almost periodic compactly covered algebra reflection.

5. <u>Corollary</u>: <u>Let S[$\mathcal{U}$] be a covered uniform monoid and let (i, T[$\mathcal{V}$]) be a weakly almost periodic compactly covered reflection of S[$\mathcal{U}$]</u>.

<u>If</u> ${}_{S[\mathcal{U}]}G[\mathcal{S}]$ <u>is a weakly almost periodic left S[$\mathcal{U}$]-module, then there is a unique left locally convex T[$\mathcal{V}$]-module structure on G[$\mathcal{S}$] such that</u>

$$i(a) \cdot x = a \cdot x \quad (a \in spS,\ x \in G)$$

${}_{T[\mathcal{V}]}G[\mathcal{S}]$ <u>is a weakly almost periodic left T[$\mathcal{V}$]-module. Moreover, if x∈G, the map</u>

$$a \to a \cdot x$$

<u>of spT into G is uniformly continuous w.r.t. σ(G, G')</u>.

<u>Proof</u>: Apply Corollary 4 and Definition 8.15.

In the special case where S[$\mathcal{U}$] is a covered uniform monoid and G[$\mathcal{S}$] is a separated, quasi-complete locally convex space, Krein's theorem would allow us to weaken statement (1) of Theorem 2 to

(1') For each P∈$\mathcal{M}$ and each x∈G, P · x is relatively σ(G, G')-compact.

In this case the conclusion of Corollary 5 is also sufficient for ${}_{S[\mathcal{U}]}G[\mathcal{V}]$ to be weakly almost periodic. In particular, this would be the case if G[$\mathcal{S}$] were a Banach space.

6. <u>Definition</u>: Let S[$\mathcal{U}$] be a covered uniform monoid (resp. a covered locally convex algebra) and let ${}_{S[\mathcal{U}]}G[\mathcal{S}]$ be a left locally convex S[$\mathcal{U}$]-module. By <u>the almost periodic submodule</u>, ${}_{S[\mathcal{U}]}G_{ap}[\mathcal{S}]$, of ${}_{S[\mathcal{U}]}G[\mathcal{S}]$, we mean the vector subspace G_{ap} of G

comprised of all almost periodic elements of ${}_S G[S]$ (see §4.4), together with the subspace topology $S|_{G_{ap}}$, which will again be denoted by S, and the natural action of S on G_{ap}.

We note that an element $x \in G$ is in G_{ap} if and only if $P \cdot x$ is S-precompact for every set P in the covering family, M, of S. For condition (a) of Definition 1 forces $S = N(S, S)$. This last equality also forces G_{ap} to be closed in G with respect to S (see 4.4.10).

7. Corollary: Let $S[U]$ be a covered uniform monoid (resp. a covered locally convex algebra), where $S = (M, M)$ and let ${}_{S[U]}G[S]$ be a weakly almost periodic left $S[U]$-module.

(1) If $x \in G_{ap}$ and $P \in M$, then $(P \cdot x)^{\infty}$ is a compact subset of G_{ap} with respect to S.

We denote by

$$\phi: \quad S \to L(G_{ap}[S])$$

the natural covered monoid morphism

(2) There is a covered algebra subobject of $L(G_{ap}[S])$ which is compactly covered with respect to the S-operator topology, has the property that, with respect to this topology, the map

$$(a, b) \to ab$$

is uniformly continuous on $P \times P$ for each set P of its covering family, and contains $\phi(S)$ as a subobject.

Proof: By using the results of Section 4.4 and an argument similar to, but simpler, than that used to prove Theorem 2, one can show that (1) → (2).

To prove (1), note that $(P \cdot x)^{\infty}$ is $\sigma(G, G')$-compact, hence $\sigma(G, G')$-complete. But S is uniform convergence on equicontinuous subsets of G' and so Proposition 3.4.1 implies that $(P \cdot x)^{\infty}$ is complete with respect to S. But it is clearly precompact with respect to S.

8. Corollary: Let $S[\mathcal{U}]$ be a covered uniform monoid (resp. a covered locally convex algebra), where $S = (M, \mathcal{M})$ and let $(i, E[\mathcal{T}])$ be a weak Bohr compactly covered algebra reflection of $S[\mathcal{U}]$. (Note that $E[\mathcal{T}]$ is a covered algebra in any case.)

If ${}_{S[\mathcal{U}]}G[\mathcal{S}]$ is a weakly almost periodic left $S[\mathcal{U}]$-module, then there is a unique left locally convex $E[\mathcal{T}]$-module structure on $G_{ap}[\mathcal{S}]$ such that

$$i(a) \cdot x = a \cdot x \quad (a \in M,\ x \in G_{ap}).$$

${}_{E[\mathcal{T}]}G_{ap}[\mathcal{S}]$ is a weakly almost periodic left $E[\mathcal{T}]$-module. If $x \in G$, the map

$$a \to a \cdot x$$

is $\sigma(G_{ap}, G'_{ap})$-continuous on spE.

Proof: Apply Corollary 7 and Corollary 8.18.

9. Corollary: Let $S[\mathcal{U}]$ be a covered uniform monoid where $S = (M, \mathcal{M})$ and let $(i, T[\mathcal{V}])$ be a Bohr compactly covered reflection of $S[\mathcal{U}]$.

If ${}_{S[\mathcal{U}]}G[\mathcal{S}]$ is a weakly almost periodic left $S[\mathcal{U}]$-module, then there is a unique left locally convex $T[\mathcal{V}]$-module structure on $G_{ap}[\mathcal{S}]$ such that

$$a \cdot x = i(a) \cdot x$$

for all $a \in M$, $x \in G$. If $x \in G$, the map

$$a \to a \cdot x$$

on spT is uniformly continuous with respect to $\sigma(G_{ap}, G'_{ap})$

We will now apply the above results to the special case $S[\mathcal{U}]$ is a uniform monoid. In this case, a weakly almost periodic compact reflection is actually a compact reflection.

10. Conventions: For the rest of this section, $M[\mathcal{U}]$ will denote fixed uniform monoid.

$(i, C[\mathcal{V}])$ will denote a weakly almost periodic compact reflection of $M[\mathcal{U}]$. $(k, E[\mathcal{T}])$ will denote a weakly almost periodic compactly covered algebra reflection for $M[\mathcal{U}]$.

(j, B[$\mathcal{W}$]) will denote a Bohr compact reflection of M[$\mathcal{U}$]. (ℓ, F[$\mathcal{Z}$]) will denote a weak Bohr compactly covered algebra reflection for M[$\mathcal{U}$].

wap(M[$\mathcal{U}$]) will denote the space of all weakly almost periodic K-valued functions on M[$\mathcal{U}$]. This space can be identified via ${}^{t}i$ with the space of all continuous functions on C[$\mathcal{V}$]. Its dual space, equipped with convolution and covered by the equicontinuous sets, can be identified bia ${}^{tt}k$ with E[$\mathcal{T}$].

ap(M[$\mathcal{U}$]) will denote the space of all almost periodic K-valued functions on M[$\mathcal{U}$]. This space can be identified via ${}^{t}j$ with the space of all continuous functions on B[$\mathcal{W}$]. Its dual space, equipped with convolution and covered by equicontinuous sets, can be identified via ${}^{tt}\ell$ with F[$\mathcal{Z}$].

If we are given a weakly almost periodic left M[$\mathcal{U}$]-module ${}_{M[\mathcal{U}]}G[\mathcal{S}]$, then we know that there is a unique left E[$\mathcal{T}$]-module structure on G[$\mathcal{S}$] such that

$$k(a) \cdot x = a \cdot x$$

for all $a \in M$, $x \in G$. It should be pointed out that, while the existence of this structure has been deduced here by rather abstract means, the action of spE on G is actually a reasonably familiar one. In effect, it is defined by weak integration. Indeed, suppose E[$\mathcal{T}$] is actually the (covered) dual space of wap(M[$\mathcal{U}$]) and e = k is evaluation. Fix $x \in G$ and $\phi \in G'$. Then it is (reasonably) clear that the function

$$M \to K$$

$$a \to \langle a \cdot x, \phi\rangle$$

is weakly almost periodic. Therefore if $\alpha \in wap(M[\mathcal{U}])'$, the number

$$\int \langle a \cdot x, \phi\rangle \, d\alpha(a)$$

is defined. However, the linear form

$$wap(M[\mathcal{U}])' \to K$$

$$\alpha \to \langle \alpha \cdot x, \phi\rangle$$

is σ(wap', wap)-continuous and so there is some $\psi \in$ wap(M[$\mathcal{U}$]) such that

$$\langle \alpha, \psi \rangle = \langle \alpha \cdot x, \phi \rangle$$

for all $\alpha \in$ wap(M[$\mathcal{U}$])'. Since if $a \in M$, we have

$$\psi(a) = \langle e(a), \psi \rangle = \langle e(a) \cdot x, \phi \rangle$$
$$= \langle a \cdot x, \phi \rangle$$

it follows that we have

$$\psi: \ a \to \langle a \cdot x, \phi \rangle$$

So we have proved that if $\alpha \in$ wap(M[$\mathcal{U}$])', we have

$$\langle \alpha \cdot x, \phi \rangle = \int \langle a \cdot x, \phi \rangle \, d\alpha(a)$$

Of course, our integral notation has only heuristic motivation if we consider the functions of wap(M[$\mathcal{U}$]) as functions on M. If we consider them as functions on C[$\mathcal{V}$], however, then this is indeed weak integration in the usual sense.

Likewise, if we assume that F[$\mathcal{Z}$] is actually the (covered) dual space of ap(M[$\mathcal{U}$]) and that ℓ is evaluation, then we have

$$\langle \alpha \cdot x, \phi \rangle = \int \langle a \cdot x, \phi \rangle \, d\alpha(a)$$

for $\alpha \in$ ap(M[$\mathcal{U}$])', $x \in G_{ap}$, $\phi \in G'_{ap}$. Again, if we consider ap(M[$\mathcal{U}$]) as a space of functions on B[$\mathcal{W}$], this is just weak integration in the usual sense.

11. Conventions: For the rest of this section, we will assume that E[$\mathcal{T}$] is the covered dual space of wap(M[$\mathcal{U}$]), that k is evaluation, that F[$\mathcal{Z}$] is the covered dual space of apM[$\mathcal{U}$], and that ℓ is evaluation. We will denote both k and ℓ by e.

${}_{M[\mathcal{U}]}G[\mathcal{S}]$ will denote a fixed w.a.p. left locally convex M[$\mathcal{U}$]-module. ${}_{C[\mathcal{V}]}G[\mathcal{S}]$ will denote G[$\mathcal{S}$], together with the unique left locally convex C[$\mathcal{V}$]-module structure such that

$$a \cdot x = i(a) \cdot x$$

for $a \in M$, $x \in G$. ${}_{B[\mathcal{W}]}G_{ap}[\mathcal{S}]$ will denote $G_{ap}[\mathcal{S}]$, together with the unique left locally convex B[$\mathcal{W}$]-module structure such that

$$a \cdot x = j(a) \cdot x$$

for $a \in M$, $x \in G_{ap}$.

We are interested in certain subsets of G. A vector $x \in G$ is called a Fluchtvector (Jacobs [1]) if 0 is in the $\sigma(G, G')$-closure of $M \cdot x$, i.e., if $0 \in C \cdot x$. It can be shown (by a proof nearly identical to that in Deleeuw-Glicksberg [2]) that x is a Fluchvector if and only if $c \cdot x = 0$ for some idempotent c in the kernel of C (i.e., the smallest two-sided ideal of C). The Fluchtvectorn do not in general form a subspace of G.

A vector $x \in G$ is called reversible (Jacobs [1]) if for every $a \in C$ there is some $b \in C$ such that $ba \cdot x = x$. It can be shown (again the proof in Deleeuw-Glicksberg [2] is sufficient, though the result stated there is weaker) that x is reversible if and only if $c \cdot x = x$ for some idempotent c in the kernel of C. The reversible vectors do not in general form a subspace of G.

A vector $x \in G$ is called unitary if it is contained in some finite--dimensional subspace of G on which C acts as a group. The closed subspace of G generated by the unitary vectors is called the space of all vectors which are almost periodic in the sense of Jacobs (Jacobs [1]). It is not hard to see that this is a subspace of G_{ap}.

It is also not hard to see that a vector $x \in G_{ap}$ is a Fluctvector if and only if $0 \in B \cdot x$ and therefore that this is true if and only if $b \cdot x = 0$ for some indempotent b in the kernel of B. Also, if $x \in G_{ap}$, then the $\sigma(G, G')$-closure of $M \cdot x$ coincides with the $\sigma(G_{ap}, G'_{ap})$-closure of $M \cdot x$ since G_{ap} is a closed, M-invariant subspace. So, if $x \in G_{ap}$, we have $C \cdot x = B \cdot x \subset G_{ap}$. This implies that if x is reversible then for each $a \in B$ there is some $b \in B$ such that $ba \cdot x = x$. Conversely, this implies that x is reversible. So, for vectors in G_{ap}, it does not matter whether we use C or B in defining the concepts of Fluchtvector and reversible vector. This is also the case with unitary vectors, though it is not as easy to prove it.

From the above discussion it is clear that if there is a unique idempotent c in the kernel of C then c · G is precisely the space of reversible vectors of G and (1-c) · G is precisely the space of Fluchtvectorn of G. Also, if $\hat{j}$: C → B is the unique continuous homomorphism such that j = $\hat{j}$oi, then it is clear that $\hat{j}(c)$ is the unique idempotent in the kernel of B and so $\hat{j}(c) \cdot G_{ap}$ is precisely the space of reversible vectors of G_{ap} and $(1 - \hat{j}(c)) \cdot G_{ap}$ is precisely the space of Fluchtvectorn of G_{ap}. One thing that is not very clear though is whether there are in this case any reversible vectors which are not in G_{ap}. Indeed, there seems to me no à priori reason to presume that there are not. However, there are not. This is a consequence of a theorem which we are about to state. There is no way (at least no convenient way) to prove this theorem within the scope of this paper, since the proof requires some deep results from the theory of almost periodic functions along with the nontrivial result that a compact uniform monoid which is also a group is in fact a topological group. (Ellis, [1] or Deleeuw-Glicksberg [2].) For an outline of the proof, modulo these facts, the reader is referred to the paper of Deleeuw and Glicksberg (Deleeuw-Glicksberg [2]). The proof there is, almost word for word, sufficient to prove the following theorem, the only difficulty being that the statement of the result proved there is somewhat weaker.

12. Theorem: Assume the following three equivalent conditions hold:

(1) wap(M[$\mathcal{U}$]) has an invariant mean

(2) C has a unique minimal ideal

(3) There is a unique idempotent, c in the kernel of C.

Then the closed, M-invariant subspace c · G of G consists precisely of the reversible vectors of G and also precisely of those vectors of G which are almost--periodic in the sense of Jacobs. In particular, we have:

(4) The set of reversible vectors of G coincides with the set of those vectors of G which are almost periodic in the sense of Jacobs.

The closed, M-invariant subspace (Id-c) · G of G consists precisely of the set Fluchtvectorn in G. In particular,

(5) The set of Fluchtvectorn of G is a closed, M-invariant subspace.

If a, b∈C and a ≠ b implies a · x ≠ b · x for some x∈G (as is the case if G = wap(M[$\mathcal{U}$])), and if (4) and (5) hold, then (1), (2) and (3) must hold.

An application of the above theorem to ergodic theory can be got in the following way: Another subset of G in which we are interested are the fixed vectors, i.e., those vectors x∈G for which a · x = x for all a∈M. In order to fit this in with the above theorem, we let P denote the closed convex hull of e(M) in wap(M[$\mathcal{U}$])' with respect to σ(wap', wap). That is, P is the set of all probability measures on C (identifying wap(M[$\mathcal{U}$]) with C(C[$\mathcal{V}$])). This set is compact in the topology σ(wap', wap) and is easily seen to be a monoid with respect to convolution. The action of wap(M[$\mathcal{U}$])' on G[$\mathcal{V}$] induces an action of P on G[$\mathcal{V}$] and, with respect to this action, $_\rho$G[$\mathcal{V}$] is a weakly almost periodic left P-module. It is quite clear that a vector x∈G is a fixed vector if and only if π · x = x for all π∈P. Moreover, if wap(M[$\mathcal{U}$]) has an invariant mean u, then, since

$$e(a) \times u = a \cdot u = u = u \cdot a = u \times e(a)$$

for all a∈M (× standing for convolution) it is quite clear that {u} is the unique minimal ideal of P and u is the unique idempotent in the kernel of P. Moreover, if x∈G and x = u · x, then we have a · x = a · (u · x) = (a · u) · x = u · x = x for all a∈M. So x = u · x if and only if x is a fixed vector, i.e, u · G is the space of fixed vectors of G. But, from the above theorem (applied to $_\rho$G) it also follows that (1 - u) · G is precisely the set of those vectors x∈G such that 0∈P · x, i.e., such that 0 is in the closed convex hull of $M \cdot x$.

Let us state this formally.

13. Corollary: Suppose that $wap(M[\mathcal{U}])$ has an invariant mean u. Then u is an idempotent in $wap(M[\mathcal{U}])'$ and we have

$$G = u \cdot G \oplus (1-u) \cdot G$$

where $u \cdot G$ is the closed M-invariant subspace of G consisting of precisely the fixed vectors of G and $(1-u) \cdot G$ is the closed M-invariant subspace of G consisting of precisely those vectors $x \in G$ such that 0 is in the closed convex hull of $M \cdot x$.

If $x \in G$, then the unique fixed vector in the closed convex hull of $M \cdot x$ is

$$u \cdot x = \int a \cdot x \, du(a)$$

where the expression on the right is taken to mean that

$$\langle u \cdot x, \phi \rangle = \int \langle a \cdot x, \phi \rangle \, du(a)$$

for all $\phi \in G'$.

Proof: All that requires any proof is the statement that $u \cdot x$ is the only fixed vector in the closed convex hull of $M \cdot x$, since all the other statements have already been proved. But if y is a fixed vector in the closed convex hull of $M \cdot x$, then $y = p \cdot x$ for some $p \in P$. So we have

$$y = u \cdot y = u \cdot (p \cdot x) = (u \times p) \cdot x = u \cdot x$$

We can also consider, instead of G, the space G_{ap}. If we also note that $(j, B[\mathcal{W}])$ is a weakly almost periodic compact reflection of $M[j^{-1}(\mathcal{W})]$ and G_{ap} is a weakly almost periodic left $M[j^{-1}(\mathcal{W})]$-module, then we obtain the following two corollaries immediately.

14. Corollary: Assume the following three equivalent conditions hold:

(1) $ap(M[\mathcal{U}])$ has an invariant mean

(2) B has a unique minimal ideal

(3) There is a unique idempotent, f, in the kernel of B.

Then the closed, M-invariant subspace $f \cdot G_{ap}$ of G_{ap} consists precisely of those vectors in G_{ap} which are almost periodic in the sense of Jacobs. In particular, we have

(4) The set of reversible vectors of G_{ap} coincides with the set of those vectors in G_{ap} which are almost periodic in the sense of Jacobs.

The closed, M-invariant subspace $(Id - f) \cdot G_{ap}$ of G_{ap} consists precisely of the set of Fluchvectorn in G_{ap}. In particular,

(5) The set of Fluchtvectorn of G_{ap} is a closed, M-invariant subspace.

If $a, b \in B$ and $a \neq b$ implies $a \cdot x \neq b \cdot x$ for some $x \in G_{ap}$ (as in the case if $G = wap(M[\mathcal{U}])$ and hence $G_{ap} = ap(M[\mathcal{U}])$) and if (4) and (5) hold, then (1), (2) and (3) must hold.

15. Corollary: Suppose that $ap(M[\mathcal{U}])$ has an invariant mean u. Then u is an indempotent in $ap(M[\mathcal{U}])'$ and we have

$$G_{ap} = u \cdot G_{ap} \oplus (1-u) \cdot G_{ap}$$

where $u \cdot G_{ap}$ is the closed M-invariant subspace of G_{ap} consisting of precisely the fixed vectors of G_{ap} and $(1-u) \cdot G_{ap}$ is the closed M-invariant subspace of G_{ap} consisting precisely of those vectors $x \in G_{ap}$ such that 0 is in the closed convex hull of $M \cdot x$.

If $x \in G_{ap}$, then the unique fixed vector in the closed convex hull of $M \cdot x$ is

$$u \cdot x = \int a \cdot x \, du(a)$$

where the expression on the right is taken to mean that

$$\langle u \cdot x, \phi \rangle = \int \langle a \cdot x, \phi \rangle \, du(a)$$

for all $\phi \in G'_{ap}$.

SYMBOL INDEX

'	E' is the dual of the locally convex space E	1.6
*	E* is the algebraic dual of the vector space E	1.5
o	Polar in a linear duality, as in B^o, B is a set	1.6
$\bigcup$	Union of a family of sets	1.2
$\bigcap$	Intersection of a family of sets	1.2
V	Least upper bound of a set of uniform structures	1.4
<, >	A duality	3.2.1, 3.2.2
∼	As in $\tilde{A}'$, $(A,\mathcal{A})[\mathcal{T}]$ a covered locally convex algebra	4.6.6
~	As in $\mathcal{A} \sim \mathcal{B}$	1.2
ap	As in A_{ap}, the almost periodic subobject	4.4.5, 6.9
$\beta(F,E)$		1.6
$\beta^*(F,E)$		1.6
c(A)		2.2.3, 2.2.2
csp	covered space functor	2.2.3
C		1.5
$\mathcal{C}_u^\ell, \mathcal{C}_u$	$\mathcal{C}$ a Cartesian category with uniformizing rule u	2.4.3
$\mathcal{C}_o, \mathcal{C}_t, \mathcal{C}_o^\ell, \mathcal{C}_t^\ell$	$\mathcal{C}$ a category of covered objects	2.4.5
CDSP		6.3.4, 6.5.1
$C(T[\mathcal{V}])$	$T[\mathcal{V}]$ a covered uniform monoid	4.5.5
$\Delta=\Delta_X$		1.2
$\mathcal{D}(A,E)$		2.6.1
$\mathcal{D}(A[\mathcal{U}],B[\mathcal{U}])$		2.6.3
DLP		5.6.2

DSP		5.6.2
E^A	E, A sets	1.2
E^S	E an object, S a set or object	3.3
$E[\mathcal{U}]^S$	E an object, $\mathcal{U}$ a uniform structure, S a set	3.3
$E[g]$	E an object, g a pseudo-metric	3.2.9
$E[\mathcal{U}]$	E an object, a uniform structure	2.4
e_S	Evaluation map	5.2
e_{SN}	Evaluation map	5.2
$E^b=(A^b,\mathcal{A}^b)$	$E = (A,\mathcal{A})$ a covered algebra	5.7
$E^{bb}=(A^{bb},\mathcal{A}^{bb})$	$E = (A,\mathcal{A})$ a covered algebra	5.7
env	Linear envelope	6.2.2
$\overline{\text{env}\phi(A)}$	Cover-closed linear envelope	6.2.2
$\mathcal{E}(A[\mathcal{U}])$	A an object, $\mathcal{U}$ a uniform structure	4.5.1
$i_{ST}: S \to T$	Inclusion map	5.2
K		1.5
$\ell im\ \mathcal{T}$	$\mathcal{T}$ a filter base	1.2
$\mathcal{L}(E)$	E a vector space	1.5
$\mathcal{LD}(A[\mathcal{U}],B[\mathcal{V}])$		2.6.3
$\mathcal{L}(E)$	E a covered vector space	5.7
$\mathcal{L}(F[\mathcal{T}])$	$F[\mathcal{T}]$ a locally convex space	4.6.5
λ	Left Arens multiplication	5.7.7
M^o	M a monoid	1.5
M^A	M a monoid, A an object	4.2.2
$M^{\mathcal{C}}$	M a monoid, $\mathcal{C}$ a category	4.2.2
$N(F,U)$		3.2.4
$N(F,\epsilon)$		3.2.9
$\mathcal{N}(C,\mathcal{U})$		3.2.4
$\mathcal{N}(C)$		3.2.9
$\phi(A)$	ϕ a map, A a set	1.2
$\phi(\mathcal{A})$	ϕ a map, $\mathcal{A}$ a family of sets	1.2
$\phi^{-1}(A)$	ϕ a map, A a set	1.2
$\phi^{-1}(\mathcal{A})$	ϕ a map, $\mathcal{A}$ a family of sets	1.2
$\phi^{-1}(\mathcal{U})$	ϕ a map, $\mathcal{U}$ a uniform structure	1.4

$\pi_{\nu\in I}\mathcal{U}_\nu, \mathcal{U}_1\times\mathcal{U}_2$	$\mathcal{U}_\nu$ uniform structures	1.4
$\psi(C)$	C an object, ψ a morphism	2.2.5
$\sigma(F,E)$		1.6
sp	Space functor	2.2.1
s.t.	such that	1.2
$\sigma(C,\mathcal{U})$		3.2.4
$\sigma(C,g)$	g a pseudo-metric	3.2.9
$\sigma(C)$		3.2.9
S^A	S a covered monoid, A an object	4.3.1
$S^{\mathcal{C}}$	S a covered monoid, $\mathcal{C}$ a category	4.3.1
$S[\mathcal{U}]^{E[\mathcal{T}]}$	$S[\mathcal{U}]$ a covered uniform monoid or locally convex algebra, $E[\mathcal{T}]$ a locally convex space	6.9.1
T_u, T_{uv}	T an admissible functor	2.4.6, 2.4.10
$\tau(F,E)$		1.6
$t(\mathcal{U})$	$\mathcal{U}$ a uniform structure	1.4
$\mathcal{T}_u, \mathcal{T}_u^i$	$\mathcal{T}$ a topology, u a uniformizing rule	2.4
$\mathcal{T}_{\mathcal{B}}$	Defined in a linear duality	1.6
t_ϕ	ϕ a morphism	2.6.1
t_ϕ	ϕ a function	3.3
$\mathcal{U}\vert_X$	$\mathcal{U}$ a uniform structure, X an object	1.4
$\mathcal{U}\vert_B$	$\mathcal{U}$ a uniform structure, B an object	2.4
u(A)	u a uniformizing rule, A an object	2.4.1
$\mathcal{U}_u, \mathcal{U}_u^i, \mathcal{U}^i$	$\mathcal{U}$ a uniform structure, u a uniformizing rule	2.4
$X[\mathcal{U}]^I$	$X[\mathcal{U}]$ a uniform space, I a set	1.4

TERMINOLOGY INDEX

absorbing set in a l.c.s:	1.6
action homomorphism	1.5
action of a covered algebra	5.7,5.10
action of a monoid on a duality	4.2.4
action of a monoid on an object	4.2.2
action of a monoid on a product object	4.2.3
action of a monoid on a set	1.5
action of a monoid on morphisms	4.2.3
action of a covered monoid on a duality	4.3.3
action of a covered monoid on an object	4.3.1
action of a covered monoid on a function space	4.5.5
adherence of a filter	1.2
admissible functor	2.2.8
admits convolutions	5.10.4
affirmative solution to an extension problem	5.2.5
almost periodic element in a duality	4.4.3
almost periodic function	4.5.5
almost periodic in the sense of Jacobs	6.9
almost periodic linear form	4.6.7
almost periodic submodule	6.9
almost periodic subobject	4.4.5
Arens multiplication	5.7.7,5.10.3
Ascoli's Theorem	3.5.1
balanced set	1.6
barrel, barrelled	1.6
bidual	5.7
bijective function	1.2
Bohr compact reflection of a uniform monoid	2.8.3
Bohr compactly covered algebra reflection of a covered uniform monoid	4.6.14
Bohr compactly covered reflection of a covered locally convex algebra	4.6.9

Bohr compactly covered reflection of a covered uniform monoid 4.5.7
bornivorous, bornivore 1.6
bornological 1.6
bornological algebra 5.7.13
bounded duality 3.2.1
bounded linear map 2.6
bounded set in a l.c.s 1.6
bounded set of morphisms 2.6.1
canonical duality of a l.c.s. and its dual 1.6
canonical duality of a vector space and its algebraic dual 1.5
Cartesian category 2.2.7
Cartesian product 1.3,2.2
category 1.3
category of covered objects 2.2.3
category of sets 2.3
Cauchy filter 1.4
chaotic structure 1.4
compact 1.2,1.4
compact reflection 2.7.7
compact reflection of a uniform monoid 2.8.3
compactifiable 2.7.4
compactification 2.7.4
compactly covered 2.4
compactly covered local reflection 2.7.7
compactly covered reflection 2.7.4,2.7.7
compactible functor 2.4.9
compatible in a context 5.2.5,5.4.3
complete 1.4
completion of a l.c.s. 1.6
completion of a uniform space 1.4
completely covered 2.4
concrete category 2.2.1
contravariant functor 1.3

convex	1.6
convex double sequence property	5.7,6.3.1, 6.3.2,6.3.4, 6.5.1
convolution	5.10.3
countably compact	1.2
covariant functor	1.3
cover-closed	2.4
cover-closed dual objects	2.6.5
cover-closed envelope	2.4.1
cover-closed linear envelope	6.2.2
covered algebra	2.3.8
covered locally convex algebra	2.5.8
covered locally convex space	2.5.6
covered monoid	2.3.4
covered set	2.2.2
covered space functor	2.2.3
covered uniform monoid	2.5.4
covered uniform space	2.5.1
covered vector space	2.3.6
covered weak locally convex algebra	2.5.8
covered weak locally convex space	2.5.6
covering	1.2
covering family	2.2.2,2.2.3
directed family of sets	1.2
double sequence	5.5
double sequence property	5.5.1,5.5.2, 5.6.2
double limit	5.5
double limit function	6.7
double limit property	5.5.1,5.5.2, 5.6.2
dual of a l.c.s.	1.6
dual object	2.6.1
duality in a category	3.2.1,5.4.2

duality over a K-vector space 6.2.1
duality over a covered locally convex space 6.2.3
entourage 1.4
equivalent coverings 1.2
evaluation map 5.2
eventually in a set 5.5
extended duality 5.3.7
extended duality of covered locally convex spaces 6.2.4
extended uniform duality 5.4.3
extension context 5.2.3,5.3.2
extension problem 5.2.5
extension property 5.4.3
factored morphisms 2.2.6
faithful functor 1.3
filter, filter base, filter subbase 1.2
final object 1.3
fixed vector 6.9
Fluchtvector 6.9
Fubini functions 6.7
full subcategory 1.3
fully stable action 4.3.1,4.3.3
fundamental system of entourages 1.4
generalized Eberlein-Grothendieck theorem 5.8.3
generalized Eberlein-Grothendieck-Krein theorem 6.6.2
generalized Pták extension theorem 5.9.2
generalized Pták linear extension theorem 6.7.3
graph of a covering 1.2
images (as in C contains images) 2.2.5
inclusion map 5.2
inductive compactly covered reflection 2.7.7
inductive reflection 2.4.7
initial object 1.3
injective function 1.2
isomorphism in a category 1.3

K as a covered K-algebra 5.7
K-algebra 1.5
K-algebra anti-homomorphism 5.7
K-algebra homomorphism 1.5
K-algebra of linear operators on a vector space 1.5
linear duality 1.6
linear envelope of a covered set 6.2.2
linear extension context 6.2.4
linear extension property 6.2.4
linear form 1.5
linearly compatible 6.2.4
local compactification 2.7.4
local duality 5.8.2
local duality over a covered locally convex space 6.6.1
local reflection 2.4.7
locally compact 1.2
locally compactifiable 2.8.9
locally compactifiable form 5.10.5
locally continuous 2.4
locally convex 1.6
locally convex algebra 2.5.7
locally convex space 1.6
locally convex uniformizing rule 6.7.2
locally equivalent 3.5.1
locally uniform duality 3.2.2
locally uniformly continuous 2.4
locally uniformly continuous element in a duality 3.2.6
locally uniformly continuous set in a duality 3.2.6
locally uniformly continuous subobject in a duality 3.2.6
locally uniformly equicontinuous subobject in a duality 3.2.6
Mackey topology or space 1.6

module	6.9.1
monoid	1.5
morphism	1.3
normed algebra	5.7
object in a category	1.3
operator topology	4.6.4
opposite K-algebra	5.7
opposite law of composition	1.5
opposite monoid	1.5
points in a Cartesian category	2.2.7
precompact	1.4
precompactly covered	2.4
product in a category	1.3
product uniform structure	1.4
projection on a co-ordinate	1.3
pseudo-metric	1.2
pseudo-metrizable	1.2,1.4
Ptak Extension theorem	5.9.4,6.7.5
quasi-barrelled	1.6
quasi-compact	1.2,1.4
refines	1.2
reflection	1.3
reflection w.r.t. a uniformizing rule	2.4.7
reflective	1.3
relation in a set	1.2
reversible vector	6.9
Samuel compact reflection	1.4
Samuel structure	1.4
semi-norm	1.6
separated module	6.9.1
separated object	2.4
separated uniform structure	1.4
separation of a uniform space	1.4
sequentially compact	1.2
space functor	2.2.1

stable family 1.5
Stone-Cech compact reflection 1.4
subbasic system of entouragès 1.4
subcategory 1.3
subbobject 2.2.4
subsequence of a double sequence 5.5
surjective function 1.2
symmetric Ascoli Theorem 3.5.5,3.5.6
the category of algebras 2.3.7
the category of covered algebras 2.3.8
the category of covered locally convex algebras 2.5.8
the category of covered locally convex spaces 2.5.6
the category of covered monoids 2.3.4
the category of covered sets 2.2.2
the category of covered uniform monoids 2.5.4
the category of covered uniform spaces 2.5.1
the category of covered vector spaces 2.3.6
the category of covered weak locally convex algebras 2.5.8
the category of covered weak locally convex spaces 2.5.6
the category of covered monoids 2.3.4
the category of covered sets 2.2.2
the category of covered uniform monoids 2.5.4
the category of covered uniform spaces 2.5.1
the category of covered vector spaces 2.3.6
the category of covered weak locally convex algebras 2.5.8
the category of covered weak locally convex spaces 2.5.6
the category of locally convex algebras 2.5.7
the category of locally convex spaces 2.5.5
the category of monoids 2.3.3
the category of sets 1.3,2.3.2
the category of uniform monoids 2.5.3

the category of uniform spaces 1.4,2.5.2
the category of vector spaces 2.3.5
topology determined by a pseudo-metric 1.2
topology determined by a family of semi-norms 1.6
topology determined by a uniform structure 1.4
transpose functor over an object 2.6.1
transpose of a function over an object 3.3
transpose of a morphism over an object 2.6.1
ultrafilter 1.2
uniform duality 3.2.2
uniform monoid 2.5.3
uniform space 1.4
uniform structure 1.4
uniform structure determined by a family of pseudo-metrics 1.4
uniform structure of finite coverings 1.4
uniformized object 2.4
uniformizing rule 2.4.1
uniformly continuous 1.4
uniformly continuous element in a duality 3.2.6
uniformly continuous set in a duality 3.2.6
uniformly continuous subobject in a duality 3.2.6
uniformly equicontinuous set in a duality 3.2.6
uniformly equicontinuous subobject in a duality 3.2.6
unitary vector 6.9
weak Bohr compactly covered algebra reflection of a covered uniform monoid 4.6.14
weak Bohr compactly covered reflection of a covered locally convex algebra 4.6.10
weak topology 1.6
weakly almost periodic compactly covered algebra reflection of a covered uniform monoid 6.8.15
weakly almost periodic compactly covered reflection of a covered locally convex algebra 5.10.10

weakly almost periodic compactly covered
reflection of a covered uniform monoid 6.8.15
weakly almost periodic linear form 5.10.6,5.10.8
weakly almost periodic function 6.8.8
weakly almost periodic module 6.9.3

BIBLIOGRAPHY

Arens, R.

[1] Operations induced in function classes; Monatshefte für Math. u. Physik. 55 (1951), 1-19.

[2] The adjoint of a bilinear operation; Proc. Amer. Math. Soc. 2 (1951), 839-848.

Bourbaki, N.

[1] General Topology, Vol. 1; Addison-Wesley (1966).

[2] General Topology, Vol. 2; Addison-Wesley (1966).

DeLeeuw, K. and I. Glicksberg

[1] Almost Periodic Compactifications; Bull. Amer. Math. Soc., 65 (1959), 134-139.

[2] Applications of Almost Periodic Compactifications; Acta Math., 105 (1961, 63-97.

Dixmier, J.

[1] les C*-algebras et leurs représentations, Gauthiers-Villars and C^le, Paris, 1964.

Eberlein, W. F.

[1] Abstract Ergodic Theorems and Weakly Almost Periodic Functions; Trans. Amer. Math. Soc., 67 (1949), 217-240.

Ellis, R.

[1] Locally Compact Transformation Groups; Duke Math. J., 24 (1957), 119-126.

Freyd, P.

[1] Abelian Categories, Harper and Row, 1964.

Grothendieck, A.

[1] Critères de compacité dans les espaces fonctionnels généraux; Amer. J. Math., 74 (1952), 168-186.

[2] Espaces Vectoriels Topologiques; Departamento de Mathemática da Universidade de São Paulo, 1954.

Herrlich, H.

[1] Topologische Reflectionen und Coreflectionen, Springer Verlag (Lecture Notes in Mathematics), 1968.

Horváth, J.

[1] Topological Vector Spaces and Distributions, Vol. 1, Addison-Wesley, 1966.

Isbell, J. R.

[1] Uniform Spaces, AMS Math., Survey #12.

Kelley, J.

[1] General Topology, van Nostrand, 1968.

Kelley, J., I. Namioka & co-authors

[1] Linear Topological Spaces, van Nostrand, 1963.

Köthe, G.

[1] Topologische Lineare Räume, Springer-Verlag, 1966.

Lang, S.

[1] Algebra, Addison-Wesley, 1965.

Mitchell, B.

[1] Theory of Categories, Academic Press, 1965.

Namioka, I.

[1] A substitute for Lebesgue's bounded convergence theorem; Proc. Amer. Math. Soc. 12 (1961), 713-716.

Pták, V.

[1] A combinatorial lemma on the existence of convex means and its applications to weak compactness, Amer. Math. Soc. Proceedings of the Symposia in Pure Mathematics, 7 (1963), 437-450.

[2] An extension theorem for separately continuous functions and its application to functional analysis; Czech Math. J., 89 (1964), 562-581.

Samuel, P.

[1] Ultrafilters and Compactification of Uniform Spaces, Trans. Amer. Math. Soc., Vol. 64 (1948), 100-132.

Schaefer, H.

[1] Topological Vector Spaces, Macmillan, 1966.

Simons, S.

[1] A Theorem on Lattice Ordered Groups, Results of Pták, Namioka and Banach, and a Front-Ended Proof of Lebesgue's Theorem; Pac. Jour. of Math. Vol. 20, No. 1 (1967),

149-153.

[2] The Iterated Limit Condition, a Fubini Theorem and Weak Compactness; Math. Annalen, 176 (1968), 87-95.

Tomita, M.

[1] The second dual of a C*-algebra, Mem. Fac. Sci. Kyushu Univ. Ser A, 21 (1967), 185-193.

Tukey, J. W.

[1] Convergence and Uniformity in Topology, Annals of Math. Studies #2 (Princeton University Press).